ARTIFICIAL STIMULATION OF RAIN

Edited by

Helmut Weickmann
Chairman, Committee on Cloud Physics, AGU
and
Waldo Smith, AGU

Assisted by

Hans J. Aufm Kampe   Horace R. Byers
Pauline M. Austin   Wallace E. Howell
Charles F. Brooks   J. Stewart Marshall
Vincent J. Schaefer

page

Part 4—Crystal growth and nucleation; laboratory and field studies

Table of Contents

Part 4—Crystal growth and nucleation; laboratory and field studies

GREETINGS FROM THE AMERICAN GEOPHYSICAL UNION

HELMUT WEICKMANN

Chairman, Committee on Cloud Physics, American Geophysical Union
Signal Corps Engineering Laboratories, Fort Monmouth, N.J.

Ladies and Gentlemen: On behalf of the American Geophysical Union and its Committee on Cloud Physics I wish to welcome all of you to the Conference on Physics of Cloud and Precipitation Particles, and especially to welcome the representatives of the two Government agencies which are sponsoring this conference: Mr. Milton Greenberg, Director, Geophysics Directorate of the Air Force Cambridge Research Center; and Mr. James Hughes of the Office of Naval Research. I wish to thank the Woods Hole Oceanographic Institution for its hospitality in making its facilities in this beautiful region available to us.

The field of cloud physics is expanding very rapidly. We all know how many hopes and desires of the public are connected with this field in connection with cloud dissipation, rain making, hail prevention, hurricane modification, etc. We also know the complexity of this field with its many applications in fields other than physics and meteorology such as chemistry, chemical physics, crystal physics, homogeneous and heterogeneous nucleation, aero- and hydrodynamics. This complexity is one reason that our understanding of processes of formation and growth of cloud and precipitation particles more often resembles a 'science fiction story' rather than a 'true-life adventure'. We are therefore trying to obtain in this conference the latter—a true life history of the particles.

Since we are here as one big family of scientists, and we all know each other, we can proceed now without formalities. I would like, however, to acquaint you with two experts who were kind enough and able to accept our invitation in order to help us in some special fields. They are Dr. David Turnbull of the General Electric Company, well known to you as an expert in nucleation problems; and Dr. G. Wolff of the Signal Corps Engineering Laboratories who is an expert on crystal physics. Dr. Wolff is a pupil of Dr. Stranski, one of the world's leading authorities on crystal growth.

May I now ask Mr. Woodcock, Woods Hole Oceanographic Institution, and Mr. Greenberg, Air Force Cambridge Research Center, for a few words of welcome on behalf of the host to the Conference and for the sponsors of the Conference.

A NOTE OF WELCOME FROM THE WOODS HOLE OCEANOGRAPHIC INSTITUTION

A. H. WOODCOCK

Woods Hole Oceanographic Institution, Woods Hole, Mass.

Admiral EDWARD H. SMITH, our director, hoped to be here to welcome you to Woods Hole and to the Woods Hole Oceanographic Institution. Unfortunately the International Geophysical Year meetings have required his presence in Brussels at this time.

The selection of an oceanographic laboratory as a place to hold cloud physics meetings may, when first considered, seem quite anomalous. However, as one remembers that most of the atmosphere rests upon sea water and that this water is a major source of the vapor required to form clouds and indirectly to drive weather systems, the anomaly fades away.

Here at Woods Hole studies of various phases of the interaction between the sea and the overlying air are emphasizing the intimate connection between various physical-chemical events in these fluids. The experience of making these studies has been exciting to many of us. It has also left the conviction that answers to some of the most important questions in cloud physics today lie in understanding the micro- and macro-physical-chemical events at and near the air-sea interface. For instance, understanding the detailed mechanics of shower rain formation in cumulus clouds in marine air seems to involve the physics of the bursting of microscopic bubbles at the sea surface, the nature of the invisible flow of vapor—and nuclei-rich air from the sea to cloud base, and the details of the density and velocity structure of the cloud and environmental air.

There are of course many other factors involved in rain formation, but those mentioned are given in order to emphasize the idea that shower formation is a multi-phase process, beginning within the sea surface and evolving upwards into the atmosphere.

These are exciting times in cloud physics and meteorology. Your meeting in this laboratory to discuss cloud physics problems indicates, we hope, a recognition of the present and potential importance of the oceans in these problems. We oceanographers welcome you to Woods Hole and hope that you will find your stay here pleasant, stimulating and useful.

ADDRESS OF WELCOME FROM THE AIR FORCE GEOPHYSICS RESEARCH DIRECTORATE

MILTON GREENBERG

Director, Geophysics Research Directorate, Air Force Cambridge Research Center,
L. G. Hanscom Field, Bedford, Mass.

Ladies and Gentlemen: It is my privilege to welcome you here on behalf of the United States Air Force. We are highly gratified by the enthusiastic response which you have shown by your attendance here, which has far exceeded our expectations. When we first discussed the idea of such a conference with Messrs. Weickmann and Smith, it was our idea that the conference would be limited to a mere handful of active cloud-physics scientists. The overwhelming enthusiasm shown by scientists in many fields of research allied to cloud physics was so great that we were forced to expand our viewpoint and enlarge the scope of our discussions.

We are delighted that it turned out this way. As you know, the Geophysics Research Directorate has been very active in the field of cloud-physics research for the past seven years, and we can well remember the time when such a conference as this would be very fortunate to attract only a dozen or so pioneer researchers.

Today the picture is sharply changed, and even the average man on the street is familiar with the basic ideas behind cloud modification and weather control. Rainmaking is fast becoming a science of its own, and is gaining respectability in the eyes of fellow scientists in allied fields.

The greatest danger which this new science faces, in my opinion, is the possibility that in its enthusiasm it will try to outrun itself before it is ready. The great amount of publicity which has been showered down upon the science of cloud seeding I feel has, in many cases, hindered rather than helped the cause.

The avid interest of the public in cloud physics is so great that only too often political pressures have tempered programs rather than cool scientific judgment. We cannot afford to run before we have learned to walk. We are only just beginning to learn how to put numbers into our speculations. It is these numbers which mean the difference between an art and a science.

Today, and in the next three days to follow, you will be discussing essentially the ways and means of formulating cloud physics as a science. We have much to learn and a long way to travel. We must proceed step by step and build this science on a firm foundation. The future and reputability of cloud physics, and weather modification in general, rests largely with the individuals gathered here today. I enjoin you to accept your responsibilities conscientiously and with scientific humility.

In closing I would like to thank Admiral Smith, and the members of the Woods Hole Oceanographic Institution for making this fine auditorium available to us, and for the wonderful hospitality we are enjoying here. I would also like to thank Dr. Helmut Weickmann, the members of the Cloud Physics Committee, and Mr. Waldo Smith for their fine efforts in working out the program and the many details which are so necessary in getting together a conference of this type.

I have felt for some time that a conference such as this has been badly needed in order to tie together the many loose ends in the field of cloud physics, and I feel that it is a real achievement that such a conference has actually come into existence.

AEROSOLS; THEIR ORIGIN, DISTRIBUTION AND MEASUREMENT

REMARKS ABOUT THE SIZE DISTRIBUTION
OF NATURAL AEROSOLS

CHRISTIAN E. JUNGE

Geophysics Research Directorate, Air Force Cambridge Research Center, Bedford, Mass.

Abstract—An explanation of certain features of the size distribution of natural aerosols is presented. It can be shown that the lower limit of the particle-size distribution (about 0.01μ radius) is caused by coagulation and the upper size limit (about 20μ radius) by precipitation by gravity. Observations and calculations are in agreement. The almost constant log volume distribution in the radius range between 0.1 and 10μ, observed over the continents, is tentatively explained by a large-scale mixing process. The profound differences between the size distribution over continent and ocean are pointed out.

IN A recent paper [JUNGE, 1955] an average size distribution of natural aerosols was derived from a series of measurements in continental air. This size-distribution plot shows certain important features which seem to have a widespread validity over continents and differs basically from size distributions over the ocean. It is the purpose of this paper to investigate carefully those processes which can be important for the formation and change of the characteristics of these size distributions.

In the first and second sections the influence of coagulation and gravity on the average-size distribution will be investigated. On the basis of the results obtained, an explanation of the size distribution over land and ocean is offered.

The effect of coagulation on the size distribution—The model distribution used in these calculations is shown in Figs. 1, 2, and 3 plotted in the convenient way as a relationship of log number and log volume to log particle-radius distribution (curve at time $t = 0$). The log number distribution has a maximum between 0.01 and 0.1μ radius and decreases cubically to the maximum size limit of about 20μ. Consequently, the log volume distribution exhibits a constant value between the radii 0.1 and 10μ. The comparison of these two figures shows that the large number of Aitken nuclei with radii less than 0.1μ comprise only about ten per cent of the total aerosol volume and, of course, mass also. The main mass is concentrated between 0.1 and 10μ radius, a fact which is of importance for a proper understanding of the role of the aerosols in the atmosphere.

It may be emphasized that this model was derived from measurements over land and is, of course, idealized. Fig. 3 compares the actual average values with this model. The individual measurements show sometimes considerable deviations from this model. For example, the radius for the maximum number concentration can shift beyond 0.01 or 0.1μ. The decrease of the number concentration above 0.1μ is not always uniform, and the exponent which characterizes this decrease may vary between 2.5 and 3.5. The observations in the range of the very small particles (Aitken-nuclei) do not show a smooth curve. For sizes below 0.05μ ion counts reveal a grouping of particles at certain sizes [ISRAEL and SCHULZ, 1932]. In our present consideration, however, these variants will not affect the conclusions.

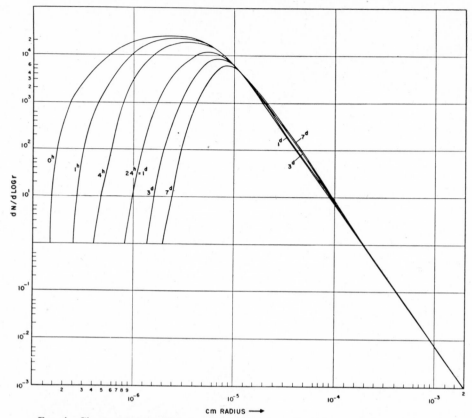

FIG. 1—Change of the model size distribution ($t = 0$) with time by coagulation; size distribution plotted as log number distribution

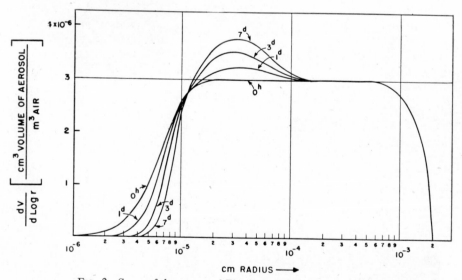

FIG. 2—Some of the curves of Fig. 1 plotted as log volume distribution

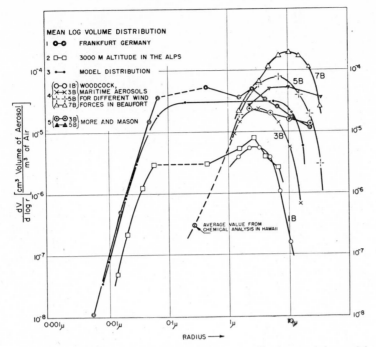

FIG. 3—Log volume plot of observed aerosol distributions and the model distribution used in Fig. 2; most of Woodcock's measurements were made at cloud-base level in Hawaii; Moore observed on a weathership at ten meters above sea level in the northeast Atlantic; the observations are averaged for certain wind speeds given in Beaufort (B)

This model size distribution is subject to change due to the coagulation of the particles by Brownian motion. This process is continuously active in clear air and in clouds. As a result, the smaller particles with their higher mobility preferentially combine with one another and with larger ones, thus decreasing more rapidly in number than the larger particles.

The laws of this coagulation process are well established [for example, see WHYTLAW-GRAY and PATTERSON, 1932]. Their application to our problem, however, is difficult because of the wide range of particle sizes encountered. Approximate analytical solutions, valid only over small size ranges, are no longer applicable.

The number $n(r) = f(r)\,dr$ of particles with radius r in the interval from r to $r+dr$ coagulate with the number of particles $n(\rho) = f(\rho)\,d\rho (\rho < r)$ according to

$$\frac{dn(r)}{dt} = \frac{dn(\rho)}{dt} = -\kappa\left(\frac{1}{r}+\frac{Al}{r^2}+\frac{1}{\rho}+\frac{Al}{\rho^2}\right)(r+\rho)f(r)f(\rho)\,dr d\rho = -\kappa F_1 f(\rho)f(r)\,dr d\rho$$

with $\kappa = \dfrac{RT}{3\eta N}$ and

$R =$ gas constant,
$T =$ absolute temperature,
$\eta =$ viscosity of air,

$N =$ Avogadro's number,

$$\frac{Al}{r^2} = \frac{a}{r^2} \neq \text{Cunningham correction,}$$

$A = 0.9$,

$l =$ mean free path length of air molecules.

It is assumed that the particles behave as droplets and that every collision is followed by coalescence. With a wide size range the calculation of the coagulation process is further complicated by the fact that the combination of two particles forms a new one of different size. If particles ρ and ρ' combine, where $\rho^3 + \rho'^3 = r^3$ the formation of r particles is

$$\frac{dn(r)}{dt} = \kappa\left(\frac{1}{\rho} + \frac{Al}{\rho^2} + \frac{1}{\rho'} + \frac{Al}{\rho'^2}\right)(\rho + \rho')f(\rho)f(\rho')\,d\rho d\rho' = \kappa F_2 f(\rho)f(\rho')\,d\rho d\rho'$$

With a size distribution ranging from $r_l \leqslant r \leqslant r_n$ the total decrease of r particles is

$$G(r)_- = -\kappa \int_{r_l}^{r_n} F_1 f(\rho)f(r)\,drd\rho$$

$$G(r)_+ = \kappa \int_{r_n}^{r \times 2^{-1/3}} F_2 f(\rho)f(\rho')\,d\rho d\rho'$$

For convenience, we divide by $f(r)$ and obtain the net fraction in the change of concentration of r particles

$$\frac{1}{f(r)}\frac{df(r)}{dt} = G(r) = \kappa \int_{r_n}^{r \times 2^{-1/3}} \left[F_2 \frac{f(\rho')r^2}{f(r)\rho'^2} - F_1\right]f(\rho)\,d\rho - \kappa \int_{r \times 2^{-1/3}}^{r_n} F_1 f(\rho)\,d\rho$$

In order to evaluate this integral, all items are developed in series of $\epsilon = \rho/r \leqslant 2^{-1/3}$. The term $f(\rho')r^2/f(r)\rho'^2$ is only used in the small interval $r \times 2^{-1/3} \leqslant \rho' \leqslant r$ and can be approximated by

$$\frac{f(\rho')r^2}{f(r)\rho'^2} \cong 1 + \frac{r^2}{f(r)}\frac{\partial\left(\dfrac{f(r)}{r^2}\right)}{\partial r}(\rho' - r)$$

With the $f(r)$ values from our model distribution the numerical integration can be performed. Since $G(r)$ gives only the rate of change at time $t = 0$, the integration must be repeated for a number of time intervals to obtain the total change over a certain time period. This stepwise integration and the approximations used result, of course, in some numerical inaccuracies which are considered unimportant for our purposes.

The results are shown in Figs. 1 and 2. After a few hours the particles of less than 0.01μ radius have almost completely disappeared. With increasing time the maximum of the distribution shifts slowly to larger particle sizes and reaches values of 0.1μ at times which are already long with respect to the age of air masses. The considerable decrease in number concentration of the smaller particles is counterbalanced by a small increase of the larger ones. The number distribution of particles above 0.1μ in the log plot is therefore influenced only to a small degree by coagulation.

Fig. 2 shows the results of the computations based on the volume distribution. Since the total volume (or mass) of the aerosol must be constant, the decrease in mass of the Aitken nuclei is equal to the mass gain of the large particles. The coagulation curves can be interpreted as a mass transport from the Aitken particles to the larger ones. This is fairly small for a day or two, but may influence the chemical composition of the larger particles as time goes on. For short times, the largest particles become at least coated with smaller ones.

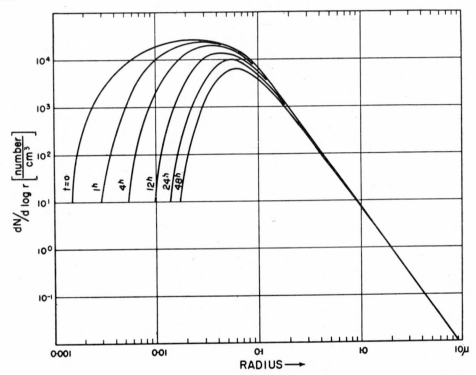

Fig. 4—Change of the model size distribution with time in a cloud of 100 droplets per cm³ with radii of 15μ by coagulation

A few remarks may be added. In the investigation of the chemical composition of aerosols, it was found that $(NH_4)_2SO_4$ is a major constituent of the particles with radii between 0.08 and 0.8μ. The amount of mass below 0.08μ as shown in Fig. 2 is comparatively small, and it is therefore very probable that this small mass has the same composition as the adjacent part of the larger particles.

It may be mentioned further in this connection that for many years the role of the numerous Aitken nuclei as contaminant of the air was obviously highly over-estimated. The role of the Aitken nuclei in cloud formation has also been over-estimated. As a rule, larger nuclei are present over continent and ocean and in the presence of these larger nuclei the Aitken nuclei are rarely involved in natural condensation. The accumulation of these facts by systematic work on natural aerosols was apparently delayed considerably simply because the availability of a very convenient instrument (Aitken counter) dictated its use. But the true nature and role of the natural aerosols can only be understood if the complete size distribution over three or four orders of magnitude in radius is considered as a unit.

If in the formula for $G(r)$ we introduce instead of $f(r)$ a distribution $kf'(r)$, where k is a constant, we obtain

$$G(f(r)) = kG(f(r))$$

The size distribution at a 10,000-ft altitude in the Alps (Fig. 3) had nearly the same shape as our model derived from ground observations except that the concentration is

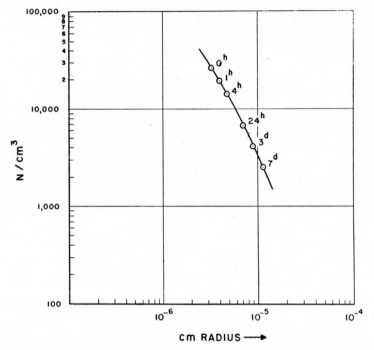

FIG. 5—Total number of nuclei as function of the mean radius and time, calculated from Fig. 1

lower by a factor of 10. The coagulation curves in Figs. 1 and 2, therefore, remain valid for these altitudes if the times are multiplied by 10. This indicates that the changes in size distribution caused by coagulation in higher levels of the troposphere are unimportant. This statement is scarcely influenced by small changes with altitudes of various constants which enter the calculation, as for instance T, η, and l.

Most of the space in the troposphere is cloud-free. It is of interest to see, however, how the size distribution is influenced by the presence of cloud droplets. A cloud of $N = 100$ droplets per cm³ with an average radius of $R = 15\mu$ was assumed. The decrease of nuclei can then easily be calculated from

$$G = -\kappa NR \int_{r_l}^{r_n} \left(\frac{1}{\rho} + \frac{a}{\rho^2}\right) f(\rho)\,d\rho$$

since $R \gg \rho$. Fig. 4 represents the results. The rate of coagulation is similar to that of Fig. 1, but does not decrease so rapidly with time. Since the lifetime of clouds is of the order of hours, the effect of clouds on coagulation of aerosols does not exceed considerably that without clouds under normal conditions. This explains the well-known fact, that a sizeable nuclei concentration is almost always found in clouds over continents.

Figs. 1 and 2 show that, during the coagulation process, the average radius increases with decreasing total number of particles. In Fig. 5 this relation was plotted as a function of time. The decrease of the total number of particles is nearly identical with that of the number of Aitken nuclei (radii below 0.1μ). This is in good agreement with the observation that aged aerosols, that is, in areas remote from smoke and other aerosol sources have low concentrations, but high mean sizes. This has been confirmed at different places over the world [JUNGE, 1955].

Summarizing the results we conclude: (a) Under normal concentrations of nuclei at ground level, the smaller Aitken nuclei decrease rapidly and limit the size distribution at radii of about 0.005 to 0.01μ. (b) The coagulation process does not influence very much the size distribution of particles with radii larger than 0.1μ.

The influence of gravity on the particle size distribution—Under the influence of gravity, particles precipitate from the atmosphere according to Stokes' law. If the particle concentration decreases with increasing altitude, as normally observed, the precipitation must be counteracted by eddy diffusion, resulting in a flux of particles from lower to higher layers in the atmosphere. With a few exceptions, the Earth's surface is the source of the atmospheric aerosols. The question of the influence of gravity on particle-size distribution, therefore, can be reduced to the question: Under normal conditions of eddy diffusion, what sized particles can be raised from the Earth's surface to penetrate to higher levels of the atmosphere?

This question can be solved by calculation under certain simplified conditions. We will start with the oceans. A number of reliable measurements of particle size distributions are available from the work of WOODCOCK [1952] and MOORE and MASON [1954] (see Fig. 3). Here the surface of the ocean is the single source, which can be assumed to be fairly uniform over wide areas, especially in the regions of the trade winds where most data are obtained. The production rate $q(r)$ per cm^2 and sec of particles with radius r is a function only of wind speed.

With good approximation the austausch coefficient is linear for the lower layers above the sea surface [LETTAU, 1939]

$$A = \rho u_5 \kappa (z+b) = a(z+b)$$

where u_5 = wind speed at an altitude of five meters (m/sec)
   κ = Karman's constant = 0.4
   z = altitude (m)
   b = roughness parameter of the sea surface (cm)
   ρ = density of air (g/cm^3).

Data on b are not too accurate and are contradictory. Most authors [for example, see NEUMANN, 1948] agree that it is not very dependent on wind speed and wave height. For average conditions 4 cm is a reasonable approximation.

Above altitudes of some 50 m the austausch coefficient sometimes goes through a more or less pronounced maximum and assumes roughly constant values with increasing altitude [LETTAU, 1939, p.115]. This value for the higher layers is determined by strength of convection. We approximate these conditions by the analytical expression

$$A = \frac{a(z+b)}{1+a(z+b)/c}$$

For small values of z, A is approximated by $A = a(z+b)$ and for large z, A becomes almost constant $A_{\infty} = c$. This expression for A covers the activity of eddy diffusion fairly well, including the convection or some semi-periodic circulation pattern.

The differential equation which controls the concentration n of particles of radius r with altitude is given by

$$\frac{\partial n}{\partial t} = \frac{\partial}{\partial z}\left(\frac{A}{\rho}\frac{\partial n}{\partial z}\right) - \frac{\partial (nw)}{\partial z}$$

The solution gives the particle concentration $n = n(r, t, z)$ as a function of particle radius, time, and altitude. If A is variable, there is no analytical solution, and even numerical solutions encounter considerable difficulties. As will be shown at another place, the observations indicate that steady conditions are often approximated, and therefore $\partial n/\partial t$ can be set equal to zero. This is especially true for the layers lower than 50 m which are the most important ones for our problem, as the results will show.

With $\partial n/\partial t \equiv 0$ the ratio $\epsilon = n_z/n_{z=0}$ as a function of particle size can be calculated. This ratio will indicate to what extent particles can penetrate to higher levels. We find

$$\epsilon = \left(\frac{z+b}{b}\right)^{\frac{wp}{a}} \exp \left(\frac{wz\rho}{c}\right)$$

This expression is evaluated in Fig. 6 with various values for the parameters. In the upper part of Fig. 6 the calculations are based on $A_{\infty} = 400$ g cm^{-1}sec^{-1}, $b = 4$ cm and three different wind speeds at 5 m, $u_5 = 5$, 10, and 20 m/sec covering the normal range of winds for those areas where measurements are available. The outstanding result is that the fraction of particles which can penetrate to higher levels, drops very sharply to zero in a relatively small size range. In order to compare these results more conveniently, we define, somewhat arbitrarily, the upper limit for the size distribution is represented by the value $\epsilon = 0.2$. Fig. 7 shows that it does not vary very much with wind speed.

In the lower part of Fig. 6, the wind speed was fixed $u_5 = 5$ m/sec, but the parameters A_{∞} and b were considerably changed. It can be seen from Fig. 7 that the ϵ values are not very sensitive to these changes. Therefore, we feel that the calculations about the upper limit of the size distribution of maritime aerosols, which are presented here, are

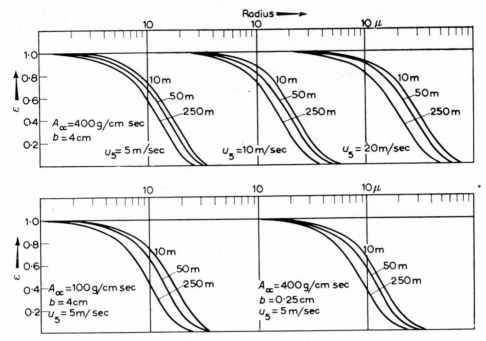

FIG. 6—Ratio ϵ over the ocean calculated for different parameters (A_∞, b, and u_5) and altitude

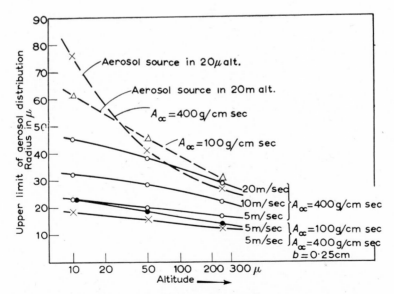

FIG. 7—Comparison of the calculated upper limits of aerosol distribution under various conditions from Fig. 5 and Fig. 8

fairly valid, although some of the parameters, especially those for the austausch, may only be approximate. In Fig. 8 the calculations are compared with Woodcock's measurements. As a matter of convenience, his measurements were plotted as log volume distributions (Fig. 3). From these curves the ϵ values can be derived under the assumption that the volume distribution would be constant without interference of gravity. Fig. 8 exhibits that the absolute values of the observed and calculated upper limits for average winds agree as well as one can expect from these calculations. The variation of the observed ϵ values with wind speed, however, is more pronounced. This probably indicates that with higher wind speed the volume distribution is not constant, but increases with particle size, a consequence which seems to be reasonable.

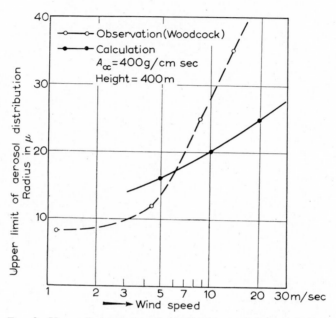

FIG. 8—Upper limit of aerosol distribution according to Fig. 6 compared with observations of Woodcock

This interpretation of the upper limit of the particle size of Woodcock's measurements indicates that the production of particles on the sea surface extends to large particles. This is supported by data of Moore and Mason, which are included in Fig. 3. Woodcock's data were obtained in the trade-wind areas in Hawaii, Florida, and south Australia, at cloud level (about 600 m). Moore measured from the deck of a weather ship about 10 meters above the sea surface. His values for Beaufort 3 and 5 agree well with Woodcock's values, except for the larger particles, which do not decrease so rapidly in Moore's data. This is at least in qualitative agreement with our calculations.

Over land, conditions are much more complicated. One of the main sources of aerosols, the smokes of industrial and residential areas in populated zones, are by no means distributed uniformly. They also are discharged from stacks into layers of the atmosphere up to more than 100 m and not from the surface proper. Because of the varying structure of the land surface, reasonable approximations of A as a function of altitude are very difficult. We tried to approximate these complex conditions by choosing the following model: We assume the sources (chimneys, stacks) to have an average height of 20 m and to be distributed uniformly. We further assume A to have the same distribution as over the ocean, and choose $A_\infty = 400$, and $A_\infty = 100$, and $b = 4$ cm. The calculation can then be done easily when we take the 20 m level as zero. Fig. 9 shows the results.

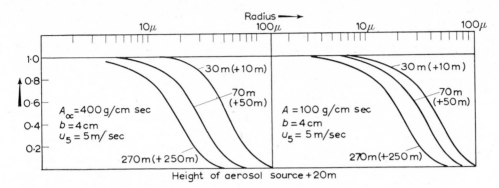

FIG. 9—Ratio ϵ for different altitudes with the aerosol source in 20 m above ground

Since the particles start in a layer with a much higher A, a much larger fraction of the larger ones can penetrate to higher levels than over the ocean (see also Fig. 7). At 50 m altitude and $u_5 = 5$ m/sec the upper limits of the particle size, according to our definition, are 46 and 41 μ for $A_\infty = 100$ and 400 respectively compared with 20μ under the same conditions over the ocean. The decrease by a factor of two roughly, however, is amazingly small compared with the considerable difference in the models. Outside the source areas, it must be expected that the upper limit drops, since the thin layers above the surface which have higher concentrations of particles above 20μ will soon be cleared by precipitation. This is in good qualitative agreement with the observation that in large towns particle sizes exceed 20μ, but that in rural districts the upper limit again fluctuates around 20μ.

Summarizing the results we conclude: (a) Size distributions below a particle size of about 5–10μ radius are not seriously affected by gravity under normal conditions over the ocean or over land. Particles of these sizes can easily penetrate to higher levels of the troposphere. (b) Gravity limits the size distribution in a rather sharp manner around radii of 20μ, depending on the conditions of eddy diffusion. This is in good agreement with the observations.

An attempt to explain the size distribution of natural aerosols—In the preceding sections, well-founded explanations could be offered for the size limitations of our natural aerosol. The question which now arises is not so easy to solve: Why is there an approximately constant log volume distribution of the particles over continents between these limits? We must admit that no physical forces come to mind which may be responsible for the trend towards an equal log volume distribution in the size range from about 0·1 to about 10μ radius. Fig. 2 shows clearly that the coagulation does not affect this size range seriously. The same is true for the precipitation by gravity. The electrical charge and the mobility of the nuclei in an electric field in this size range are, under normal conditions, so small that such forces can have no bearing on our problem.

On the basis of these facts, we feel that the observed size distribution may be the result of a vast mixing process of the large number of aerosol sources over the continent. It is a statistical phenomenon rather than the result of a physical process.

In order to explain this in more detail we have to start with a single aerosol source. Enough evidence is available in the literature to show that the mean radius of particle sizes of different smoke and dust sources can vary over a wide range between 0·01 and 100μ, depending on the individual conditions. This includes the size range in which we are interested. In general, the single source exhibits a size distribution which can be well represented by a Gaussian distribution. Experience shows that in order to get a symmetrical Gaussian distribution the log r scale rather than the linear scale must be used [HERDAN, 1953]. Because of the complexity of the processes of formation, no explicit reason can be given for this experimental fact. However, it is reasonably clear that differences of equal amount in excess or deficiency from the mean radius are not equally likely, but that ratios of equal amount in excess or deficiency from the mean value may be expected to be equally likely. It can be shown theoretically that the grinding process, for instance, very likely yields a log normal distribution. If r is the radius, the log normal size distribution is given by

$$n = (2\pi)^{-\frac{1}{2}}(\log \delta)^{-1}\exp\left[-\tfrac{1}{2}\left(\frac{\log r - \log r_m}{\log \delta}\right)^2\right]$$

where δ is the geometric standard deviation of the distribution of ratios around the geometric mean volume r_m. Most commonly a log normal probability graph is used to verify if a certain distribution obeys a log normal law, which would be represented by a straight line.

From these experiences we may conclude that the log r scale describes in the best way the complexity of processes which result in particle-size distributions. This is considered to be an important fact for further discussion, for it indicates that the log r scale is also most likely the one which describes the mixing process of a large number of aerosol sources. From the size distributions the volume distributions can easily be obtained. In the case of the log normal distribution we find

$$V = (8\pi)^{\frac{1}{2}}r^3(3\log \delta)^{-1}\exp\left[-\tfrac{1}{2}\left(\frac{\log r - \log r_m}{\log \delta}\right)^2\right]$$

We now assume a large number of aerosol sources with a wide range of geometric mean radii r_m and standard deviations δ. If these aerosols are mixed, a very broad distribution will result. The size and volume distribution of our natural aerosols between the radii $r = 0·1$ and 10μ is expected to be the result of such a mixing process. On the basis of this hypothesis, the observation of a nearly constant log volume distribution means that the absolute amount of substance contributed by the various sources in the different log r intervals is nearly equal. It would be hard, of course, to accept this explanation if the third power law would hold true exactly. But the observations indicate that the exponent three is but a first approximation and often fluctuates between the limits 2·5 and 3·5. Although this does not show up too much in the number distribution curves if they are plotted on the log scales as is usually done (see Fig. 1), it creates considerable differences in log volume distribution plots. The exponents 2·5 and 3·5 respectively, result in concentration ratios between particles of 0·1 and 10μ radius of 10 : 1 or vice versa. The mixing process, therefore, has only to yield a very rough approximation of a constant log volume distribution in order to explain the observation. However, the trend toward the constant log volume distribution is without doubt obvious, and seems to be a basic feature of the continental aerosol sources (Fig. 3).

We feel that this trend toward an approximate constant log volume distribution is the basic problem of the size distribution of aerosols over the continent. Unfortunately, it will be hard, perhaps impossible, to prove this hypothesis because it implies a survey of the size distribution of all the numerous sources which contribute to the aerosol content of an air mass. But a number of observations can easily be explained on the basis of this theory. Strong deviations should occur when a single source of aerosol becomes predominant in a large air mass, as with volcanic eruptions or huge forest fires. The unusual optical phenomena observed during these periods and only then confirm our conclusion that only a single source of geophysical scale is able to disturb severely the normally balanced mean distribution in the absence of condensation (for example, see PENNDORF [1953]). Condensation and cloud formation is another process which can disturb profoundly the size distribution between 0·1 and 10μ radii. VOLZ [1954] observed characteristic optical phenomenon of the scattering function around the sun after the dissipation of cloud layers which he related to deviations from the normal aerosol size distribution. Finally, it has to be expected from our theory that systematic local deviations will occur according to the characteristic composition of the local aerosol sources, the local 'climate' of the aerosol mixture.

The oceans are a widespread single source in this sense. Recent observations indicate that the production of sea-spray particles below 0·8μ radius is very small and that the particle-size distribution in pure maritime air is considerably different from that over the continents. Fig. 3 shows the log volume distribution of the measurements of Woodcock, and Moore and Mason. These are the only measurements so far available, but unfortunately they do not extend below 1μ radius, so that nothing is known about maritime aerosol size distributions below 1μ. From our chemical analysis data in Hawaii we can draw the conclusion that the size distribution must drop considerably as indicated by the single point at $r = 0.28\mu$ radius.

In accordance with the fact that the oceans present a single source the log volume distribution is constant only over a narrow part of the log r scale. This, of course, will hold true only in pure maritime air remote from continental influences. Over wide areas along the coast of the continents a mixture of the continental and maritime type will be observed. Our chemical analysis data strongly indicate that even in the center of big oceans (Hawaii) traces of continental influence can be detected. A wide variety of aerosol distributions will, therefore, be encountered in coastal zones, depending on the history of the air masses.

REFERENCES

HERDAN, G., *Small-particle Statistics*, Elsevier Pub. Co., Houston, 113pp., 1953.

ISRAEL, H. and L. SCHULZ, Ueber die Groessenverteilung der atmosphaerischen Ionen, *Met. Zs.*, v.49, pp.226–233, 1932.

JUNGE, CHR., The size distribution and aging of natural aerosols as determined from electrical and optical data on the atmosphere, *J. Met.*, v.12, pp.13–25, 1955.

C

LETTAU, H., Atmosphaerische Turbulenz, Akademische Verlagsges, Leipzig, pp.72–00, 1939.

MOORE, D. J. and B. J. MASON, The concentration, size distribution and production of large salt nuclei over the oceans, *Q.J.R. Met. Soc.*, v.80, pp.583–590, 1954.

NEUMANN, G., Ueber den Tangentialdruck des Windes und die Rauhigkeit der Meeresoberflaeche, *Zs. fuer Met.*, v.2, pp.193–203, 1948.

PENNDORF, R., On the phenomenon of the colored sun, especially the blue sun, September 1950, *Geophysical Res. Pap.*, no.20, 41pp., 1953.

VOLZ, F., Die Optik und Meteorologie der atmosphaerischen Truebung, *Ber. Deut. Wetterdienst*, no.13, pt.2, 47pp., 1954.

WHYTLAW-GRAY, R. and H. S. PATTERSON, *Smoke: a Study of Aerial Disperse Systems*, E. Arnold and Co., London, pp.27–00, 1932.

WOODCOCK, A., Salt nuclei in marine air as a function of altitude and wind force, Tech. Rep. 3, Naval Res. Contract Nonr–798(00), 8pp., 1952.

DISCUSSION

Mr. Alfred H. Woodcock—In making estimates of the Austausch over the sea, I wonder what kind of assumption you made concerning the size of the turbulence elements?

Dr. Junge—The Austausch coefficient comprises all sizes of turbulent elements as they influence the eddy diffusion. The larger elements are, of course, much more efficient for the mixing process than the smaller ones. The value of the Austausch in my paper is representative of average convective conditions which prevail over the oceans, especially in the trade-wind areas.

It is very hard to derive exact values of the mean free-path length. The structure of turbulence is very complicated, and the use of the Austausch coefficient eliminates these difficulties. I do not know, however, how far the presence of large, rotating convective cells, which are sometimes present over the oceans, is included in the Austausch values. But it is fortunate that our results are fairly independent of details in the vertical structure of the eddy diffusion.

Dr. E. M. Fournier d'Albe—Do you think the discrepancy between Woodcock's measured size and your calculated size distributions can be explained on the basis of the evaporation of the droplets as they leave the surface and rise?

Dr. Junge—I think the explanation is simply that with increasing wind speed the larger particles are produced at a higher rate and not a rate which is independent of the size. Though this effect should be expected, no data are available up to now.

Mr. Woodcock—I want just briefly to mention bubbles in the sea. I notice that during high winds the production of bubbles and the introduction of bubbles into the sea is much greater and the bubbles are carried down much deeper in the water. On looking out a porthole in the *Atlantis* on the lee side of the ship, and when the ship was rolled under, I could see that the bubbles were carried much deeper under strong wind conditions than under light conditions. I think this would favor coalescence of bubbles and thus make more large bubbles. We know that large bubbles make more large droplets than small ones.

We find that melting snow produces a prodigious number of small bubbles, and we expect that raindrops also produce many bubbles upon striking the sea surface.

Dr. Richard M. Schotland—Did you assume in your analysis that the particle coagulation resulted from strictly Brownian motion? Also, since the collision efficiency is probably quite small for these particles, would this have a significant effect upon your calculations?

Dr. Junge—I assumed that collision occurred strictly by Brownian motion. Since the majority of the aerosol particles are droplets with normal relative humidities the coalescence efficiency is probably not too far from unity, as we assumed. With a smaller coefficient of coalescence the time scale would be stretched, but otherwise there would be no effect on the results. Our calculations are supported by observations in closed rooms, although a strict comparison is not possible.

Dr. H. J. aufm Kampe—I think Schotland's point is important. For the large sizes there is a certain compromise between the coagulation due to the Brownian motion and the complicated coagulation theory which Hitschfeld may bring out tomorrow. It is difficult to make it really a strict theory because we do not exactly know at what point regular coagulation comes into the picture.

Dr. Junge—The only open question in my calculations is the coefficient of coalescence. Nothing definite is known, but it seems to be fairly high.

Dr. James P. Lodge, Jr.—We have some data which have not actually been published. The published data break up our salt particles only into: <3 microns, 3–6, 6–10, and >10. However, at Chicago we actually measured three size classes below three microns. I believe those were: 0–0·7, 0·7–1·2, and 1·2–3 microns in diameter. A plot of a few mean distributions checked very nicely with your constant volume distribution. But it might be worthwhile for someone at Chicago now to dig out those distributions from my data and plot them, because I think they would tend to confirm the distribution you assumed.

THE QUESTION OF METEORITIC DUST
IN THE ATMOSPHERE

VINCENT J. SCHAEFER

The Munitalp Foundation, Inc., Schenectady, New York

Abstract—Attempts to collect meteoritic dust from melted snow and warm frontal rain samples by the magnet method showed that, although samples are obtainable wherever the method is tried, analysis and observation indicate that most of the residues gathered are of terrestrial origin. Experiments directed towards testing the magnet gathered dust for ice nucleating properties resulted in negative results at $-25°C$. A further attempt to form ice nuclei by vaporizing bits of an iron-nickel-cobalt meteorite also produced negative results at $-25°C$.

THE entrance of meteors into the Earth's atmosphere, some of which reach the ground as meteorites, has been noted for many centuries. Those reaching the Earth's surface, in the size ranging from a few ounces to a few tons and which are easily found and recognized, represent a small fraction of the total quantity of extra-terrestrial material that enters the atmosphere. The largest meteorites of the type that produced the craters in Arizona, northeastern Canada, and eastern Siberia, probably exploded upon impact with some of the vapor subsequently condensing to form the tiny iron-nickel pellets, such as are found in certain areas near the crater in Arizona.

Smaller meteors, many of them not larger than grains of sand, may be seen as they make a momentary streak of light in the night sky as they enter the upper atmosphere and burn. The smaller dust in the micron-size range, consisting probably of the burned residues of larger meteors or the condensate of the vapor from explosions, is thought to settle into the atmosphere without further modification.

The literature contains many references to dust falls which have been attributed to extra-terrestrial intrusions of meteoritic dust clouds. The more interesting and important of these have been reviewed and summarized by BUDDHUE [1950].

Recently, due to the studies of BOWEN [1953], interest in the subject of meteoritic dust has received new stimulus. He has published a number of graphs showing precipitation anomalies, which he suggests may have resulted from the seeding of clouds by meteoritic dust settling into them. To support this theory, he has shown that the four precipitation peaks in the month of January occur about thirty days after the Earth's passage through the orbits of the Geminids, the Ursids, and the Quadrantids, which occur on December 13, 22, and January 3, respectively. If his thesis can be established by observation and experiment, it would represent an important advance in experimental meteorology and atmospheric physics.

Attempts to obtain meteoritic dust for study of its ice-nucleating properties—
Early in 1948, while conducting an extensive survey of the ice nucleation properties of naturally occurring terrestrial dusts, I made an attempt to secure samples of meteoritic dust for studies. In this search I was unsuccessful, although I found a number of soils

and clays (mostly of volcanic origin), which served as excellent ice nuclei in the temperature range of −15 to −25°C [SCHAEFER, 1949]. About two years ago, I renewed my efforts to obtain meteoritic dust and finally decided to attempt to collect samples myself. Since that time I have obtained samples from a number of different places, using the magnet method described by Buddhue.

This method is quite simple. It consists essentially of covering a strong magnet with a sheet of thin plastic. The magnet is swept through the water, snow, dust, or air sample for varying lengths of time, and the catch examined by removing the thin plastic sheet from the magnet. If the search is successful, localized regions of dust will be concentrated at the poles of the magnet, especially at corners and edges where the magnetic flux is greatest.

The residue may then be pulled into a tiny pile by manipulating the magnet under the plastic sheet, or by sweeping it with a drop of water moved with a glass rod, which leaves the dust in a localized zone upon evaporation. Under some conditions, a magnet may be used effectively with the water drop. Under no condition should the dust collection be permitted to touch the bare magnet, since it is virtually impossible to recover the fine particles from a strong magnet.

The gathering of particles by the magnet method would presumably only recover residues from metallic meteorites of the iron-nickel complex. However, since these comprise the type that have been studied most intensively under the term 'meteoritic dust', it seemed worthwhile to study such particles, especially with respect to their appearance, composition and ice-nucleating properties.

Collection of dusts concentrated by magnet—The samples studied thus far in my laboratory have been gathered in the eastern Mohawk Valley of New York, the Green Mountains of Vermont, the White Mountains of New Hampshire, the Selkirk Mountains of Idaho, and the Wallowa Mountains of Oregon. Most samples have been obtained by melting snow accumulated during the winter of 1954–55, although some earlier samples were obtained from rainwater coming from warm front rains and local thunderstorms. There has been no difficulty in obtaining adequate samples of particles that are attracted to a magnet. While the quantities gathered are measured in micrograms, the techniques used for preliminary studies have not suffered because of lack of material. All samples were gathered by magnet from water suspension or sediments, after the rain had fallen or the snow melted. An average sample consisted of 20 liters of water. When concentrated on an area of one cm², the sample appeared as a grey, dusty area with most particles smaller than one micron. It was found desirable to use polyethylene trays or bags to collect the water. Trouble was encountered while using enamel-coated photographic trays. As these have a steel core, it was found that a considerable number of the particles were apparently magnetized, since they tended to stick to the bottom of the tray, and were only recovered after repeated and careful sweeping of the bottom with a strong bar magnet. Thin transparent sheets of vinyl plastic, of the type used for wrapping food, were found to be eminently suited for covering the magnet. An Alnico V bar magnet, having a cross section 1·5 cm × 20 cm long, was employed for sampling.

The analysis of dust collected by the magnet method—A common procedure for indicating that dust gathered by the magnet method is of extra-terrestrial origin is to test for nickel. If the test for nickel is positive, the material is assumed likely to have a meteoritic source.

A highly sensitive and more discriminating method now available is the x-ray spectrometer. The sample is placed on a plastic sheet in a goniometer head, rotated slowly in the axis of a collimated beam of x-rays, and the diffracted rays measured by a Geiger counter. This signal is totalized continuously and recorded on a moving chart. The various metallic elements have the property of diffracting x-rays at specific wavelengths. These are known and can readily be identified. Thus the finished curve shows the relative amount of each metallic constituent in the sample being tested, as well as the various elements present.

To establish a reference curve for comparing the samples obtained from snow and rainwater, filings from an iron-nickel meteorite found in Africa were prepared in a concentration equivalent to the samples at hand. A curve was run for this sample on the x-ray spectrometer, and the values obtained are shown in Table 1. A similar run was then made for a sample gathered by magnet from the meltwater of snow, which fell during the passage of an intense cold front during February 10–11, 1955. This storm was the most intense of the winter and occurred along a line extending along the East coast, from the Middle Atlantic states to western New England, with a trajectory from the west and southwest. The x-ray spectrometer values for this sample are compared to the meteorite filings in Table 1. These values are quite similar to those observed with a good grade of terrestrial iron.

Table 1. Sample Source

Element	Iron-nickel Meteorite	Mt. Washington, N.H. Snow	Mt. Gisborne, Ida. Snow	Priest River, Ida. Varve Clay	Russel Mt., Oreg. Snow
Iron	>1000 C.P.Sec.	>1000 C.P.Sec.	>1000 C.P.Sec.	>1000 C.P.Sec.	600 C.P.Sec.
Nickel	>1000	200	0	150	40
Cobalt	500	0	0	0	0
Manganese	10	20	50	10	...
Chromium	0	15	30	25	...
Vanadium	0	0	...	6	...
Zinc	0	0	...	5	2
Lead	0	0	30	2	...
Titanium	0	10	100	...	...
Copper	...	...	50	...	10

An examination of this sample, under the light microscope, showed it to contain many spherical particles, semi-transparent and opaque. These have the appearance and size very similar to those described and illustrated by Buddhue, and described as samples of meteoritic dust.

A sample of dust, obtained by magnet from the same snow storm, was tested for its effectiveness as an ice-crystal nucleus. The sample was spread as a very thin layer of dust on a piece of filter paper, held with one hand in the top zone of a cold chamber, and given several sharp snaps with the thumb and second finger of the other hand. This procedure is a simple but very effective method of producing an aerosol from a small sample of dust.

Although the temperature of the cold chamber was −25°C, no ice crystals could be observed to form in the supercooled cloud into which they were projected. Under similar conditions most samples of volcanic soils and ash would show much activity.

Samples from several other localities have been tested by the x-ray spectrometer, but thus far none has produced curves resembling the iron-nickel meteorite filings. The presence of only iron, nickel, and cobalt in the meteorite sample contrasts with the absence of cobalt, the predominance of iron and the presence of manganese, titanium, and chromium in easily measurable quantities in the snow-dust sample. This demonstrates the sensitivity of the method, as well as its value for studying such small samples of atmospheric residues.

Since the result of the snow-dust evaluation indicates the collected dust particles are of terrestrial iron origin, it is likely that they are from the open hearth or Bessemer furnaces of Michigan, Indiana, or Pennsylvania, upwind from the region where the tested sample was obtained.

Another approach was made to finding traces of meteoritic dust in precipitation. This utilized a porous ion-exchange membrane, designed to absorb metal ions from water preferentially. By stirring the water sample for 12 hours with a small piece of the rubber-like membrane, and then scanning it with the x-ray spectrometer as described earlier, the relative concentrations of the metallic ions that had been in the water were determined.

Although the results of this study are not sufficiently completed for final publication, the efforts to date have failed to show evidence of the iron-nickel-cobalt ratios, which might indicate the presence of very small particles or dissolved residues of metallic meteoritic dust. In the snow-water samples from the Selkirk Mountains of northern Idaho, the dust attracted to the magnet appeared, under the microscope, to be considerably different from the samples obtained in the northeastern United States. The particles were angular, with a crystalline appearance, and probably consisted mostly of magnetite from the glacial clays of the region that becomes airborne during snow-free periods of the winter.

Problems posed by the analysis of magnet-collected dust—The results to date indicate the serious problems encountered in attempts to collect meteoritic dust. In view of the ease of collecting dust from precipitation with a magnet, even in regions which would seem to be free of air pollution, the big question arises: How is it possible to avoid contamination from terrestrial sources? The selection of collecting regions far distant from pollution sources becomes an increasingly difficult, if not impossible problem. The tremendous distances over which polluted air moves illustrates the situation. During the summer of 1954, on two occasions I followed, by airplane, a smoke plume from western Washington to Los Angeles, where it originated. The smoke was spilling over the rim of mountains to the north of the basin. In the Spokane, Washington, area, it had risen to a level of about 20,000 ft. At several breaks in the mountains, notably the gap between Mt. Lassen and Mt. Shasta, long streamers could be seen flowing eastward from the main plume of smoke.

This problem has been pointed up even more clearly by the long distances over which the radioactive fallout from nuclear explosions have been observed. Because of the probable widespread distribution of particles from terrestrial sources that are attracted by a magnet, it is questionable whether this method can be relied upon to obtain meteoritic dust samples. The quantity of material, found in precipitation and attracted to a magnet, is usually so large that, if meteoritic dust is present, it can only be a very small fraction of the sample collected. Unless obtained from ancient sea sediments, deep peat bogs and similar deposits, the samples could easily have been contaminated with recent pollution from industrial sources. But even the ancient deposits may be suspect, since it is likely that volcanic eruptions would emit spherules containing enough iron to be attracted by a magnet. How to separate the small amount of extra-terrestrial dust, which may be present, from the larger quantity of terrestrial material is a problem that is not easy to solve.

Studies of the ice-nucleating properties of the residues from an iron-nickel-cobalt meteorite—Failing in an attempt to obtain bona fide meteoritic dust samples for study of their ice-nucleating properties, an experimental approach was tried. A small sliver of an iron-nickel meteorite was mounted on the end of a Tesla coil, and a large spark was drawn between the sliver and a large piece of the meteorite. The vaporized residue was formed in a cold chamber at $-25°C$, both before and after a supercooled cloud was formed. No trace of ice-crystal formation could be detected from the residues, although the large increase in nuclei following the sparking procedure indicated that particles had been formed.

When this procedure is performed, using silver contacts with a trace of iodine vapor present to coat the silver residues, to form silver iodide, tremendous numbers of ice crystals develop within a few seconds.

Conclusions—The results of this study indicate that if meteoritic dust is important in the modification of clouds and the increase in precipitation as suggested by Bowen, the metallic iron-nickel-cobalt type is not the dust which is important. Further study should be made of the stony types, which are probably as common. However, unless the concentrations of these latter residues are considerably higher than that of the natural foreign particle nuclei of terrestrial origin, it is difficult to assess the role which they might play.

Our studies at Mt. Washington have shown the great variability in concentration of foreign-particle ice nuclei [SCHAEFER, 1954]. However, there are times when the concentration reaches values of at least a million per cubic meters at $-20°C$. At least half of the time, the concentration is of the order of 10,000 per cubic meter. The occurrences of the higher concentrations are highly variable, however, since they depend on such phenomena as dust storms, volcanic eruptions, etc.

If effective ice nuclei enter the atmosphere, when the Earth encounters the orbit of a meteoritic dust cloud, and in some manner the smaller particles affect precipitation over wide areas, the phenomenon is of primary importance to meteorological science. The results described in this paper indicate some of the experimental difficulties that must be surmounted, if one intends to investigate the significance of meteoritic dust to cloud and atmospheric physics, as well as experimental meteorology.

Acknowledgments—Grateful thanks are extended to Paul Zemany and his co-workers of the General Electric Research Laboratory, who made the x-ray spectrometer runs on the dusts collected by magnet from rain and snow samples as described in this paper.

REFERENCES

Bowen, E. G., The influence of meteoritic dust on rainfall, *Austral. J. Phys.*, v.6, pp.490–497, 1953.

Buddhue, J. D., *Meteoritic Dust*, University of New Mexico Press, 102pp. Albuquerque, 1950.

Schaefer, V. J., The formation of ice crystals in the laboratory and the atmosphere, *Chem. Rev.*, v.44, pp.291–320, 1949.

Schaefer, V. J., The concentration of ice nuclei in air passing the summit of Mt. Washington, *Bul. Amer. Met. Soc.*, v.35, pp.310–314, 1954.

DISCUSSION

Mr. Duncan C. Blanchard—Could you take a dozen different meteorites and expect to find the same relative abundance of the elements you have listed there? I was wondering how the ratio would vary from one meteorite to the next.

Dr. Vincent J. Schaefer—I can't answer that definitely. Off hand, I would expect that these other trace materials would undoubtedly be present in very low concentration. Unless one can show cobalt in the samples, it is difficult to prove they are meteoritic, because the cobalt is outstanding relative to the other materials, which are just traces.

Of course, this does not answer the case of the stony meteorite, which might well be a good source of meteoric material.

Mr. James E. Manson—I agree with Dr. Schaefer that this x-ray technique is a versatile one. Are these numbers total counts, or are they maxima?

Dr. Schaefer—Maxima.

Mr. Manson—I found the total count is more reproducible if you have the time to wait.

Dr. Schaefer—One could probably work this out with a planimeter.

Mr. Manson—If you use the standard Norelco unit, you can totalize them directly. But I'd also like to know if you examined the residue from the Tesla coil.

Dr. Schaefer—No. There was so little material that you couldn't even see it.

Mr. Manson—There is a method using a cheaper powder camera which I mentioned a couple of years ago that might be more applicable under limited budgets.

Mr. D. Lee Harris—A few months ago, when Bowen was discussing this hypothesis in Washington, I asked him why he would expect these iron particles to serve as ice nuclei. One suggestion he made was that approximately 40 per cent of the meteoritic material is silica. Of the six crystalline forms of silica, one has a form similar to ice; and so he assumed this silica material falling out might have a rather large percentage of this form.

His second way out of the difficulty is to call attention to the fact that we have such things as mother-of-pearl cloud and water vapor in the high atmosphere, that these particles might become coated with water and that the water would freeze in the very low temperatures in the upper stratosphere, and so we would really have homogenous nuclei.

Therefore, he feels that even though particles didn't test out in the cold box, it is of no real consequence.

SOME FACTS ABOUT METEORITIC DUST

CHRISTIAN E. JUNGE

Geophysics Research Directorate, Air Force Cambridge Research Center, New Bedford, Mass.

Abstract—A brief review is given of recent papers on meteoritic dust in an effort to substantiate Bowen's theory of periodic rain due to a large-scale natural seeding process. The present knowledge of the size distribution of meteoritic dust particles in the atmosphere makes it difficult to find sufficient proof for Bowen's theory.

Introduction—BOWEN [1953] recently claimed that certain peaks in rainfall intensity over wide parts of the world may be caused by ice nuclei originating from the dust of periodic meteor showers. The peaks of rainfall are restricted to narrow time intervals of a few days and are related to meteor showers occurring about thirty days previously.

As an essential part of his thesis, Bowen has to assume a mechanism, which makes it possible for a sharply defined cloud of meteoritic dust particles to arrive a month after formation at the upper troposphere over wide areas of the Earth. A more or less constant flux of meteoritic particles entering the troposphere is of no significance in this connection.

It is still an open question as to what extent the peaks in rainfall are statistically significant [OLIVER and OLIVER, 1955]. Assuming that they are real, the question may be raised about the occurrence of meteoritic dust in the atmosphere and the physics of its behavior based on our present knowledge. A number of recent papers deal with this subject, but they are scattered in various periodicals and are primarily concerned with optical and astronomical problems. The purpose of this paper is to relate this literature to cloud physics, and specifically to Bowen's theory.

Origin of meteoritic particles—The meteoritic particles which enter the atmosphere belong, with rare exceptions, to the solar system. VAN DE HULST [1947], ÖPIK [1951] and SIEDENTOPF and others [1953] find that the interplanetary dust is concentrated in a lens around the plane of the ecliptic and gives rise to the zodiacal light. This dust envelope is probably composed of particles with diameters between 1 and 1000μ. Smaller particles are completely removed by the Poynting-Robertson effect. Similarly, the larger particles spiral slowly into the Sun and those which are now between Sun and Earth must have passed the orbit of Jupiter. But, Jupiter removes all particles larger than about 1000μ. These limits are, of course, not exactly known because certain assumptions enter these calculations. However, van de Hulst found that the optical properties of the zodiacal light are in good agreement with these limits and with a continuous size distribution between them.

Although this quiescent dust cloud, which seems to exist in addition to the rapidly moving meteors and meteor showers, is of secondary importance for the present question, it should be mentioned. Since the particles of this cloud move around the Sun in orbits similar to that of the Earth, they enter the atmosphere with small geocentric velocities. The minimum velocity is 11·5 km/sec due to the gravitation of the Earth, so that the total geocentric velocity of these particles may range from 11·5 to about 20 km/sec. ÖPIK [1951] calculated from these data the fraction of particles entering the atmosphere which (a) melt and evaporate and do not reach the Earth's surface; (b) melt but do not evaporate and reach the surface of the Earth as 'spherules', that is, little spheres of magnetic iron components or glass-like material; (c) do not melt and reach the Earth's surface almost unaltered as so-called angular particles (Table 1).

Table 1. *Fraction of surviving and not surviving meteoritic dust particles, entering the atmosphere at 16 km/sec, according to* ÖPIK [1951]

Diameter limits	Original frequence of Van de Hulst	Particles which do not survive	Spherules	Angular particles
micron				
300–190	36	36	0	0
190–120	76	73	2	1
120– 75	160	145	12	3
75– 47	330	252	62	16
47– 30	690	280	330	80
30– 19	1400	0	1000	400
19– 12	2900	0	900	2000

Particles of these types (b) and (c) are observed at various places all over the Earth. Most of the particles have been collected with rain water, separated by a magnet from other (terrestrial) dust, and chemically and physically investigated [BUDDHUE, 1950; THOMSON, 1953]. They have also been found in deep-sea sediments [LAEVASTU and MELLIS, 1955]. There seems to be no doubt about their cosmic origin. Their size distribution and limits are in good agreement with the ÖPIK calculations. Considerably differences occur only with respect to the total annual deposit for the entire Earth calculated by these observers (Table 2).

Table 2. *Comparison of annual deposit of meteoritic dust calculated by different observers*

Total annual deposit for the whole earth in kg/year	Rate of deposit of 10μ (diameter) particles per cm²sec.	Concentration of 10μ particles in the troposphere per m³
Thomson (Wisconsin) 2×10^9	$0·6 \times 10^{-5}$	1·5
Buddhue (New Mexico) 5×10^7	$1·6 \times 10^{-7}$	0·04
Laevastu and Mellis (Pacific) $1·3 \times 10^5$ ...	$0·4 \times 10^{-9}$	0·0001

Angular particles together with spherules are also observed in rain water. But they are difficult to distinguish from ordinary dust particles so that exact data, as with the spherules, could not be obtained.

Although the agreement between observed and calculated sizes of spherules supports the idea that their origin is the dust cloud of the zodiacal light, Buddhue finds strong evidence in his long and careful observations that they are composed of the molten material swept away by the heated air from the surface of falling meteors. He, and also others, find, for instance, an increase of spheres after meteor showers which is sometimes considerable, as in his observations of an early part of the Orionid shower, October, 1947 [BUDDHUE, 1950, p.89ff]. The composition and size distribution of these particles were very similar to the 'normal' spherules. They cannot represent original (but molten) particles of the shower, because such small particles are likely to be expelled by the Poynting-Robertson effect [WYATT and WHIPPLE, 1950] soon from the swarm. But even if they were present in the swarm they could not have reached the Earth's surface because of the higher geocentric velocities of meteor showers (about 50 km/sec) which results in an upper limit of only a few microns for particles surviving in the atmosphere. Thus, sizes of particles of about 10μ diameter which would correspond to BOWEN'S [1953] fall times of thirty days are very likely secondary particles formed by the crumbling and melting of meteors in the atmosphere.

The particle concentration of the aforementioned Orionid shower was considerable, with a maximum around 10μ diameter. We calculated a concentration of these particles in the troposphere of $1500/m^3$. This value is orders of magnitude higher than the concentrations derived for the same particle size on the basis of the values for annual deposit (Table 2). Most observers agree that the spherules appear shortly, that is, a few days after the observed meteor showers.

Almost no spherules and angular particles were observed below 10μ diameter. This may be because of the sampling process, which prefers the larger particles. But the considerable agreement between different observers, places, and techniques support the idea that this limit is real. If we assume that these particles stem from the interplanetary dust cloud, such a limit should be expected and would be in agreement with Öpik's calculations (Table 1). The lower limit of the angular particles should then be different from that of the spherules and equal to the lower limit in this dust cloud, which is assumed to be 1μ.

If, on the other hand, spherules and angular particles are fragments of meteors, nothing can be said about their lower limit. Further and more careful observations are necessary to decide between these possibilities.

The average concentration of meteoritic material in the interplanetary space, calculated from observed meteors (visible and telescopic), is about three orders of magnitude less than that of the meteoritic dust cloud. Only in the case of the more dense showers will the concentration of meteoritic material in the atmosphere exceed that of the constant flux from the dust envelope around the ecliptic.

Although very little is known, the evaporation process is likely to create very fine particles, ranging in size from molecular dimensions to an estimated value of micron size. Their number may be especially large because the total mass of these fine particles is a considerable fraction of the meteoritic material entering the atmosphere (the non-surviving particles in Table 1). These secondary particles may be of special importance to our problem. There is indirect evidence of their presence (see below) but they have not been observed directly. Before we discuss them in more detail, some remarks should be made about the fall of meteoritic particles through the atmosphere.

Fall time and particle size—Link [Svesta, 1954] calculated the time of fall through the atmosphere of particles of different sizes and material (Fig. 1). The radius of spherical particles which correspond to Bowen's time of thirty days is 4·6 and 6μ respectively for different materials. But if a cloud of these particles is to arrive at the troposphere within 30 days after formation, this size must be uniform within a few per cent. The brief outline in the preceding section showed, however, that this is a rather

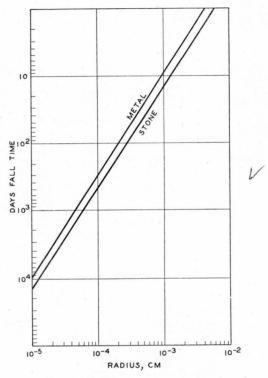

FIG. 1—Fall time of meteoritic dust as a function of size and material according to Link [Svesta, 1954]

unrealistic claim. Dust clouds with size distributions of the expected kind will spread over considerable vertical distances on their way down. These difficulties are even increased if turbulence and large-scale vertical and horizontal circulations are taken into account, for which there is good evidence in the layers between 70 and 100 km which is the level at which most particles come to a stop or melt and evaporate. These micro and macro wind structures will tend to smooth out existing variations in the vertical density distribution of meteoritic dust in the atmosphere, rather than to sharpen them.

Special evidence of fine meteoritic dust—A number of recent papers deal with optical phenomena related to meteor showers, which cannot be produced by the spheres and angular particles discussed under 'Origin of meteoritic particles'.

The most important phenomena are: (*a*) enlargement of the Earth's shadow, which is more intense at times of large meteoritic showers [Svesta, 1954]; (*b*) decrease in transparency of the atmosphere close to the time of Perseid activity [ZACHAROV, 1952]; and (c) a correlation between noctilucent clouds and meteor showers [BOWEN, 1953].

Careful investigation of these effects have left little doubt as to their reality. Svesta, Zacharov, and Giovanelli [GIOVANELLI, 1954] arrive at the conclusion that the particles which cause these phenomena must be in the size range of $0\cdot1$ to 1μ. Particles of this size, however, need more than a year to fall out (Fig. 1). In most cases, the listed optical disturbances disappear in about one month, however. To explain this considerable time discrepancy, several hypotheses have been made:

(a) The fall out by gravity is accelerated by eddy diffusion between 80 and 10 km, the troposphere acting as a sink for these particles by water vapor condensation upon them [SVESTA, 1954].

(b) Coagulation decreases the number of particles. This would explain the disappearance of the optical phenomena, but Giovanelli shows that the coagulation rate is far too small at the low concentrations of dust particles, which must be assumed.

(c) The particles consist of ice, sublimated on smaller meteoritic nuclei around 80 km altitude [SVESTA, 1954; GIOVANELLI, 1954]. The region between 70 and 85 km has the lowest temperatures, and therefore the highest probability of high relative humidities. Size and concentration of these particles would suffice to let them appear as noctilucent clouds, which are observed at about 80 km. When these ice-coated particles leave this zone on their way down, the ice evaporates and the optical phenomenon disappears.

(d) We may add here one more possibility: The dust layers are carried away by large-scale circulation systems, concentrating them in convergence zones and transferring them to lower layers. The few wind observations to date between 70 and 100 km altitude make it impossible to say anything concrete, but tentative circulation models support this idea [KELLOGG and SCHILLING, 1951].

Regardless of which explanation may be true, the meteoritic particles which are responsible for these phenomena are relatively small, and are possibly those secondary particles originated by evaporation of larger meteors. However, there is no indication of a mechanism by which these particles can reach the tropopause as a sharply defined cloud unless by large-scale subsidence. But, it is improbable that this will result in the arrival of such clouds over wide areas of the Earth after a constant time interval of 30 days.

Conclusions—The following conclusions are drawn:

(a) Particles with radii above a few microns occur in meteor showers in abundance. But their broad size distributions make it almost impossible to explain limited rain periods after thirty days.

(b) There is also evidence of particles below 1μ connected with meteor showers which seem to disappear much faster than can be expected by the usual fall time calculations. Several suggestions to explain this discrepancy, however, offer no possibility that these particles are responsible for the type of cloud seeding claimed by Bowen.

REFERENCES

BOWEN, E. G., The influence of meteoritic dust on rainfall, *Austral. J. Phys.*, v.6, pp.490–497, 1953.
BUDDHUE, J. D., *Meteoritic Dust*, University of New Mexico Press, 102pp., 1950.
GIOVANELLI, R. G., The attenuation of light by meteoric dust in the upper atmosphere, *Austral. J. Phys.*, v.7, pp.641–648, 1954.

Kellog, W. W. and G. F. Schilling, A proposed model of the circulation in the upper stratosphere, *J. Met.*, v.8, pp.222–230, 1951.

Laevastu, T. and O. Mellis, Extraterrestrial material in deep-sea deposits, *Trans. Amer. Geophys. Union*, v.36, pp.385–389, 1955.

Oliver, M. B. and V. J. Oliver, Rainfall and stardust, *Bul. Amer. Met. Soc.*, v.36, pp.147–151, 1955.

Öpik, E. J., Astronomy and the bottom of the sea, *Irish Astron. J.*, v.1, pp.145–158, 1951.

Siedentopf, H., A. Behr and H. Elsasser, Photoelectric observations of the zodiacal light, *Nature*, v.171, pp.1066–1067, 1953.

Svesta, Z., The problem of meteoritic dust layer in the earth atmosphere, *Bul. Astron. Inst. Czechosl.*, v.5, pp.91–98, 1954.

Thomsen, W. J., The annual deposit of meteoritic dust, *Sky and Telescope*, v.12, pp.147–148, 1953.

Van de Hulst, H. C., Zodiacal light in the solar corona, *Astrophys. J.*, v.105, pp.471–488, 1947.

Whipple, F. L., The theory of micro-meteorites, Part II, In heterothermal atmospheres, *Proc. Nat. Acad. Sci.*, v.37, pp.19–30, 1951.

Wyatt, S. P. and F. L. Whipple, The Poynting-Robertson effect on meteor orbits, *Astrophys. J.*, v.111, pp.134–141, 1950.

Zacharov, I., Influence des Perseides sur la transparence atmospherique, *Bul. Central Astr. Inst. Czechosl.*, v.5, pp.91–98, 1953.

DISCUSSION

Dr. David Atlas—I wonder if Dr. Bowen might suggest that the nucleating particles had a preference for the five micron diameter particles which were the ones which did take 29 days to settle?

Dr. Roscoe R. Braham, Jr.—I couldn't answer for Dr. Bowen. But I have talked with him at length about these problems, and I think some of his thoughts might run along this line.

We know a form of quartz called beta tridymite which at a temperature of about 700°C changes to a crystal form reasonably close to that of ice. The temperature to which incoming meteor particles are heated is a direct function of their size. If they exceed a certain size, they vaporize, whereas the ones quite small come into the atmosphere without being heated very much. Some particles with restricted size range could be heated to the inversion point of beta tridymite without being completely vaporized. It is likely that a five-to ten-micron diameter would be about the size to do this.

Dr. E. J. Workman—It seems to me that the biggest difficulty with Bowen's theory is the claim that the abundance of an ice-producing nucleus would influence precipitation considerably over the surface of the Earth. I think the Bergeron-Findeisen mechanisms play a very small, or at most not a controlling role in precipitation in New Mexico. I think they play a correspondingly small role in central Ohio thunderstorms, as you and some of my colleagues have pointed out.

It seems that we should go back now and ask what is the mechanism by which these particles increase rainfall over the world. An abundance of sublimation nuclei might produce the opposite effect. This has good physical basis and its validity does not depend upon any particular process of precipitation, but only upon the necessity for supercooled clouds.

If this ('negative' mechanism) applies, maybe we won't need to worry about the width of the time interval in Bowen's rainfall pattern quite so much, but rather we would have to worry about how it shuts off in exactly 30 days.

Dr. E. M. Fournier d'Albe—Could Dr. Junge tell us what effect the electrical charges carried by meteoritic dust would have on their movement in the Earth's magnetic field?

Dr. Christian E. Junge—Mr. Dubin of the Cambridge Research Center has developed a theory that meteoritic dust should be concentrated around the magnetic poles, because the particles are likely to carry charges, when they enter the atmosphere. In Table 2 the places are arranged in an order of increasing distance from the magnetic pole. In fact, the annual deposit decreases, but unfortunately this is not very conclusive, because the order is also one of decreasing industrial influence.

There are no observations or other indications of electrical charges. But a survey of reported meteoritic dust falls reveals that they occur more often in arctic areas than in middle latitudes. This would prove an electrical charge. This question is of great interest for geophysics.

Dr. Charles F. Brooks—There is so much more snow in the Alps than in the Arctic that meteoric dust would be so greatly diluted as not to be visible. The opportunity for concentration by sublimation, as in the Arctic, is also far less, for the warm season removes Alpine snow mostly by active melting and runoff.

Prof. Charles L. Hosler—I tested some beta tridymite but was unable to get ice crystals from it by dusting it into the chamber, even at —23°C. I wonder if anybody else has gotten the same results?

Dr. Helmut Weickmann—G. Schulz, Findeisen's assistant, found —10·5°C as the nucleating temperature of tridymite (Der Einfluss von Fremdköpern auf die Unterkühlungsfähigkeit des Wassers, Met. Rundschau, v.1, pp.237–241, 1947–48).

Dr. G. A. Wolff—There might be a positive result when the beta tridymite crystals are cleaved and used immediately.

Dr. Raymond Wexler—I remember talking Bowen's theory over with Prof. Houghton when it first came out, and we came to the conclusion that the biggest argument against Bowen's theory is actually in the statistics of rainfall itself.

Of the 50 years of data, with which he was concerned, the chances of moderate to heavy rain on any one calendar date might be one out of ten. This means he had an average of five cases per year which might vary from about two cases on one calendar date to perhaps ten cases on another.

As a result, you are bound to get an extremely irregular curve of rainfall from one calendar date to the next. Some peaks would be very much larger than others merely from chance. Hence from the statistical viewpoint alone, you cannot accept his conclusions as valid.

Dr. Brooks—Mr. Pauls Putnins in a detailed statistical study of singularities in the daily precipitation at Blue Hill for 68 years found no support for Bowen's theory.

Dr. James E. McDonald—With regard to that question of a charge on meteoric particles, I should think that this would be rather unreasonable to expect, even though the meteors may well be charged when they enter the atmosphere. In view of the very long fall times and the high conductivity of the layers through which they fall, surely the charges ought to be low by the time they got to the region where they could affect the clouds.

In regard to Dr. Hosler's experiment, one member of our group has been working on tridymite, and finds nucleation at temperatures of —18°C and even —13. There are a lot of problems in sizing and grinding, but, at least, there is some evidence that this form of SiO_2 is a good nucleating substance.

I want to comment on Dr. Workman's implied suggestion that Bowen's hypothesis really ought to be put aside for a moment to look at the question of whether ice can seriously influence rainfall amounts. It wasn't very long after Bowen first enunciated his hypothesis that everyone was interested in seeing it examined just because it seemed to afford the first clearcut test of the very question of whether adding nuclei would do any good. So Dr. Workman's question comes back full circle, then, to the original one.

FACTS AND PROBLEMS OF CHEMICAL COMPOSITION OF CONDENSATION NUCLEI IN UNPOLLUTED AND POLLUTED ATMOSPHERES

CHRISTIAN E JUNGE

Geophysics Research Directorate, Air Force Cambridge Research Center, Bedford, Mass.

Abstract—Sea spray particles seem to have the same chemical composition as sea water, but it is an open question if they are not decomposed over land. Nitrate is found predominantly in particles above 1μ radius. The possible source and formation process is discussed. Ammonium and sulfate are found predominantly in particles below 1μ radius. The possible sources and formation processes are discussed.

Introduction—The purpose of this paper is to give a brief survey of the results of recent measurements of the chemical composition of atmospheric condensation nuclei. In these investigations the stress was put on the soluble ions, chloride, sodium, sulfate, nitrate, and ammonium, because they affect the relationship between particle size and humidity, and are therefore of importance in the condensation processes. The progress in this field was mainly activated by the fact that particles of two different size ranges (0.08 to 0.8μ and 0.8 to 8μ radius) could be collected and analyzed separately.

The results exhibit some general rules which are valid in many geographical areas, and which indicate new processes of particle formation and growth.

Most of the measurements discussed here are concerned with 'unpolluted' air at places far remote from man-made sources of contamination. But it is apparent that these sources influence larger areas than heretofore assumed. There is, in fact, no possible separation of polluted and unpolluted atmospheres, because contaminants spread over vast areas of the continents and even the oceans, and are of importance for the understanding of the physics of water vapor condensation. We therefore incorporate here some recent and interesting measurements by the U.S. Department of Public Health, which were made at a large number of American cities and some non-urban districts.

The sea-spray component—About 99 per cent of the mass of natural sea spray is concentrated in particles above 0.8μ radius. This statement is based on measurements made near the coast of Massachusetts [JUNGE, 1954], and in the trade winds of Florida (unpublished), and Hawaii [JUNGE, in press]. Separate analyses of Cl and Na in Florida (in Hawaii, no Na analysis was made) indicate that within the experimental limits of accuracy the ratio of Cl to Na is the same as in sea water. TWOMEY [1954] arrived at the same conclusion by combining the isopygnic method with a Cl analysis. Measurements of the Cl and SO_4 content of the sea spray aerosols in Hawaii showed that their ratio was about the same as the sea water. The ratio Mg/Na at Round Hill [JUNGE, 1954] was found to be 0.18, which is only slightly higher than the sea water value of 0.12. In co-operation with A. H. Woodcock, analyses were performed on particles produced by the bubble process so that they were in the same size range as the natural sea-spray particles. Within the limits of accuracy, these particles had the same composition as the mother solution.

All these results indicate that the composition of the sea-spray particles cannot deviate very much from that of sea water. They were obtained by straightforward micro-chemical analyses at the coast or in well defined maritime air masses, and are therefore reliable.

A certain confirmation can be seen in the fact that electron microscope pictures and electron diffraction patterns of natural aerosols reveal the presence of cubic sodium chloride crystals [KUROIWA, 1953; YAMAMOTO and OHTAKE, 1953; ISONO, 1955]. It must be kept in mind, however, that the electron microscope can only be regarded as a quali-tative tool, inasmuch as any particular substance must be present in a recognizable shape or crystal structure.

Over land, no separate analyses for Cl and Na or other sea-water components were made for particles between one and 10μ radius. But, the results of a considerable num-ber of rain-water analyses for these substances are available. The most recent and com-prehensive results from the Swedish rain collecting network [ROSSBY and EGNER, in press] indicate that the Cl/Na ratio (in sea water $1\cdot8$) fluctuates between $0\cdot2$ and $3\cdot5$, depending on the general circulation (NE and S wind respectively). These considerable deviations may be explained either by a decomposition of the sea-spray particles over land [ROSSBY and EGNER, in press], or by the admixture of continental aerosols with independent sources of Cl and Na. We favor the latter explanation, because on the aver-age, the fairly large-sized sea-spray particles are eliminated over land fairly rapidly by rain. Over distances of about 100 miles the Cl content of rain water drops to 25 per cent [ROSSBY and EGNER, in press]. Continental aerosol sources will therefore soon become important and predominant. These sources are known to contain Cl; for instance, the Cl-content of particles in the size range below $0\cdot8\mu$ (where no sea spray can be present) increases with increasing distance from the sea and the Cl content of rainfalls is also higher in the vicinity of highly populated areas. Independent Na sources are not known yet and further work is necessary before this interesting problem can be answered satisfactorily.

The nitrate content of aerosols—A considerable number of aerosol samples in the vicinity of Boston (unpublished), coast of Massachusetts [JUNGE, 1954], Florida (un-published) and Hawaii [JUNGE, in press] were analyzed for nitrates. With very few excep-tions (in the Boston area during rainfall) the nitrate was concentrated in particles with radii above one micron, and very little was found in the smaller particles. This regularity seemed to indicate that the process of nitrate formation is the same at the various places, and a basic one in our atmosphere.

In Table 1 the average amounts of nitrate for the two particle sizes are listed. We see from the very low values in Hawaii that NO_3 cannot be of maritime origin. But the values for West Newton indicate clearly that pure continental air masses also have low nitrate contents. Note that continental air masses in West Newton (ten miles west of Boston) are not affected by Boston and are fairly representative for undisturbed condi-tions. Simultaneous measurements between Boston and West Newton further indicate that a big city is not of considerable influence on the nitrate content. This is in agreement with Table 2, which lists the total amount of particular matter found in a large network

Table 1. NO_3 content in γ/m^3 in the aerosols at various places. The figures beside the place name indicate the number of analyses.

Place		Range of particle radius	
		$0\cdot08–0\cdot8\mu$	$0\cdot8–8\mu$
West Newton:			
Continental air mass	23	<0·030	0·053
Maritime air mass	27	0·038	0·69
Round Hill ...	27	0·086	0·70
Florida	13	<0·030	0·32
Hawaii	14	<0·026	0·064

Table 2. Average total amount of sulfate and nitrate in γ/m^3 at various places according to results of the Public Health Service: figures in parentheses indicate number of places

	SO_4	NO_3
Cities with population 2,000,000	12·4 (5)	1·3 (4)
Cities with population 2,000,000	2·0 (7)	0·82 (6)
Non-urban areas	0·62 (5)	0·7 (1)

by the Public Health Service [CHAMBERS and others, 1955]. Although NO_3 analyses were made for only one non-urban place, the table clearly indicates that the nitrate content is not strongly affected by density of population and industry as, for example, that of SO_4. We may summarize these results by the statement that big towns, the ocean, and the continent are not considerable sources of nitrate. We therefore believe that the high values in Round Hill and in maritime air masses in West Newton are formed at the border area between ocean and (polluted?) continent. This again is supported by the two exceptionally high values of nitrate content in the Public Health network, which were therefore excluded from the average values of Table 2. These values were found in Los Angeles ($14\cdot4\ \gamma/m^3$) and San Francisco ($3\cdot4\gamma/m^3$), both places being in coastal areas.

The question about the origin of the nitrate content of aerosols is still unsolved. We incline to the following explanation: Traces of NO_2, which are always present in the atmosphere [JUNGE, in press], are dissolved in the solution droplets of hygroscopic nuclei and oxidised to nitrate. Experimental investigations, which are on the way, indicate, however, that this process is not sufficient for a quantitative explanation. But this process is irreversible, and a repeated exposure to high humidity should therefore accumulate the nitrate content. This is favored in areas of high sea-fog frequency, as Round Hill and the California Coast. Since the very hygroscopic sea-spray particles may be expected to accumulate the most nitrate, an explanation would also be given for the fact that the nitrate is found in the same particle-size range as the sea spray. If this explanation can be confirmed, the nitrate content of the aerosols may be an indicator of the history of the air mass with respect to condensation processes.

The ammonium and sulfate content—In the first two sections it was mentioned that the particle-size range between $0\cdot1$ and $1\cdot0\mu$ radius contains almost no chloride and nitrate. Rather, our measurements at various locations showed that the predominant part of their soluble material consists of NH_4 and SO_4. No exception from this rule was found. The average values are listed in Table 3. The ratio of NH_4 to SO_4 indicates that these substances are present as a mixture of $(NH_4)_2SO_4$ and $(NH_4)HSO_4$. The highest concentrations are found in Frankfurt, and the values drop

Table 3. NH_4 and SO_4 values in γ/m^3 for various locations in the radius range of $0\cdot08$ to $0\cdot8\mu$

Location				NH_4	SO_4
Frankfurt, Germany	...	...		3·6	11·1
Round Hill, Mass.	...	...		0·8	4·1
Florida	...	...	...	0·085	0·32
Hawaii	...	...	...	0·027	<0·3

continuously when we proceed to more maritime places. Their formation in densely populated areas by human activity seems obvious. But the surprising result is that they are still present to a small degree in the center of the Pacific. It appears that we have to think in fairly large geographical scales with respect to continental and maritime influences in aerosol composition. From the few data which are available, it appears further that the continental influence (mainly represented by the particles below one micron radius) extends much further into the center of the oceans than the maritime influence (represented by the sea-spray particles above one micron radius) extends into the continents. This is to be expected, since the larger nuclei are eliminated more rapidly by atmospheric condensation processes than the smaller ones.

The overall presence of the ammonium sulfate component raises the question as to its origin. There is strong evidence that it is formed by a gas reaction between NH_3 and SO_2. Experimental investigations show that this reaction occurs with very small concentrations, and field measurements indicate that NH_3 and SO_2 are always present in the atmosphere in amounts large enough to account for the ammonium sulfate in the aerosols [JUNGE, in press]. We feel that the successful investigation of this process will be an important step towards the understanding of the kinetics of formation of the natural condensation nuclei.

REFERENCES

CHAMBERS, L. A., M. J. FOTER and J. CHOLAK, A comparison of particulate loadings in the atmospheres of certain American cities, presented at Third National Air Pollution Symposium, Pasadena, California, April 1955.

ISONO, K., Identification of ice-crystal nuclei and other substances found in snow crystals by means of micro-diffraction, *J. Met. Soc. Japan*, ser.2, v.33, pp.37–38, 1955.

JUNGE, CHR., The chemical composition of atmospheric aerosols, I, Measurements at Round Hill Field Station June–July 1953, *J. Met.*, v.11, pp.323–333, 1954.

JUNGE, CHR., In Report of Project Shower, Hawaii, in press.

KUROIWA, D., In Studies on fogs in relation to fog-preventing forest (edited by T. Hori, Sapporo, Hokkaido, Japan), Tanne Trading Co., pp.349–380, 1953.

ROSSBY, C. G. and H. EGNER, On the chemical climate and its variation with the atmospheric circulation pattern, *Tellus*, v.7, pp.118–133, 1955.

TWOMEY, S., The composition of hydroscopic particles in the atmosphere, *J. Met.*, v.11, pp. 334–338, 1954.

YAMAMOTO, G. and T. OHTAKE, Electron microscope study of cloud and fog nuclei, *Science Reports, Tohoku Univ.*, ser.5, v.5, no.3, 1953.

DISCUSSION

Dr. Helmut K. Weickmann—It is known that nitrate nuclei are produced by lightning. Did you consider this important?

Dr. C. E. Junge—I do not think that NO_3 formation by lightning is of great importance for air chemistry. My data cannot give an answer to this question, because their number is too small and the measurements were not arranged to investigate this question.

Major C. S. Downie—In your Table 3, the results obtained at Frankfurt, Germany, indicate the ratio of NH_4 to SO_4 approximates that found in $(NH_4)_2SO_4$, while at Round Hill, Massachusetts the ratio is identical to that of $(NH_4) H SO_4$. Can the Frankfurt results be attributed to local contamination caused by any one specific industry?

Dr. Junge—The ratio of sulphate to ammonium at Frankfurt is not very much different from that of Round Hill. In places like Florida and Hawaii the content of sulphate was too small to be measured, because the sulphate method is relatively insensitive. I believe that the same ratio would have been found with a better method.

Dr. E. S. Workman—I should like to suggest something concerning a possible mode of formation of free chlorine in the atmosphere. If you imagine a hail stone which is shedding some water as it falls, freezing water which contains salt, and forming wet hail, this freezing action will result in almost a complete separation of the sodium chlorine, leaving the sodium with the shedded water and the chlorine with the ice.

Now it would be good (I suggested a test this summer, but we didn't get a chance to make it) to catch some water from a hailstorm, or hailstones themselves, and examine them for Chlorine. Hail formation should be an effective geochemical process for separating these elements in the atmosphere. This will take place in a range of concentrations in which sodium chloride water exists in the atmosphere, and I do not see how the freezing can avoid making the separation.

Dr. James P. Lodge, Jr.—I think we might mention some results that I don't remember in vast detail, but which have been obtained on analysis of rainfall. This work was done for the University of Chicago by the Illinois State Water Survey; they analysed practically all of the precipitation that arrived in sufficient quantity for analysis at all over the course of a year. There were no extremely obvious correlations of composition with meteorological conditions, but there were correlations between the proportions of certain cations and anions.

The rather curious thing that emerged was that the potassium was extraordinarily high compared with sea water. The potassium content was about one-fifth of the sodium content and the chlorine content was exactly equivalent to the sum of sodium plus potassium.

This, I think, suggests Dr. Junge's alternative explanation very strongly, that the real reason for the lack of correlation between sodium and chloride is due entirely to the introduction of other halides.

ELECTRON-MICROSCOPE STUDIES ON THE NUCLEI OF SEA FOG AND SNOW CRYSTALS

UKICHIRO NAKAYA

Hokkaido University, Hokkaido, Japan

Nuclei of snow crystals—This experiment is the continuation of Kumai's study on the nuclei of snow. In order to study the mechanism of sublimation of snow crystals, fine particles of carbon black were scattered on the crystal surface, and the motion of these particles was examined under a microscope during the course of sublimation.

The center nuclei of snow crystals were studied with an electron-microscope and at the same time the diffraction pattern was taken. Some of the nuclei were found to have the same crystal structure constant as the ice crystal and the similar lattice constant. Six microphotographs made by Kumai are shown here (Figs. 1–6).

Nuclei of sea fog—D. Kuroiwa has engaged in an electron-microscope study of nuclei of sea fog since 1944, and the earlier results were published in *Studies on Sea Fog* in 1953. The investigation is still continuing and the recent results are reported here.

In parallel to the electron-microscope study of sea fog, the hygroscopicity of nuclei was studied by changing the relative humidity. In some cases the nuclei were treated chemically by the use of a micromanipulator, and the electron-microdiffraction pattern was taken in order to study the crystal structure of the nuclei.

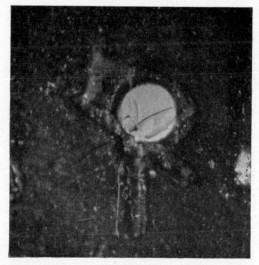

FIG. 1—Snow crystal of stellar type, the center nuclei of which was examined in figs. 2 and 3, × 150

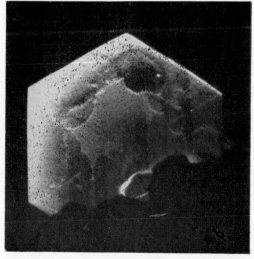

FIG. 2—The electron-microphotogram of the center nuclei of the crystal fig. 1, × 2,250

36

FIG. 3—The diffraction pattern of the nucleus fig. 2;
the lattice constant is very near to that of ice

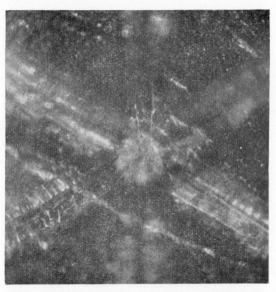

FIG. 4—Snow crystal of dendritic type, the center
nucleus of which was examined in figs. 5 and 6, × 80

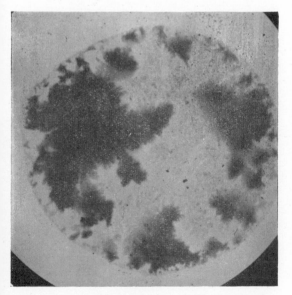

FIG. 5—The electron-microgram of the center nucleus
of the crystal fig. 4, × 4,600

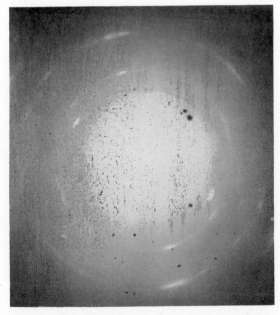

FIG. 6—The diffraction pattern of the nucleus fig. 5;
from the lattice configuration is considered as a sea-salt
nucleus

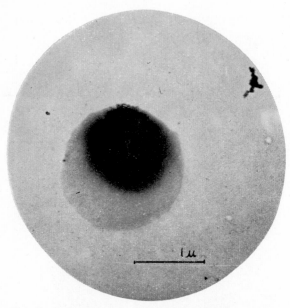

FIG. 7—Sea-salt nuclei; within the circular area covered by a thin deposit, one sees a substantial nucleus residue appearing black, that is, opaque to electron beam

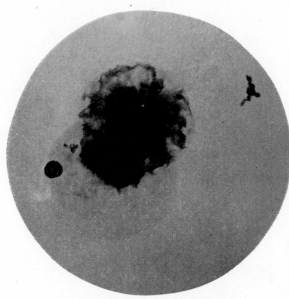

FIG. 8—The same nucleus which has undergone a marked change after being wetted and redried in the moisture vessel

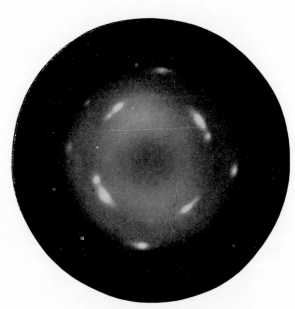

FIG. 9—Electron-diffraction pattern of the nucleus in fig. 8

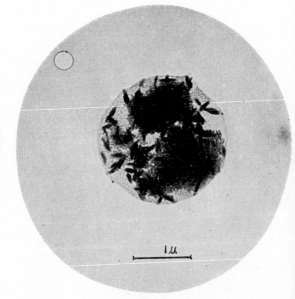

FIG. 10—Sea-salt nuclei; water-soluble nucleus where a number of tiny crystals having fish-like shape are dispersed, being partly overlaid with some massive, dark material

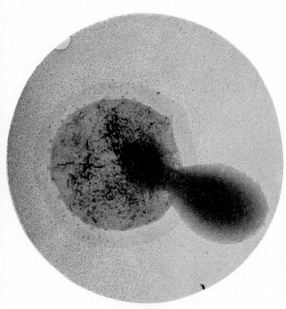

FIG. 11—Modification after artificial condensation on the nucleus fig. 10; a dark material is seen to have protruded in the form of liquid from the thinly deposited area

FIG. 12—The largest sea-salt nucleus ever found in advocation sea fog (dark ground illumination)

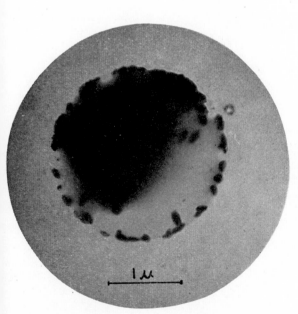

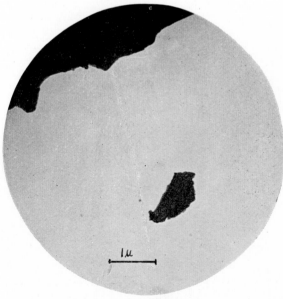

FIG. 13—Another type of sea-salt nucleus where a thick deposit is seen within the enclosure of tiny crystals distributed along a circle

FIG. 14—Combustion products (water-insoluble nuclei); one of the typical water-insoluble nuclei, the upper dark area being the image of the periphery of specimen-supporter

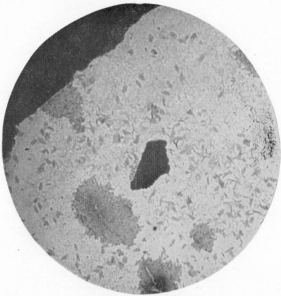

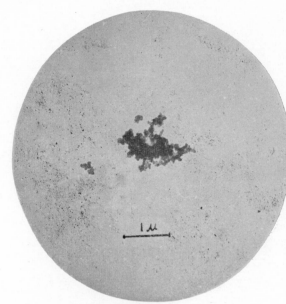

FIG. 15—Nitric acid treatment on nucleus fig. 14 by means of micromanipulator; a droplet of ten per cent nitric acid solution was brought into contact not only with the nucleus but also, by accident, with the periphery, and consequently the copper metal was dissolved in the nitric acid to form copper nitrate, which spread all over the collodion film; the nucleus itself remains unaffected so that it may well be considered to be a combustion product

FIG. 16—The typical appearance of a combustion product

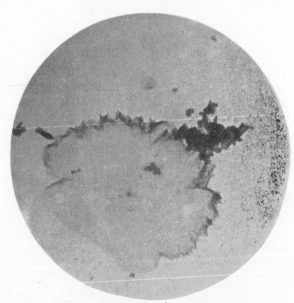

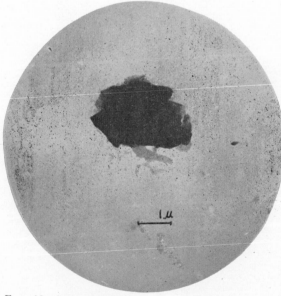

FIG. 17—The nucleus fig. 16 is partially affected by nitric acid and the dissolved substance is spread over the collodian film; the nucleus must therefore contain some unknown acid-soluble substance

FIG. 18—Soil material; water-insoluble nuclei, which is to be identified as a soil material from its general appearance

From investigation of 255 samples of sea fog, it was found that the nuclei can be classified into three kinds; combustion nuclei (50 per cent), sea-salt nuclei (40 per cent), and soil nuclei (10 per cent). Of the sea-salt nuclei, about 80 per cent were found to be one micron or more in size, 20 per cent less than one micron. These results are concordant with Junge's observations of the aerosols of continental and maritime air. Thirteen of Kuroiwa's microphotographs are shown in Figs. 7–19.

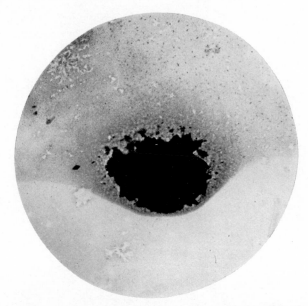

FIG. 19—After being treated with nitric acid, the nucleus fig. 18 came out in a form different from that in the first examination, the periphery having been disintegrated through erosion and spread uniformly on the collodion film

DISCUSSION

Dr. E. J. Workman—What percentage of snow crystals observed had nuclei in the center?

Dr. Ukichiro Nakaya—About 80 per cent.

Dr. David Atlas—Since there was no relationship between the size of the hygroscopic nuclei and that of the fog particles for diameters as large as 90 microns, this would seem to be indirect evidence that even the largest particles grew strictly by condensation, instead of by condensation and coalescence combined.

Dr. G. A. Wolff—Where did you find most of those sublimation nuclei?

Dr. Nakaya—At the mountain summit and at a height of about one kilometer.

Dr. Wolff—And how often did you find it?

Dr. Nakaya—On the four examples.

Dr. Helmut Weickmann—It seems to me, according to your investigations, that snow crystals act like a sink for small nuclei and upon evaporation act as a source for large nuclei. They absorb small nuclei, but as they evaporate the small ones come together and form large nuclei.

Mr. S. J. Birstein—You apparently investigated the nucleus in the electron microscope, removed the sample and put it back in the electron microscope. This seems to be a rather difficult technique to be certain that you find the same nucleus each time.

Dr. Nakaya—Not so difficult.

Mr. Birstein—What assurance have you that it was not the electron beam or some other agents that were changing the material? There were many other factors that could enter into the changing of the material, manipulating the outside or distorting the crystal that way.

Dr. Nakaya—Because we take a photograph first. Then we take it out, give it the acid treatment, and replace it in exactly the same position.

Mr. Birstein—Suppose the length of exposure to the electron beam changes the shape of the crystal. In other words, if you irradiate it twice, you will get a different looking crystal, or if you expose it to air, you may get a change. You may get a breaking up of the crystal. How can you be sure that you can classify these materials?

Dr. Nakaya—I have the photographs, many photographs, which show the change.

Mr. Birstein—But the photographs show changes which I cannot explain or accept on the basis of your explanations, where there might be other crystals.

Dr. Nakaya—There might be. But in one case they don't change shape at all; of that we are sure. And in other cases they change shape. So we think it all right.

Mr. Birstein—There is no definite way of being able to tell what happens to the nucleus as you take it out, except that it appears to have changed shape after exposure or manipulation.

Dr. Nakaya—If we expose it too long to the beam, it is no good, and in some cases we see the change of shape by irradiation itself.

Mr. Charles E. Anderson—I was interested to hear that sea salt apparently was present in these snow particles, which you felt was possibly a nucleus for the snowflake formation. Is that true?

Dr. Nakaya—Yes, but not frequently. Most of them have the solid nucleus, but also the sea salt nucleus.

TECHNIQUES FOR THE CHEMICAL IDENTIFICATION
OF MICRON AND SUBMICRON PARTICLES

JAMES P. LODGE, JR.* AND BARBARA J. TUFTS

Cloud Physics Project, Department of Meteorology,
The University of Chicago, Chicago, Illinois

A summary—Interest among meteorologists, geochemists, and air pollution chemists in the chemical nature of airborne fine particles has led to the development of new techniques for their identification. Classical methods, such as microscopical examination, micrurgy, or the bulk analysis of impinger or filter collections, are limited in their application, and generally fail in some fashion to meet the requirement for a reasonably rapid method that will give (*a*) the chemical species present, (*b*) the size ranges in which they occur, (*c*) the particle number concentration of the species, and (*d*) the mass concentration. The technique developed by JUNGE [1953; 1954] of analyzing washings from the slides of a two-stage impactor represents one acceptable method, although the size separations provided by an impactor are by no means sharp.

Several workers have attempted to identify particles by electron microscopy, with or without the aid of electron diffraction. However, the difficulty of identifying crystal forms by their outlines, and the uncertainty of electron diffraction images, together with the danger of evaporating or changing the samples in a vacuum under the electron beam, have led to results that are at best open to question.

WOODCOCK [1952; WOODCOCK and GIFFORD, 1949] and TWOMEY [1953; 1954] developed methods based upon the differing hygroscopicities of different species. Woodcock's technique appears to lack specificity, however, and Twomey's, since it involves collection on a spiderweb, seems incapable of sampling sufficient numbers of particles to define accurately their size distribution.

A distinctly different approach to the problem is represented by use of microscopic spot tests on a gelatin surface.

The gelatin method was developed by SEELY [1952; 1955] and by FIDELE and VITTORI [1953; VITTORI, 1954] based on Liesegang's work on reactions in this medium, especially as developed for microchemistry by WINCKELMANN [1931; 1933; 1935]. The gelatin is pre-impregnated with a selective reagent, for example, acidified mercurous fluosilicate for halides; it is examined microscopically after impaction of the particulates. At the original site of each particle of the substance sought, a characteristic reaction spot develops.

PIDGEON [1954] and SEELY [1952] both showed that, in the case of the above halide test, and under appropriate conditions, the reaction spot size was related to the equivalent dry size of the reacting particle. Unfortunately Pidgeon also showed that the spots corresponding to the smaller halide particles faded rapidly, so that quite rapid examination

---

* Present affiliation: Robert A. Taft Sanitary Engineering Center, U.S. Public Health Service, 4676 Columbia Parkway, Cincinnati, Ohio.

was necessary. Lodge and Fanzoi [1954] also developed several additional tests using this technique.

Lodge and co-workers [Lodge, 1954; Lodge, Ross, Sumida and Tufts, 1955] developed a number of spot tests utilizing 'Millipore', a commercial membrane filter. Millipore retains on its surface particles below 0·1 micron. It also becomes transparent when treated with microscope immersion oil, so that reaction spots may be examined microscopically. In general, the filter with its sampled particles was floated on the surface of a specific reagent, causing reaction spots to appear wherever the sought substance was present, as in the gelatin method. After washing to remove excess reagent, drying, and treatment with immersion oil, these spots could be detected easily under the microscope. For several of these tests, the relation between spot size and particle size was determined.

Tufts and Lodge [1955] extended the lower range of this general method by collecting particles on Formvar films supported by electron microscope grids, using thermal precipitation. The samples were then treated in roughly the same fashion as the Millipore collections; they were floated on a specific reagent, washed, dried and examined in this case by electron microscopy. Tests for halide and sulfate were developed, and again the spot-particle size relation was determined. The halide test is remarkably sensitive; particles as small as 10^{-18} grams gave recognizable reaction spots.

Acknowledgments—The research reported in this paper has been sponsored by the Geophysics Research Directorate, Air Force Cambridge Research Center, Air Research and Development Command, under Contracts AF19(604–618 and AF33(038)–25913. This article is a summary of a paper submitted to *Tellus*.

REFERENCES

Fidele, D. and O. Vittori Antisari, Determinazione delle particelle di cloruro nell'atmosfera e metodi di misura, *Riv. Met. Aeronaut.*, v.13, no.4, pp.9–13, 1953.

Junge, Chr., Die Rolle der Aerosole und der gasförmigen Beimengungen der Troposphäre, *Tellus*, v.5, pp.1–26, 1953.

Junge, Chr., The chemical composition of atmospheric aerosols, I, Measurements at Round Hill Field Station, June–July, 1953, *J. Met.*, v.11, pp.323–333, 1954.

Lodge, J. P., Analysis of micron-sized particles, *Anal. Chem.*, v.26, pp.1829–1831, 1954.

Lodge, J. P. and H. Fanzoi, Extension of the gelatin method for the detection of micron-sized particles, *Anal. Chem.*, v.26, p.1829, 1954.

Lodge, J. P., H. F. Ross, W. K. Sumida and B. J. Tufts, Analysis of micron-sized particles, II, Determination of particle size, Paper submitted to *Anal. Chem.*, 1953.

Pidgeon, F. D., Controlling factors in identification of microscopic chloride particles with sensitized gelatin films, *Anal. Chem.*, v.26, pp.1832–1835, 1954.

Seely, B. K., Detection of micron and submicron chloride particles, *Anal. Chem.*, v.24, pp.576–579, 1952.

Seely, B. K., Detection of certain ions in 10^{-10} to 10^{-15} gram particles, *Anal. Chem.*, v.27, pp.93–95, 1955.

Tufts, B. J. and J. P. Lodge, Chemical identification of halide and sulfate in submicron particles, Paper submitted to *Anal. Chem.*, 1955.

Twomey, S., Identification of individual particles in the atmosphere by a phase-transition method, *J. Applied Phys.*, v.24, pp.1099–1102, 1953.

Twomey, S., The composition of hygroscopic particles in the atmosphere, *J. Met.*, v.11, pp.334–338, 1954.

Vittori Antisari, O., La rivelazione de particelle costituite da particolari sostanze chimiche nell'indagine sui nuclei di condensazione e sul nuclei di sunlimazione artificiale, *Riv. Met. Aeronaut.*, v.14, no.2, pp.17–22, 1954.

Winckelmann, J., Über einige neue Methoden der präparativen Mikrochemie, *Mikrochemie*, v.10, pp.437–439, 1931.

WINCKELMANN, J., Über einige neue Methoden der qualitativen Mikroanalyse, *Mikrochemie*, v.12, pp. 119–128, 1933.

WINCKELMANN, J., Aus der Praxis der Tupfelanalyse, *Mikrochemie*, v.16, pp.203–210, 1935.

WOODCOCK, A. H., Atmospheric salt particles and raindrops, *J. Met.*, v.9, pp.200–212, 1953.

WOODCOCK, A. H. and M. M. GIFFORD, Sampling atmospheric sea salt nuclei over the ocean, *J. Marine Res.*, v.8, pp.177, 1949.

DISCUSSION

Dr. James E. McDonald—In the sulfate test with the electron microscope, are some of the particles barium and some lead sulfate?

Dr. James P. Lodge Jr.—The phenomenon of co-precipitation is very complex, and I wouldn't be prepared to say. I think it's more likely that you have something resembling mixed crystals here. You can take lead sulfate, which is soluble in a large excess of acetate ion, in solution and add a drop of barium chloride or barium nitrate, and the precipitate which is thrown down is about half barium sulfate and half lead sulfate.

Mr. Charles E. Anderson—I was wondering whether or not the test for sodium chloride is specific for sodium chloride?

Dr. Lodge—No. It is specific for any soluble halide. That is, it is not specific for sodium at the sizes involved here; with exceedingly large particles one might get a central spot of sodium fluosilicate, but one couldn't count on it. So any soluble chloride, in the first place, will give such a reaction; and in the second place, mercurous halides are all insoluble, so bromide and iodide will give the same reaction—fluoride will not.

Mr. Anderson—Even with that limitation, it might be a valuable test for some of the work that Dr. Nakaya and his associates were doing on identifying the residues from snowflakes and ice crystals, because his method of identifying them, electron diffraction, I think, suffers even more severe limitations.

Dr. Lodge—That is correct, I think this technique should be quite specific. We have actually checked most of the cases where we would expect any interference. Mercurous sulfate is somewhat insoluble, for example, so we actually made a very heavy collection of sulfate and got no halos whatsoever treating it with chloride reagent. And we did the reverse test, where we thought there might be trouble, and showed that halides do not interfere with the sulfate test.

Dr. Hans J. aufm Kampe—Do you need a different filter for each reaction?

Dr. Lodge—No, a different reagent. The filter is identical. It is simply a commercial membrane filter. We use the 'HA' grade.

Dr. aufm Kampe—I mean that you couldn't use the same filter for more than one test.

Dr. Lodge—This is both right and wrong. You need a different portion of filter for each test, but the filters are just a two-inch circle of something that looks like paper, and if your concentrations are high enough on the surface that you don't need the whole area for statistically valid size determination, you can cut the filter into say, four pieces and test for four different substances.

Dr. Vincent J. Schaefer—I might just point out one thing. As you indicated, you do have trouble with the electron beam evaporating these things, and in our work with electron microscope we found one could take a thing as destructible as stearic acid, and by merely putting a thin, fifty-angstrom film of polyvinylformal over the sample you could cut down the evaporation almost completely. This is a technique that is extremely valuable.

Dr. Lodge—I don't know what this would do to the subsequent reaction.

Dr. Schaefer—I would do it after reaction. Then you put the film over it.

Dr. Lodge—We had no difficulty with the reaction spots evaporating. It was the primary particles where we wished to examine them first. Then when we reacted them we would get sometimes an anomalous looking reaction spot, or none. I think it might still work, because it is easy for salts to dialyze through. But there are some practical difficulties with the technique.

FURTHER DISCUSSION

(at the closing session)

Dr. C. E. Junge—Our analyses of atmospheric nuclei indicated that in particles below one micron radius, chloride was present in populated and industrial areas which was definitely not of maritime origin. This fact should be kept in mind when conclusions are drawn from the presence of chloride particles as indicators of the maritime origin of air masses.

I further think that the role of sea salt for cloud physics over the continent is strongly overestimated. Here, chloride is only a small fraction of the total amount of hygroscopic material concentrated in the nuclei. Over land we should therefore look for the total amount of soluble or hygroscopic material rather than for sea spray, because only this total amount is important for cloud physics and not the chemical composition.

I would like to ask Dr. Lodge the following question: Did you check how enlargement factors changed when the particles consisted of a mixture of, say, nitrates, chlorides, sulfates, etc.? Is your method applicable to such mixed particles as we encounter in the air?

Dr. Lodge—I would like first to complete the earlier discussion. There are certainly a lot of halides contributed by industrial processes. One possible source in the Middle West is the coal piles, which are customarily sprayed with either sodium or calcium chloride to keep them from freezing in the winter and to keep down dust in the summer. The result is that whenever coal is burned tremendous quantities of chloride particles in the smallest size ranges are set free. If you will remember the data on Flight 105 from the figures in Dr. Byers' paper they showed an abnormal concentration of particles below three microns in the sample taken over St. Louis.

We are not trying to say that sea salt is the sole hygroscopic agent responsible for the initiation of warm rain. It happens that chlorides are very easy to test for, and if we can show that there are enough chloride particles to initiate precipitation, then whatever else is present is just so much extra.

In answer to your other question, nitrate, water, or any other dilutant will be ineffective over a certain range. Take water for example; water, nitrate, sulfate or any other foreign substance would be equally ineffective as far as the halide test is concerned. Consider a given dry mass of chloride. It will yield a reaction spot roughly five times its diameter. If an equal mass of water is added the particle diameter will be increased about 50 per cent and we would expect the reaction spot size to be unaffected; but if enough water is added the droplets will cover a greater area than the reaction spot should for the mass of chloride actually involved. Thus, if you dilute too much you will get very thin reaction spots which are too large for the particle size that caused them, so the stated relationships hold only within limits.

Dr. aufm Kampe—I would like to ask about a paper by Fedele and Vittori, two Italian scientists. They claim to have a method (Liesegang reaction) by which they can detect particles (I think it was sodium and calcium chlorides) having a mass as small as 10^{-16} grams, that is, particles having a radius of approximately 10^{-5} to 10^{-6} cm. On a mountain about 2000 m high they found small chloride particles in a concentration of ten to 100 per cc and they believe that these particles play an important role as condensation nuclei.

I would like to have an opinion of the reliability of the Liesegang reaction with respect to the findings of Fedele and Vittori.

Dr. Lodge—The term Liesegang reaction is a general term which Vittori has applied to all reactions on gelatin. The only test for which a lower detection limit of 10^{-16} grams was claimed was the chloride test. This makes use of physical development, an autocatalytic photographic development processes. The presence of some reduced silver catalyzes the deposition of more reduced silver and so on, so that from a very minute initial reaction a much larger reaction spot is obtained. A full discussion of this phenomenon can be found in Fritz Feigl's book, Spot Tests. The reaction is actually extremely non-specific. Virtually any insoluble particle will set off exactly the same chain of events. Feigl, for example, points out that the test is applicable only on extremely clean filter paper, and then only if the location of the expected reaction is precisely known. I think this may account for the very high concentration of supposed chloride particles found by Vittori.

DISTRIBUTION IN THE ATMOSPHERE OF CERTAIN PARTICLES CAPABLE OF SERVING AS CONDENSATION NUCLEI

HORACE R. BYERS, JOHN R. SIEVERS AND BARBARA J. TUFTS

Department of Meteorology, The University of Chicago

Abstract—Collections of chloride particles on flights in Illinois and in the Lower Mississippi Valley are compared with those made in Puerto Rico and some ground data. Large chloride particles are numerous at flight altitudes even though scarce at the ground in the interior of the continent. Giant particles giving the sulphate and magnesium reaction appear to be somewhat more numerous than the chlorides. The previous air trajectory does not seem to have a very great effect on the counts.

METHODS for collection of identifiable atmospheric particles of micron size and larger (very large condensation nuclei) have been developed in recent years. In the present paper the technique of identifying and sizing particles collected on the surface of Millipore filters will not be emphasized. This method has been developed [LODGE, 1954; LODGE and others, 1956] at the University of Chicago. Some impactor measurements based on an improvement of the SEELY [1952] technique and some results of a flame photometer, patterned after SOUDAIN's [1951] sodium counter, have been reported by others [REITAN and BRAHAM, 1954] of this Project.

Most previous upper-air measurements of particles have been made over the sea or in maritime locations [WOODCOCK and GIFFORD, 1949; WOODCOCK, 1950, 1952, 1953; LODGE, 1955], although CROZIER, SEELY, and WHEELER [1952] collected unsized chloride particles on a cross-country flight. Additional new collections will be reported in this paper.

LODGE [1955] has reported on the Chicago University — Air Force flights made in the neighborhood of Puerto Rico. These showed high chloride counts in excess of 10^5 particles per m^3 having diameters $\geqslant 3$ microns and up to 10^3 per m^3 with diameters $\geqslant 10$ microns. More recent analysis for magnesium particles in the atmosphere, over the same area of the Caribbean, shows concentrations which are comparable to the chloride counts at most elevations, with the 'giant' sizes ranging up to one order of magnitude greater than the large chloride particles. Data at the ground in Central Illinois, reported by REITAN and BRAHAM [1954] showed an average of about two chloride particles per m^3 with diameters $\geqslant 10$ microns. This seemed to imply that in contrast with Puerto Rican conditions, giant seasalt nuclei were not playing an important role in condensation and precipitation over the continent.

When we took to the air from Chanute Air Force Base, we were surprised to find that the counts in fresh tropical air at around 5000 ft were nearly the same as in Puerto Rico. This was especially true of the larger particles, $\geqslant 10$ microns. The counts of these giant nuclei aloft exceeded those at the ground by one to two orders of magnitude.

The great difference between maritime and continental locations appears to be in the circumstance that the surface of the continents provides a very pronounced sink for the salt particles. One imagines that trees and other vegetation strain out at least the larger particles. Also a considerable number of them might be scavenged out by showers. The showers probably would not reduce the numbers very much at cloud levels since, as shown by Braham [1952], most of the cloud-condensed water (80 per cent) evaporates without reaching the ground. Furthermore, as shown by Cunningham [1951; 1952], the collection efficiency of falling raindrops as well as the total collection by them has a pronounced maximum in the lowest levels. The Swedish measurements [Rossby and Egner, 1955] of chloride in rainwater decreasing inland probably must reflect mainly an inland decrease of number of large particles at the near-surface levels. Some measurements of these effects at the ground were made by Lodge [1955] in Puerto Rico.

Particles identifiable as sulphates were found to be numerous and uniformly distributed over large distances in the Mississippi Valley and Gulf of Mexico region. They appeared to form an ever-present particulate constituent of the upper air, occurring in

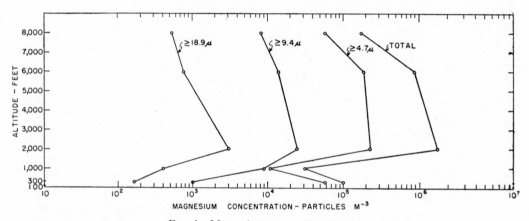

FIG. 1—Magnesium counts, Puerto Rico

'giant' sizes in about the same manner as the chlorides, although less variable in geographic distribution. Analysis for magnesium particles reveals that the larger 'giant' sizes occur in numbers of the same order of magnitude as do the chloride particles. There is a suggestion of greater variability in these counts in their geographic distribution over the Mississippi Valley. The total counts, however, do appear to be more uniform over the same area and in greater concentration than the total chloride particles.

Results of collections—Fig. 1 shows counts from airborne Millipore collections made in the vicinity of Puerto Rico. The magnesium counts show total particle concentrations similar to the total chloride particle numbers, shown in Fig. 2 [after Lodge, 1955], at least above 2000 ft. The number of 'giant' sized particles differ by approximately one order of magnitude.

Fig. 3 shows the counts from impactor collections at the ground at the Champaign, Illinois, airport, as reported by Reitan and Braham. For particles having a mass greater than 10^{-9}g, the values averaged about 2 m^{-3} and rarely exceeded 20 m^{-3}.

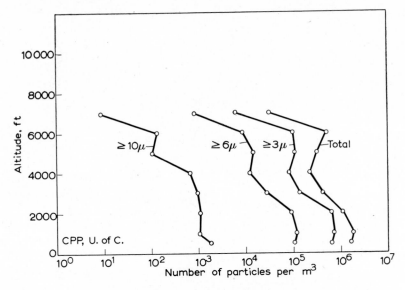

Fig. 2—Chloride counts, Puerto Rico

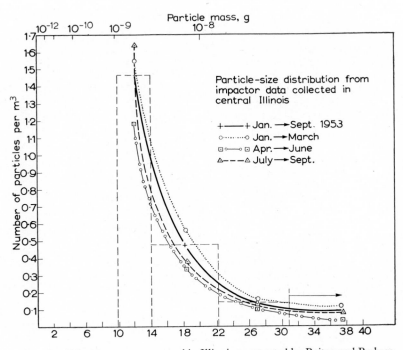

Fig. 3—Chloride counts at ground in Illinois as reported by Reitan and Braham

Fig. 4 shows the first airborne Millipore collections made in the Mississippi Valley from the Missouri River to the Gulf of Mexico at 5000 ft. Note that among the large chloride particles we have numbers approaching those of Puerto Rico. For comparison with chloride distributions, the sulphates counted for Flight 105, the same flight as is

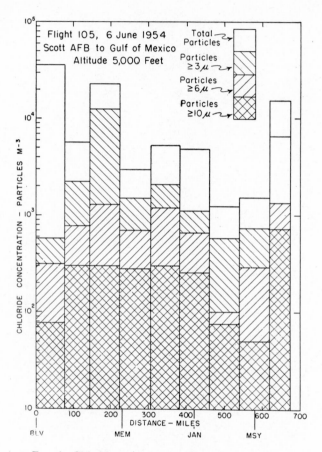

Fig. 4—Chloride counts, flight 105, Mississippi Valley

represented for chlorides in Fig. 4, are shown in Fig. 5. The large numbers and uniform geographical distribution are striking features. The flight was made in a fresh maritime-tropical air influx as shown by the trajectories in Fig. 6.

Fig. 7 shows a similar run coming back from the Gulf a few days later at 2500 ft. The values of the giant nuclei counts are not quite as large as on the southbound flight, but the air trajectories shown in Fig. 8 may not be as favorable.

Fig. 9 shows a flight made at various altitudes west and southwest of Chanute Field. Again the counts are relatively high. As shown in Fig. 10, the air trajectories show the air to be of Gulf origin except at 12,000 ft where the air seems to have come from central Mexico.

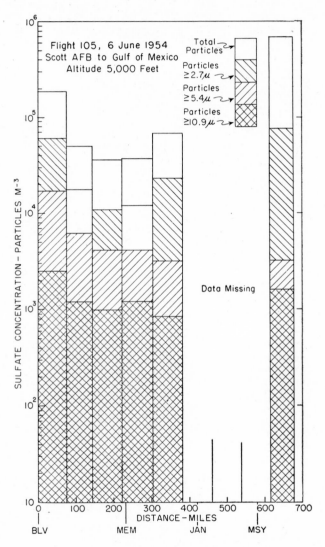

FIG. 5—Sulphate counts, same flight as Fig. 4

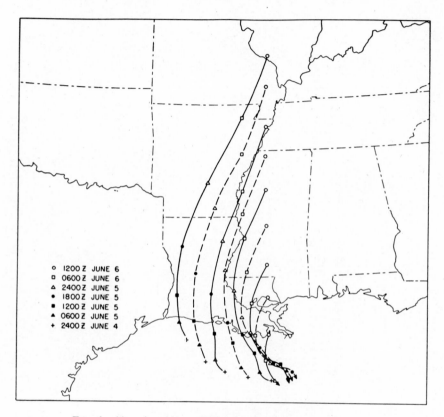

Fig. 6—Air trajectories at 5000 ft for 36 hours before flight 105

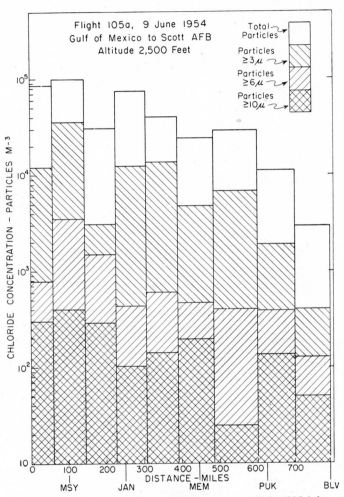

Fig. 7—Chloride counts taken at 2500 ft on return flight (105a) from Gulf of Mexico

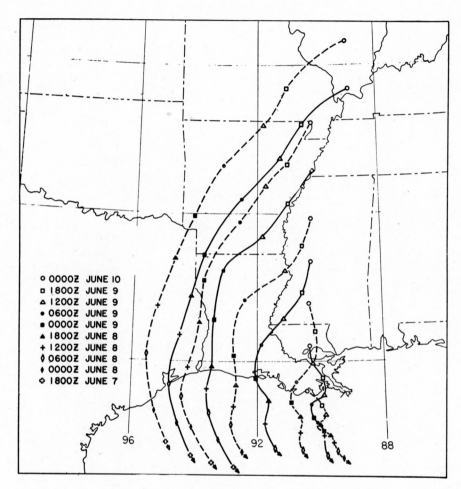

Fig. 8—Air trajectories at 2500 ft for 54 hours prior to Flight 105

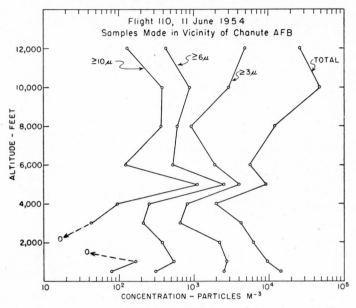

FIG. 9—Chloride counts at various altitudes west and southwest of Chanute
Field, Ill, Flight 110

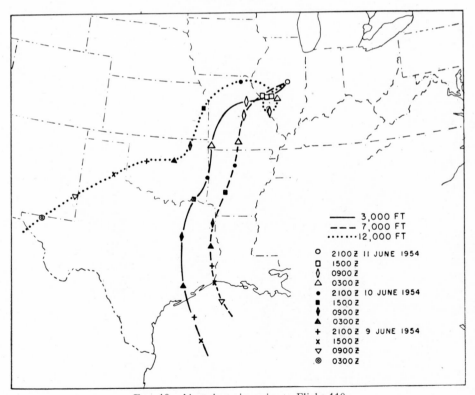

FIG. 10—Air trajectories prior to Flight 110

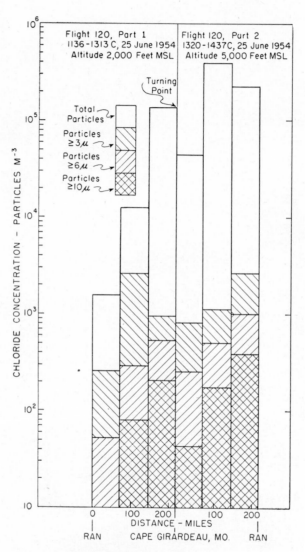

Fig. 11—Chloride counts in flight at two levels in the
Mississippi Valley, Flight 120

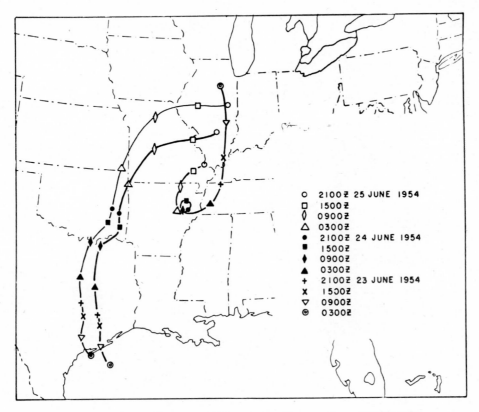

Fig. 12—Air trajectories at 3000 ft corresponding to outbound Flight 120

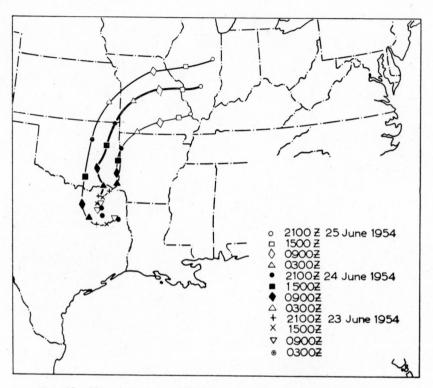

FIG. 13—Air trajectories at 5000 ft corresponding to return flight 120

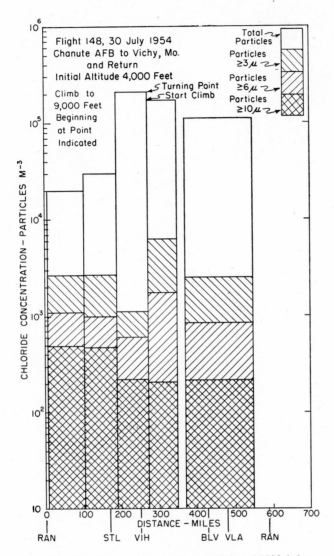

FIG. 14—Chloride counts in flight at 4000 ft and 9000 ft from
Chanute Field, Ill., Flight 148

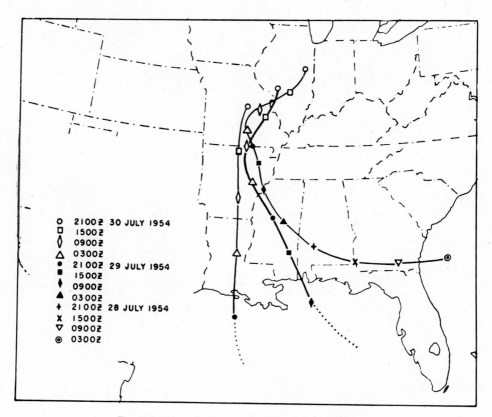

Fig. 15—Air trajectories at 4000 ft prior to Flight 148

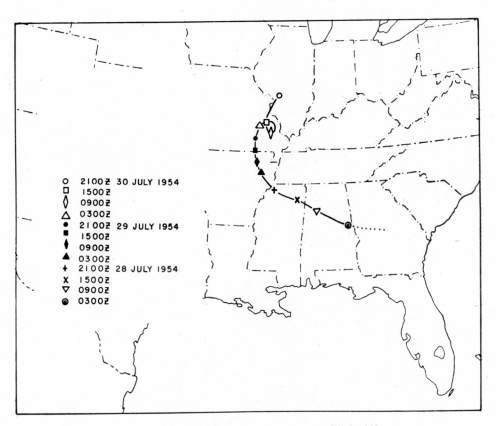

Fig. 16—Air trajectories at 9000 ft prior to Flight 148

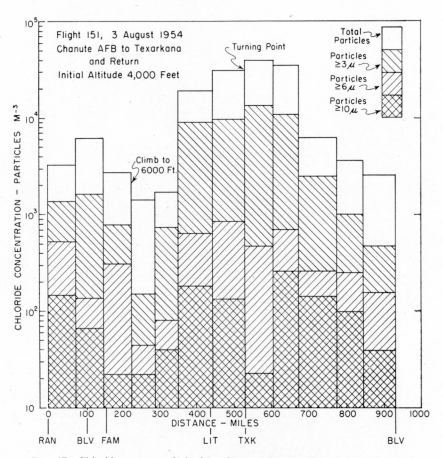

Fig. 17—Chloride counts on flight from Chanute Field to Texarkana and return, Flight 151

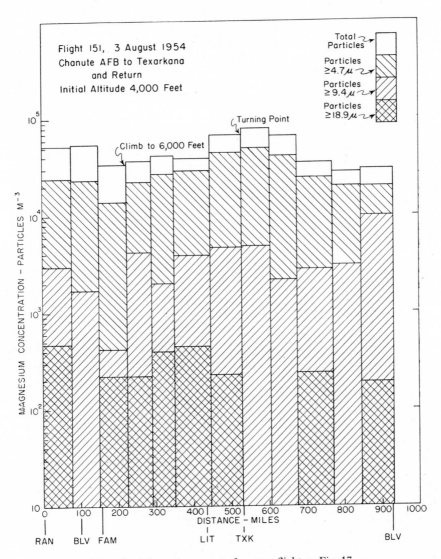

FIG. 18—Magnesium counts for same flight as Fig. 17

F

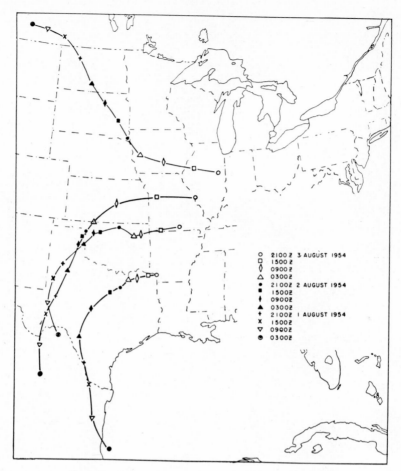

FIG. 19—Air trajectories at 5000 ft prior to Flight 151

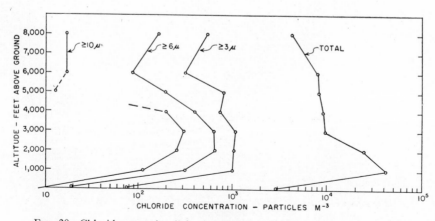

FIG. 20—Chloride counts in a light aircraft flight, Champaign, Ill., Nov., 5, 1954

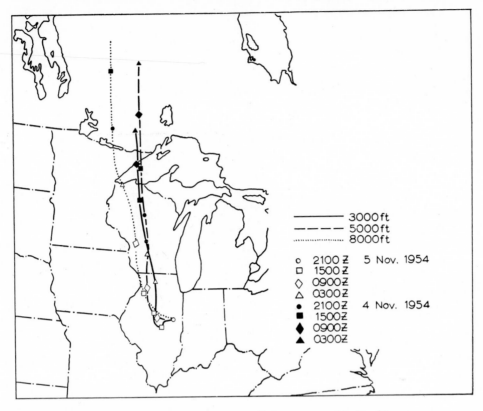

FIG. 21—Air trajectories prior to flight represented in Fig. 20

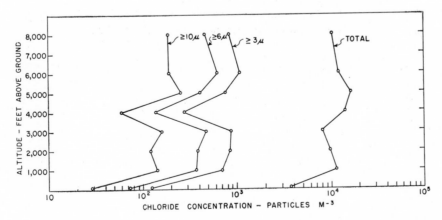

FIG. 22—Chloride counts in a light aircraft flight over the same area as Fig. 20, Nov. 10, 1954

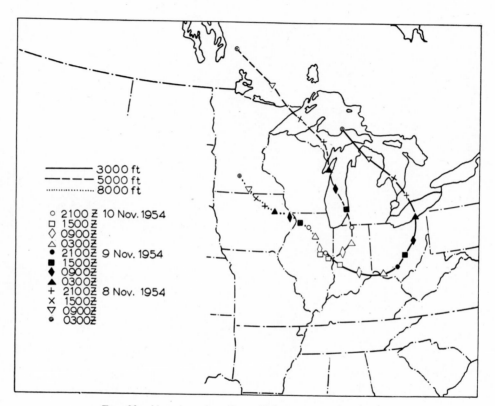

Fig. 23—Air trajectories prior to flight represented in Fig. 22

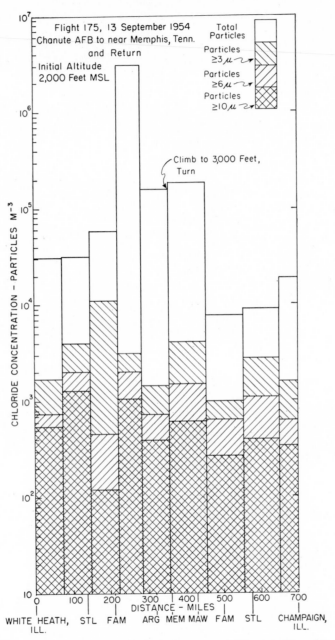

FIG. 24—Chloride counts in flight from central Illinois to Memphis
and return, Flight 175

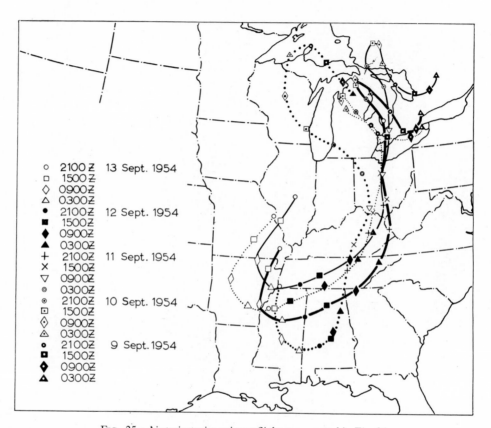

FIG. 25—Air trajectories prior to flight represented in Fig. 24

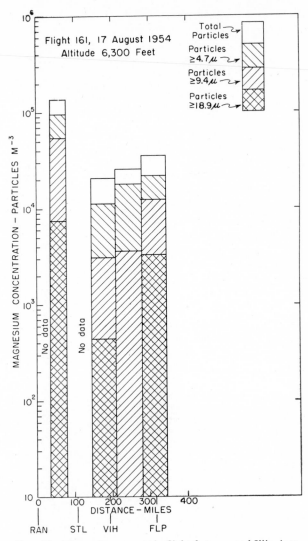

FIG. 26—Magnesium counts in flight from central Illinois to
northern Arkansas

Fig. 11 represents a flight at 2000 ft from Chanute to Cape Girardeau, on the Mississippi River in southern Missouri, and return at 5000 ft. The air trajectories in Figs. 12 and 13 show that the air came mostly from the south-central states.

Fig. 14 gives the collections on a flight to a point about 275 mi southwest of Chanute Field at 4000 ft and return at 9000 ft. The air trajectories indicated in Figs. 15 and 16 show the air to be from the Gulf of Mexico and the tropical Atlantic.

Figs. 17 and 18 represent a flight from Chanute Field to Texarkana and return at altitudes of 4000 and 6000 ft and show counts for chloride and magnesium particles, respectively. The 5000-ft air trajectories show the air to be of mixed origin (Fig. 19).

In Fig. 20 we are dealing with a flight in Central Illinois with air of polar origin, as indicated in the trajectories of Fig. 21. The distribution of giant chloride particles above 4000 ft is unusual.

Fig. 22 shows a flight in the same area five days later resulting in fairly high counts. The trajectories are shown in Fig. 23.

Flight 175, from central Illinois to Memphis and return, shows fairly high salt concentrations (Fig. 24) even though the trajectories appear unfavorable (Fig. 25).

Fig. 26 shows the magnesium concentrations on a flight from central Illinois to northern Arkansas at an altitude of 6300 ft. Although the data are not continuous, the number and variability, over some distance, of the magnesium particles appear to be similar to the data taken on Flight 151 (Fig. 18), with the exception of the higher concentrations of large particles between Rantoul, Illinois and St. Louis, Missouri.

Acknowledgments—James P. Lodge inaugurated and supervised the particle collection, identification and counting. Edward L. Harrington assisted in the computation of trajectories. Louis J. Battan's help in assembling the material and in general supervision is acknowledged. The research reported in this paper has been sponsored by the Geophysics Research Directorate of the Air Force Cambridge Research Center, Air Research and Development Command, under Contract AF19(604)–618.

REFERENCES

BRAHAM, R. R., JR., The water and energy budgets of the thunderstorm and their relation to thunderstorm development, *J. Met.*, v.9, pp.227–242, 1952.

CROZIER, W. D., B. K. SEELY and L. B. WHEELER, Correlation of chloride particle abundance with the synoptic situation on a cross-country flight, *Bul., Amer. Met. Soc.*, v.33, pp.95–100, 1952.

CUNNINGHAM, R. M., Some observations of natural precipitation processes, *Bul., Amer. Met. Soc.*, v.32, pp.334–343, 1951.

CUNNINGHAM, R. M., Distribution and growth of hydrometeors around a deep cyclone, Mass. Inst. Tech. Dept. Met., Tech. Rept. 18, 1952.

LODGE, J. P., Analysis of micron-sized particles, *An. Chem.*, v.26, pp.1829–1831, 1954.

LODGE, J. P., H. F. ROSS, W. K. SUMIDA and B. J. TUFTS, Analysis of micron-sized particles, II, *An. Chem.*, v.28, pp.423–424, 1956.

LODGE, J. P., A study of sea-salt particles over Puerto Rico, *J. Met.*, v.12, pp.493–499, 1955.

REITAN, C. H. and R. R. BRAHAM, JR., Observations of salt nuclei over the midwestern United States, *J. Met.*, v.11, pp.503–506, 1954.

ROSSBY, C. G. and H. EGNER, On the chemical climate and its variation with the atmospheric circulation pattern, *Tellus*, v.7, pp.118–133, 1955.

SEELY, B. K., Detection of micron and sub-micron chloride particles, *An. Chem.*, v.24, pp.576–579, 1952.

SOUDAIN, G., Realisation d'un compteur automatique de noyaux de chlorure de sodium, *J. Sci. Met.*, v.3, p.137, 1951.

WOODCOCK, A. H., Sea salt in a tropical storm, *J. Met.*, v.7, pp.397–401, 1950.

WOODCOCK, A. H., Atmospheric salt particles and raindrops, *J. Met.*, v.9, pp.200–212, 1952.

WOODCOCK, A. H., Salt nuclei in marine air as a function of altitude and wind force, *J. Met.*, v.10, pp.362–371, 1953.

WOODCOCK, A. H. and M. M. GIFFORD, Sampling atmospheric sea salt nuclei over the ocean, *J. Marine Res.*, v.8, pp.177–197, 1949.

DISCUSSION

Dr. Raymond Wexler—Presumably the observations were taken over open farm country. There are not too many trees; doesn't your explanation give too much weight to the effect of trees?

Dr. Horace R. Byers—I don't know. We certainly don't have very many trees around the airport at Champaign. Of course we are a long distance from the Gulf of Mexico and other possible sources, so a great deal of it may not have been removed locally.

Prof. Charles L. Hosler—For the past couple of years we have been making studies of the distribution of ragweed pollen during this nasty season of the year. We had concentrations of 3000 per cubic meter. At 400 meters these concentrations fell to the order of 50 to perhaps 200, and in a forested region four or five feet above the ground, we got concentrations of 2 or 3, or at most 10, showing almost 98 pct or better collection efficiency of those surfaces within the forest for particles of that particular size. These particles are uniformly 20 microns.

Dr. Byers—In explanation of the ground measurements you should notice from the slide that it cuts off at around ten microns. The impactor technique was used in these measurements. As a result we don't know what the concentrations might be in the smaller sizes. They could be very great. By the time one gets the record into the laboratory, fading has removed most of the smaller spots.

Dr. Helmut Weickmann—We have made similar measurements, with an Aitken nuclei counter, on a tower 400 feet high. The lowest level of the tower is surrounded by forest; the upper level is above the forest. And on a windy day we get fewer nuclei at the low level than at the upper level. The forest definitely seems to act as a filter.

We had a fairly marked decrease of particle numbers from the ground to high altitude whereas in your case the number is roughly constant. It should be interesting to compare your measurements with those of Aitken nuclei, that I'll report on later.

Mr. Alfred H. Woodcock—Concerning the collection of aerosols by vegetation, I remember a Japanese paper of several years ago showing vegetation differs in collection. Runoff from hillsides showed that certain types of vegetative cover, particularly pine forests, were much more effective in collecting chlorides.

Mr. James D. Wilcox—The Department of Agriculture for some years has been interested in deposition on foliage and in forests. Even with small particles, such as smoke, you find quite a filtering action in the forest. It's more or less a matter of the amount of surface present. With chemical warfare agents in woods, we find there are definite particle sizes that will pass through these woods.

Mr. Charles E. Anderson—I thought it a very provocative statement made by Byers concerning the apparent constant source of chlorides over the continents. How do you explain this? Is it possible that these chlorides are not removed by gravity even after being over the continents for prolonged periods?

Mr. Woodcock—Concerning this problem, I have often wondered about the rain-out of particles from very high levels. Large regions of convergence occasionally develop in the trades at Puerto Rico. Clouds will grow to perhaps 30,000 feet during periods of days. Of course, these clouds will carry nucleating materials with them, and that portion which evaporates will leave last aerosols at high levels. You could have materials raining down to the lower levels and seem to have an extraordinary persistence of chlorides at low levels, which might not occur at a time when the air entered the continent with the aerosols distributed up to say only 10,000 feet.

Dr. Wallace E. Howell—We have made observations in Peru that seem to indicate rapid rain-out of giant nuclei from the stable air along the coast and fail to show persistence of salt nuclei in the easterly air stream coming across from the Amazon basin. Counts ranging from 10^5 up to 5×10^6 large nuclei per cubic meter, depending on surf conditions, were found on the beaches, falling off to the order of 10^3 at a distance of about 50 km inland within the stable low-level Pacific air brough inland by the sea breeze. No measurable number of large nuclei was found at any time in the air mass associated with the easterlies.

Dr. J. S. Marshall—Is there any natural process that could conceivably give us upper air that was relatively free of such particles?

Dr. Byers—I should think rain and snow would be the most effective way of removing salt from the upper air. These flights were made in the summer and fall during a drought period; so it is possible that there was not enough rain to deplete it as much as might normally be expected.

On the other hand, there was quite a lot of cumulus cloud activity. The processes for carrying particles up were about normal for summer. But for carrying them down there was a deficiency because of drought conditions.

Dr. Christian E. Junge—I have tested the chemical composition of nuclei in the subsidence layer above the trade-wind inversion of Hawaii. The inversion was so strong that no sea salt was present at all, or at least in such small concentrations that it could not be detected, which means orders of magnitude below normal concentrations.

Dr. Vincent J. Schaefer—I think it's very important that we don't extrapolate these effects too far, because we are dealing in most cases with highly polluted regions, and I would like to second what Junge just said, that over in the Hawaiian Islands one finds an optical clarity such as one never sees here or in Puerto Rico, or any place I have ever seen between here and Europe. So I think we have to be a little careful in assuming that one can consider the whole world as being contaminated in this way. I think there are great areas where it is not; probably the optics of the atmosphere will be the best indication of whether we have these high concentrations or whether we are relatively free of them.

SOME OBSERVATIONS OF THE GEOGRAPHICAL DISTRIBUTION OF GIANT HYGROSCOPIC NUCLEI

E. M. FOURNIER D'ALBE

Instituto de Ciencias Aplicadas,
Universidad Nacional de México, Mexico D.F., Mexico

Abstract—The concentration and size distribution of giant hygroscopic nuclei in the surface air was measured twice weekly throughout a period of two years at five stations in West Pakistan. The results suggest that the sea surface and coasts are the only important source of such particles in this area. The loss of particles by fall under gravity is negligible except for those of mass greater than 10^{-9} g, and the main agent in their removal from the atmosphere appears to be precipitation. On the other hand, the evaporation of rain or large cloud droplets may produce locally high concentrations of giant nuclei. Some measurements have also been made in Mexico which tend to support these conclusions.

Introduction—The results of sampling of giant hygroscopic nuclei by cascade impactors in Pakistan and Mexico are analyzed for the light which they throw on the sources, transport and removal from the atmosphere of these particles.

The observations—Throughout a period of two years from May 1952 to May 1954, samples of the particulate matter in the air near the ground were taken twice weekly at five meteorological observatories in West Pakistan (namely Karachi, Hyderabad, Lahore, Peshawar, and Quetta).

The instrument employed for sampling was the cascade impactor designed by MAY [1945] and manufactured by a British firm. These instruments have the advantages of cheapness and simplicity and can take samples from sufficiently large volumes of air. They were used successfully by the regular staff of the Pakistan Meteorological Service after a short period of training, without interruption of their normal duties.

The technique of sampling and analysis has been described fully elsewhere [FOURNIER D'ALBE and LATEEF, 1953]. Briefly, the airborne particles are captured on clean glass slides, which are enclosed for examination in a small chamber where the relative humidity is controlled by the presence of a solution of sodium chloride of fixed concentration. The hygroscopic particles grow into droplets on the slide; they are counted and their diameters measured with the aid of a special graticule. By making assumptions as to the chemical nature of the nuclei it is then possible to estimate from the droplet diameter the mass of salt in each particle. The results presented later are in a form based on the assumption that the nuclei are of sodium chloride, for which there is some experimental support. However, the significance of the results for cloud physics does not depend vitally on the correctness of this assumption, since it is not the chemical structure of a nucleus as much as its mass and hygroscopic properties which determine its role in the formation of rain.

Similar observations have now been started in Mexico, where six nucleus sampling stations have just been put into operation. The results of these measurements are not yet available, but some preliminary observations from this country are quoted to illustrate points in the discussion of the Pakistan results.

Size distribution of hygroscopic nuclei—Each sample yields a size-distribution curve of the hygroscopic nuclei present in the air near the ground at the time and place

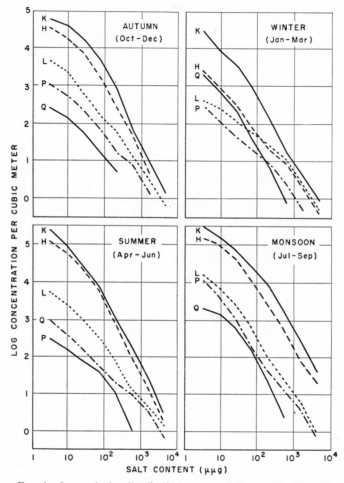

Fig. 1—Seasonal size-distribution curves, Pakistan: K, Karachi; H, Hyderabad; L, Lahore; P, Peshawar; Q. Quetta

of the experiment. In Pakistan no means were available for taking samples in aircraft, but the surface observations were always made in the afternoon when the convective mixing of the lower atmosphere was at its maximum.

Counting was limited to those particles which formed droplets of radius greater than two microns when in equilibrium with an aqueous solution containing ten per cent by weight of sodium chloride, and which thus contained the equivalent of at least 3×10^{-12} grams NaCl.

At each station both the total concentration and the size distribution varied considerably from day to day, but we may consider first the seasonal mean size distribution curves for each station in Pakistan which are given in Fig. 1. Each curve here represents the mean of some 50 observations.

The curves for Karachi, which is on the coast of the Arabian Sea, resemble those obtained in other oceanic areas [WOODCOCK, 1952, 1953; MOORE, 1952]. The variations from season to season reflect changes in the strength of the prevailing southwesterly wind. The concentration of particles of $10\mu\mu g$ is about ten times higher at the height of the monsoon in August than it is in January, when there is only a local sea breeze

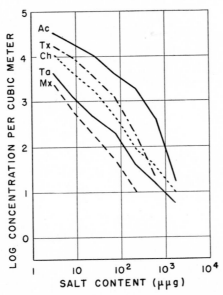

FIG. 2—Size-distribution curves, Mexico: Ac, Acapulco, on coast, July 31, 1955; Tx, Tuxpan, 5 km from coast, August 7, 1955; Ch, Chilpancingo, 95 km from coast, July 31, 1955; Ta, Taxco, 180 km from coast, July 31, 1955; Mx, Mexico City, 250 km from coast, August 7, 1955

bringing particles from the ocean. The change in concentration of the very large particles of mass greater than $10^3\mu\mu g$ is even more marked, it being nearly 100 times greater in August than in January. No means were available for making observations at sea, and it is not possible to say what proportion of the nuclei were formed at the open sea surface and what proportion by the breaking of waves on the coast.

At Hyderabad, some 120 miles from the coast, the change of monsoon is equally evident, though here the change in concentration is nearly independent of particle size.

At the three inland stations (Lahore, Peshawar, and Quetta) the seasonal changes are less well-marked, but the influx of maritime air during the monsoon season was often reflected in the values of hygroscopic particle concentration. At these stations, the situation is complicated by the fact that the air masses may have rather complex histories.

Also, the particles captured so far from the coast may have had other sources than the ocean. This point will be discussed in the following Section.

A significant feature of the particle concentration at Quetta, which was also observed, though less clearly, at Hyderabad and Karachi, was its high correlation with the dew-point. This may be due to the fact that Quetta is surrounded in all directions by desert for some hundreds of miles and therefore the main source of both water vapor and hygroscopic particles in the air at Quetta is the Arabian Sea. Karachi and Hyderabad also lie in desert areas. The correlation was not observed either at Lahore or Peshawar, where the relatively abundant vegetation supplied water vapor but no salt particles to the surface air.

In Fig. 2 are shown some size-distribution curves obtained from single observations in Mexico. The samples at Acapulco, Chilpancingo, and Taxco were obtained within a few hours of one another on July 31, 1955, and those at Tuxpan and Mexico City on August 7. The first notable feature of these results is the much lower particle concentrations observed on the coasts of Mexico, at Acapulco and at Tuxpan, than at Karachi at the same season. This is no doubt due to the much lighter winds prevailing in the Mexican area. The second is the more rapid decrease of concentration inland in Mexico, which is probably accounted for by the mountainous topography. On flying between Mexico City and the Gulf coast the author has noticed that the coastal haze layer is not always deep enough to rise on to the plateau of Mexico. In West Pakistan there is no such barrier to the invasion of the fairly shallow layer of maritime air. Thus the interior plateau of Mexico, although less than 200 miles from the ocean, appears to have particle concentrations during the rainy season comparable to those of the Punjab, more than 500 miles from the nearest sea.

Sources of giant hygroscopic particles; the oceans—There is no doubt that the main source of the particles is the oceans and coasts. In the absence of precipitation, the main agent for the loss of particles from the atmosphere will be fall under gravity. In an atmosphere kept mixed by convection this loss c, should be exponential, and expressed by the equation

$$C = C_0 \exp(-vt/h)$$

where C_0 is the concentration at time $t = 0$ of particles whose terminal velocity of fall is v cm/sec assuming that the atmosphere is mixed up to a height h cm above the ground. At least during daylight hours, this assumption may generally be justified. If v is expressed in cm/sec and h in km, then the time t for the concentration of particles of any size to decrease by a factor of 2 is given by

$$t = 19{,}25h/v \text{ hours}$$

Table 1 shows the 'half-life' of particles of various masses, with various assumptions as to the mixing height. The terminal velocities of the particles, calculated from modified Stokes' Law have been assumed equal to those of spheres of equal mass and of the density of dry salt.

It is clear that even on the severe assumption of a mixing height of 1 km, particles of up to 10^{-9} gram may remain airborne long enough to penetrate far into the interior of continents.

Table 1. *'Half-life' of airborne particles*

Mixing height	Mass of particles (grams)			
	10^{-11}	10^{-10}	10^{-9}	10^{-8}
	day	day	hr	hr
1 km	45	10	50	11
2 km	90	19	101	22
5 km	225	49	252	54

During the monsoon season in West Pakistan, a fairly regular current of maritime air sweeps up from the Arabian Sea into the western Punjab. It may take approximately 30 hours to travel from Hyderabad, where the air is already mixed at least up to 1 km, to Lahore. Using (1) one may calculate the loss of particles by fall under gravity during this time. Fig. 3 shows the distribution curve at Hyderabad at this season, and the distribution curve for Lahore calculated on the above assumptions.

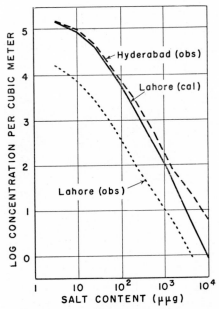

Fig. 3—Observed distribution curve at Hyderabad, and the observed and calculated distribution curves at Lahore during the monsoon season

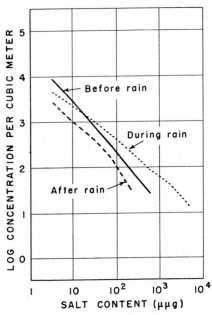

Fig. 4—Distribution curves at Mexico City, August 5, 1955

It is clear that loss by fall under gravity is negligible as an agent of removal of the particles, except of those of mass greater than 10^{-9} gram. The decrease in concentration from Hyderabad to Lahore may be due to several causes: (a) dilution by mixing of the maritime air stream with continental air from Baluchistan; (b) dilution by convective mixing with upper air which may be relatively poor in nuclei, or (c) removal by precipitation. Processes (a) and (b) would tend to reduce concentrations without altering the slope of the distribution curve, and in any case are not likely to account for a decrease by as much as a factor of 10.

Sources of giant hygroscopic particles; clouds and precipitation—The role of precipitation is more complex, as it is not known what effect it is likely to have on the shape of the size distribution curve. Furthermore, the evaporation of falling raindrops may produce large nuclei as a result of the aggregation of the nuclei of numerous cloud droplets. A series of samples taken at Mexico City, August 5, 1955, is illustrative of this effect.

In Fig. 4 sample A was taken in the morning, with some convective clouds in the sky but no rain. In the early afternoon a violent thunderstorm developed over the city and sample B was taken during light rain just after the main storm. Sample C was taken when rain had ceased though the sky remained covered with altocumulus. The visibility was then extremely good.

The notable increase in the numbers of the largest particles in Sample B taken during the rain may have been due to the evaporation of small raindrops of radius between 150 and 250 microns, which are just not large enough to reach the ground from a cloud base 600 m above. If this indeed was the case, it indicates a concentration of salt in these small raindrops of 20–30 mg/l, which is comparable only with the highest values of chloride content found in rainwater in Hawaii by Woodcock and Blanchard [1955], or in Scandinavia by Rossby's group. It is difficult to assess the importance of the evaporation of small raindrops as a source of giant nuclei, but on a local scale it may be of importance, since it provides a mechanism by which one raincloud may eventually 'seed' others in its vicinity.

Even without precipitation, it is possible that giant nuclei may be formed by the coalescence and subsequent evaporation of cloud droplets, for instance in 'fair-weather' cumulus clouds. This was suggested independently by Facy and Fournier d'Albe at the recent Symposium on Experimental Meteorology in Zurich as a possible explanation of the observation reported by Byers that on some occasions the concentration of hygroscopic particles is greater aloft than at ground level.

The net effect of precipitation, however, is to remove nuclei from the atmosphere, and it is probably the main agent in their removal. This is well illustrated by sample C in Fig. 4, which was taken about an hour after the cessation of general light rain in Mexico City.

Sources of giant hygroscopic particles; land sources—At first it was thought that the areas of salt desert in West Pakistan might be an important source of giant nuclei. Quetta in summer often experiences thick dust haze from the deserts to the west, but no significant rise in hygroscopic particle content of the air was observed on these occasions. The difficulty of access prevented the author from visiting the salt-desert areas in Baluchistan, but it is possible that the salt lies on the surface in grains too large to remain airborne for long even if raised by strong winds.

There was little opportunity in Pakistan to investigate the possible production of giant nuclei by industrial processes, though in Lahore the concentration was usually slightly greater in the early morning than in the afternoon, possibly due to the production of nuclei by domestic fires. The only terrestrial source so far positively identified by cascade impactor is the laboratory of the Institute of Chemistry in the University of Mexico.

Conclusions—It appears that the main source of giant hygroscopic nuclei is the sea, and that the main agent of their removal is precipitation. If they escape precipitation near the coasts, giant nuclei of maritime origin may easily penetrate far into the interior of continents.

There is a need for a closer investigation of their removal from the atmosphere by precipitation. It seems likely that chemical analyses of precipitation and of aerosol samples collected on a synoptic basis will yield some very useful information on this point. It is hoped to undertake such observations in Mexico within the course of the next few months.

Acknowledgments—The author is indebted to the Director, Pakistan Meteorological Service, for permission to use the data from nucleus samples in that country. The author is at present working in Mexico as member of a UNESCO Technical Assistance Mission.

REFERENCES

Fournier D'Albe, E. M. and A. M. A. Lateef, Preliminary note on the large hygroscopic particles suspended in the atmosphere, *Bul. Obs. Puy de Dôme*, ser.2, no.1, pp.1–12, 1953.

May, K. R., The cascade impactor: an instrument for sampling coarse aerosols, *J. Sci. Instrum.*, v.22, pp.187–195, 1945.

Moore, D. J., Measurement of condensation nuclei over the North Atlantic, *Q.J.R. Met. Soc.*, v.78, pp.596–602, 1952.

Woodcock, A. H., Atmospheric salt particles and raindrops, *J. Met.*, v.9, pp.200–212, 1952.

Woodcock, A. H., Salt nuclei in marine air as a function of altitude and wind force, *J. Met.*, v.10, pp.362–371, 1953.

Woodcock, A. H. and D. C. Blanchard, Observations supporting the salt-nuclei hypothesis of raindrop formation, unpublished manuscript no.55–19, Woods Hole Oceanographic Institution, 16pp., 1955.

DISCUSSION

Dr. Vincent J. Schaefer—Where did you obtain your sample during the rain? Was it near the surface of the roof?

Dr. E. M. Fournier d'Albe—Yes, it was about two meters above the roof surface.

Dr. Schaefer—The Splash effects of large raindrops on slides show tremendous numbers of bubbles. Isn't there danger of bubbles being projected from the splashing water, producing the large nuclei, and then maybe being carried up?

Dr. Fournier d'Albe—I don't think that any droplets were splashed directly from the roof surface into the impactor during these experiments. However, it seems quite probable, as you say, that the splashing of raindrops on the ground may produce droplets small enough to become airborne and to leave behind large nuclei when they evaporate. This process may well contribute to the relatively high concentration of very large airborne nuclei observed during rain.

Dr. James P. Lodge, Jr.—There are a couple of our flights that have been worked up for sulfate, and I believe that Miss Tufts is currently making some magnesium determinations. There is quite a bit of magnesium over the ocean, and a not too negligible amount over the continent. Miss Tufts has also worked out a test for potassium. It would be very enlightening to test a few of these samples aloft for potassium content.

Mr. D. Lee Harris—The air-pollution studies at Los Angeles report a tremendous amount of nitrates being put into the air in that city. I presume that would be true of other industrial cities. Have there been any studies of nitrates?

G

Dr. Lodge—We have a test for nitrate that is not too satisfactory. It doesn't detect particles below two microns. It seemed to be more to the point initially to make a thorough study of halides and come back to the nitrates later.

Dr. James E. McDonald—Fournier d'Albe and Byers have both given data here that lead to some speculation about the possibility of interception of the particles. Isn't it a very serious difficulty that the very particles with which you are concerned here are down in the range of a few microns, for which the collection efficiency of a leaf must be very close to zero at the speeds involved?

Mr. Alfred H. Woodcock—Concerning the collection by plants, one point that hasn't been brought up is the effects of the diurnal radiation cycle over land and the consequent cooling of the surface layers of the atmosphere. As a result, the humidity goes up, the particle size increases by condensational growth and the possibilities of direct rainout or impingement on vegetation are increased. One can see, in an ordinary grass field in the early morning, spiderwebs festooned with droplets. I find that when the water has evaporated, most of these droplets leave a crystalline nucleus residue.

Dr. Horace R. Byers—I have seen some data showing that the salt concentration in dew on the California coast is very high, and it is probable that a great deal of salt comes out of the lower atmosphere in that form.

RECENT MEASUREMENTS OF THE VERTICAL DISTRIBUTION OF AITKEN NUCLEI

HELMUT WEICKMANN

Evans Signal Laboratory, Belmar, N.J.

Abstract—The vertical distribution of Aitken nuclei was measured during flights with a B-17 aircraft. The exchange layer of the lower atmosphere is clearly indicated by a high concentration of nuclei which decreases suddenly at the top of this layer.

THE attached figures (Figures 1–13) show some results of condensation nuclei counts versus altitude. The counts have been carried out using an Aitken nucleus counter, which was kindly loaned to us by the Carnegie Institution of Washington. The measuring range has been extended to below 100 nuclei per cc. In the figures the abscissa is the number of nuclei per cc of environmental air. The measurements were made during the ascent in order to be sure that the air in the counter would not be contaminated. Only outside air was sampled.

Usually tops of haze layers were marked by a sudden decrease of the particle concentration, whereas the layer itself was not necessarily characterized by high absolute concentration. During the flights of February 24–25 and July 19–21, 1955, measurements were made almost without interruption during a slow rate of climb of about 200 ft per

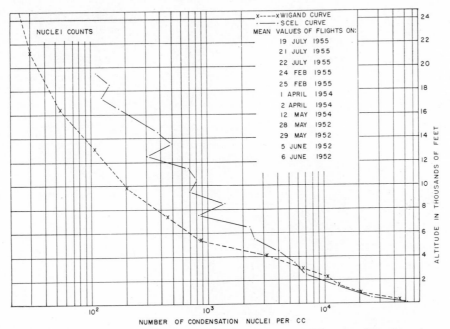

FIG. 1—Mean curve of number of condensation nuclei after Wigand and by these data

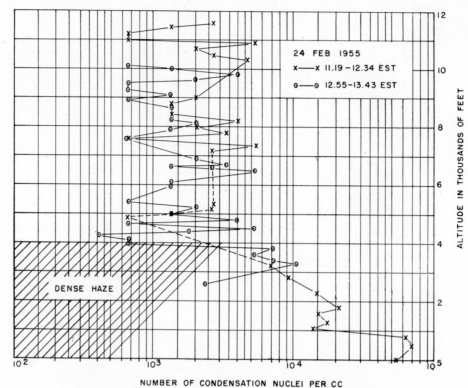

FIG. 2—Number of condensation nuclei, flights of Feb. 24, 1955

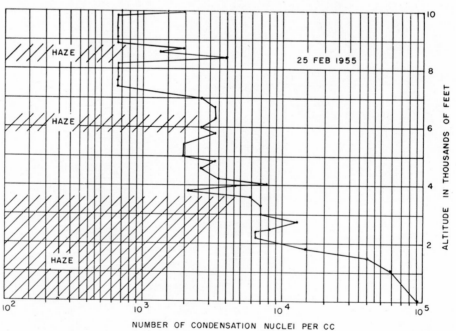

FIG. 3—Number of condensation nuclei, flight of Feb. 25, 1955

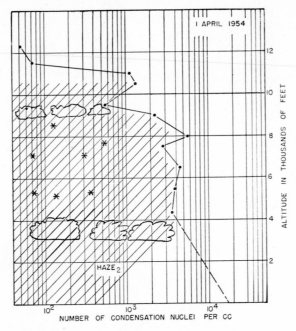

FIG. 4—Number of condensation nuclei, flight of Apr. 1, 1954

minute, in order to obtain the fine structure of the aerosol distribution. It turned out that above the main haze layer the concentration continuously changed back and forth up to one order of magnitude. The flight of February 24, 1955, indicates that we may have some confidence in the reality of these variations. On that day the top of the haze

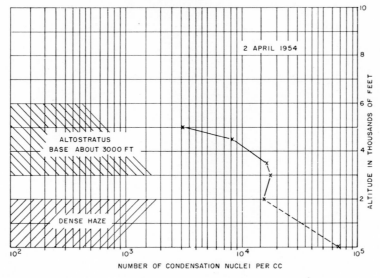

FIG. 5—Number of condensation nuclei, flight of Apr. 2, 1954

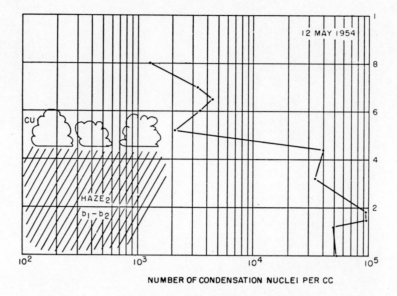

FIG. 6—Number of condensation nuclei, flight of May 12, 1954

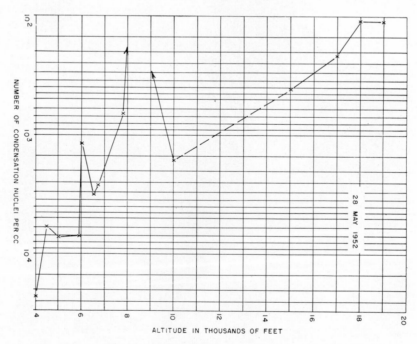

FIG. 7—Number of condensation nuclei, flight of May 28, 1952

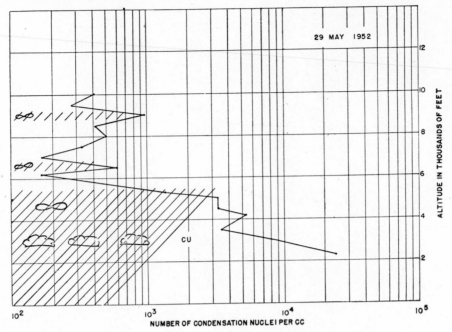

FIG. 8—Number of condensation nuclei, flight of May 29, 1952

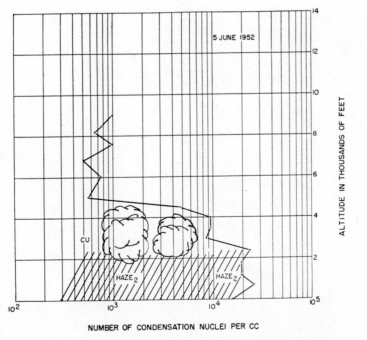

FIG. 9—Number of condensation nuclei, flight of June 5, 1952

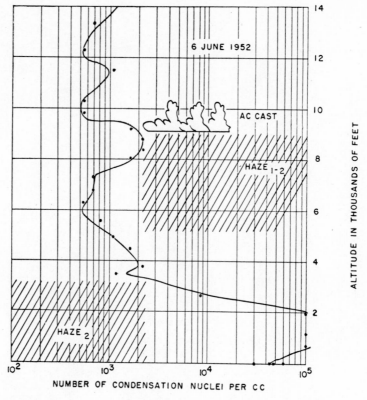

FIG. 10—Number of condensation nuclei, flight of June 6, 1952

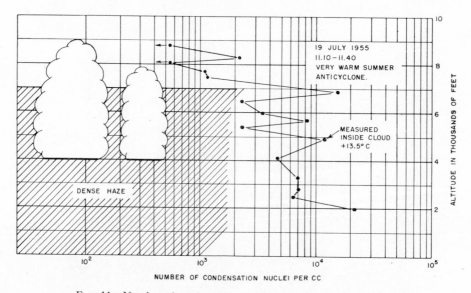

FIG. 11—Number of condensation nuclei, flight of July 19, 1955

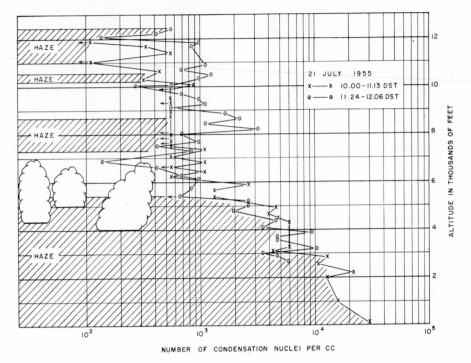

FIG. 12—Number of condensation nuclei, flight of July 21, 1955

layer was very sharp. Based on eye observation of the pronounced top of the layer two consecutive measurements were made; one just below the top of the layer at 3800 ft, and one just above it at 4000 ft. The first one yielded 7400 nuclei per cc and the second one 670. The two values are shown on the diagram of the flight of February 24 during the time interval between 12h 55m and 13h 43m EST. If we may have confidence in the reality of these fluctuations, then the question arises how they form. They would indicate either a pronounced layer structure of the atmosphere or fluctuations in the concentration along the flight path due to aerosol clouds. In a level flight at an altitude of 5000 ft

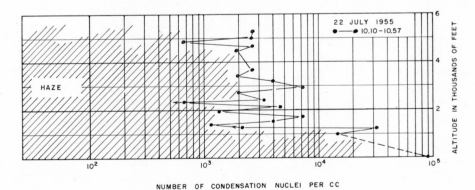

FIG. 13—Number of condensation nuclei, flight of July 22, 1955

on April 2, 1954, no such fluctuations were found. This would indicate that they are due to the layer structure of the atmosphere. Also these fluctuations seem to be less pronounced in the well-mixed turbulence layer near the ground. For definite conclusions, however, the data are still too sparse.

A few words should be said about the mean curve of the values presented here (Fig. 1) in comparison with the Wigand curve. It appears questionable if a mean curve of nuclei concentration actually means anything. Since, however, the Wigand curve is well known but was obtained only during one or two free-balloon flights, the mean curve here is probably more justified. Whereas the two curves agree rather well for the lowest 5000 ft, they differ roughly one order of magnitude for the remaining common height interval.

Credit is due to J. J. Kelly for his participation in these observations and to pilots and crew members of the Flight Test Division, Griffiss Air Force Base, Rome, N.Y.

DISCUSSION

Mr. D. Lee Harris—In the February 24 flights the counts varied in a peculiar way above 4500 ft. They oscillated back and forth and with only a couple of separations came down to the same minimum, about 700 nuclei per cc. Is that real or do you suppose that it is due to some characteristic reading method?

Dr. Helmut Weickmann—This is due to the reading method and is the lowest count which I could obtain in this particular series of measurements. Actually the concentration in some of these points was still lower but could not be determined due to unfavorable circumstances. The lowest concentration obtainable under optimum conditions was 11 nuclei per cc.

Mr. Duncan Blanchard—About a year and a half ago Mr. Spencer of our laboratory built a modified form of Vonnegut's continuously operating nuclei counter. He built it so as to be portable and compact in size. The operating unit was placed within a streamlined object about the size of a football and mounted on the wing of our laboratory plane. With this arrangement we made many nuclei soundings in the atmosphere. On days when the air was stable the high nuclei counts were found near the surface and on days when mixing occurred the nuclei count tended to be uniform throughout the sounding.

We could more or less tell what was going on in the atmosphere from the variation of nuclei with altitude. On one occasion, with the wind coming from the Boston area, we noticed two very prominent haze layers. The nuclei sounding showed high nuclei counts as we passed through the layers.

This was not the first time that a continuous recording nuclei counter has been flown. Vonnegut while working with Project Cirrus, made several nuclei soundings over New Mexico.

THE VERTICAL DISTRIBUTION OF AEROSOLS
OVER THE OCEAN

CHRISTIAN E. JUNGE

Geophysics Research Directorate, Air Force Cambridge Research Center, Bedford, Mass.

Abstract—Recent observations of sea-spray particles at various altitudes over the ocean by Woodcock, Moore, Lodge and others are compared, and the major features discussed. They can be explained satisfactorily as a non-steady case of eddy diffusion.

Introduction—Recent investigations of sea-spray aerosols over the oceans yielded some information as to the dependence of their concentration on wind speed and altitude. Although the material is still fairly incomplete, some general features are recognizable, which may justify a quantitative consideration of the basic process involved. The purpose of this paper is to show that these observations can well be explained by the action of eddy diffusion in a non-steady case.

The main observational results—Data on sea-spray particle concentration over the ocean, useful for this analysis, are available from Woodcock [1953], Lodge [1954], Moore [1952], and a few of my own measurements [Junge, 1954]. The observations give information about the two interesting, but not completely independent, inter-relationships of particle concentration with wind force and particle concentration with altitude.

Fig. 1 reproduces a graph of Woodcock with additional values of Moore, Fournier d'Albe [Moore, 1952] and Junge, outlining sea-salt density as a function of the wind force. Woodcock's numerous measurements, made mostly in the Hawaiian trade winds, represent the sea-salt content at the cloud base level (500 m) of all particles larger than about 4×10^{-12} gr. They scatter in a comparatively narrow area, limited by the two dashed lines, and very well suggest a functional dependence of particle size on the wind force.

We added some data by Moore, obtained on weather ships in the eastern Atlantic at about ten meters above sea level, and of Fournier d'Albe in the Bay of Monaco. They represent the total mass of sea-salt particles larger than 10^{-11} gr and are comparable to Woodcock's data. Our own measurements were made near Round Hill, Massachusetts about 300 ft from the beach to eliminate the effects of the surf. This is a fairly exposed place with respect to the various wind directions. Our data, plotted as a function of wind speed, can be limited by a line representing the maximum salt content possible at various wind speeds. This is the heavy broken line reproduced in Fig. 1. Values below this maximum line were obviously caused by insufficient contact of the air masses with the sea. Our data give the total sodium chloride content for particles with radii between $0 \cdot 08$ and 8μ and are comparable with Woodcock's data.

Fig. 1 shows that all these data agree to a certain extent, even though Woodcock's data were obtained at cloud-base level and the other data near sea level. It appears that, within some limits, the sea-salt content is a function of the wind speed and that this function varies but little with geographical area, observational technique, and altitude in the lower few hundred meters.

There are fewer measurements of concentration versus height. Woodcock measured primarily at cloud-base level and between the clouds. He found that between the trade-wind cumuli, the particle concentrations decreased rapidly because of condensation and mixing with the clean layers above the inversion. Here we are concerned with the layers

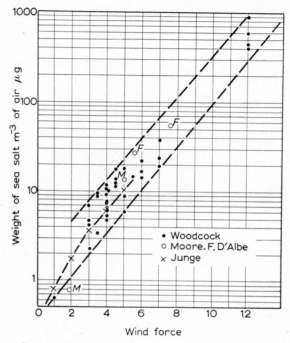

FIG. 1—Relation of wind force to weight of sea salt
according to Woodcock and other observers

below cloud-base level. For this layer, Woodcock states that the decrease with altitude is, in most cases, not very pronounced, but he gives almost no data. One general feature readily apparent is that the size distribution down to particles of about 1μ stays nearly the same at various places and altitudes. The largest particles are excluded from this rule, for they decrease with altitude a little faster than the smaller ones.

The only systematic measurements below cloud level were done by LODGE [1954] in the trade-wind area at Puerto Rico. His valuable material shows again that the character of the size distribution does not change with altitude. He finds a decrease of particle concentration with altitude which varies from day to day. The fluctuations in his curves are fairly large, but there seems to be an exponential decrease of concentration with altitude which is well pronounced in the trade winds approaching Puerto Rico. We summarize the main results: (a) A fairly well-pronounced interrelationship exists between wind and sea-salt content under various conditions (Fig. 1). (b) Often a small decrease of particle concentration with altitude is found in the lowest 1000 m. When this decrease is more pronounced, it can be well approximated by an exponential law. (c) The character of the particle size distribution for particles above 1μ is fairly independent of the altitude.

Possible explanation for the observed facts—It is very likely, on the basis of these facts, that the particle size distribution does not represent a steady state condition, although Fig. 1 suggests this strongly. The reasons are twofold.

If gravity counteracts the upward flux of particles to establish this equilibrium, a pronounced dependence in particle size should appear in contradiction with (c).

If the cloud level acts as a sink, because particles are eliminated by the condensation process, the steady state should be characterized by a vertical flux which is independent of altitude. In other words, the vertical gradient of particle concentration is inversely proportional to the Austauch coefficient. The knowledge of the vertical distribution of the eddy diffusion over sea, although not very complete, makes it impossible to explain an exponential distribution.

With gravity and condensation ruled out, we see no other process which could remove the particles and establish a steady state. We are forced, therefore, to assume unsteady conditions, which will be investigated in more detail.

The non-steady state solution—We approximate the natural conditions over the ocean by the following model: The sea surface (altitude $z = 0$) is a uniform source of particles with a production rate of q particles/cm² sec. No particles shall penetrate the inversion layer, $z = L = 2000$ m, and no clouds shall be present. For the lowest layers over the water surface the Austauch (g/cm sec) can be expressed by $A = 6 \times 10^5 u_5$ $(z+b) = a(z+b)$ where u_5 is the windspeed (cm/sec) at $z = 500$ cm and b, the roughness parameter of the sea surface [LETTAU, 1939].

The value of b is not very well known as a function of windspeed or wave height, and various observers arrive at different conclusions [see NEUMANN, 1948, for example]. Most probably b is about four cm and fairly independent of wind speed. Our results later will show that the value for b is not critical for the solution. After the linear increase in the lowest layers, A assumes a roughly constant value with increasing altitude, determined by the intensity of convection. Before this value is reached, A is thought to go through a maximum, although not very much is known. A sufficient approximation for our present problem is given by the analytical expression

$$A = \frac{a(z+b)}{1+a(z+b)/c}$$

which satisfies the conditions that for small values of z, $A \simeq a(z+b)$ and for larger values of z, $A \simeq c$. Under trade-wind conditions with convection, a reasonable value for c is 400. In Fig. 2 A is plotted as a function of altitude.

The one-dimensional diffusion equation for the particle concentration $n = n(t,t)$

$$\frac{\partial n(z,t)}{\partial t} = \frac{\partial}{\partial z}\left(\frac{A}{\rho}\frac{\partial n(z,t)}{\partial z}\right) \text{ with } A > 0$$

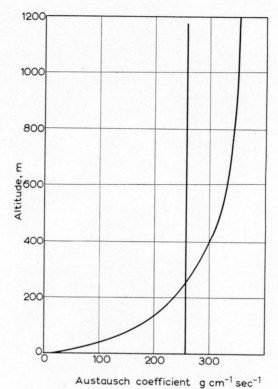

FIG. 2—Relation of the austausch coefficient to altitude; the curve represents the variable austausch coefficient used for Fig. 3; the straight line represents the constant austausch coefficient used for Fig. 4 and which is approximately the average of the curve

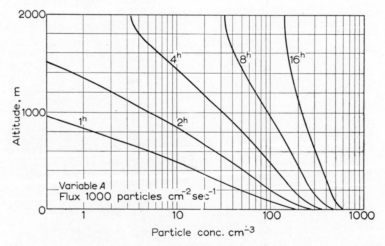

FIG. 3—Calculated particle concentration as a function of time and altitude with a variable austausch coefficient

can only be solved by numerical calculation. The boundary conditions are

$$-\frac{A}{\rho}\frac{\partial n(z,t)}{\partial z}\bigg]_{z=0} = q \quad 0 < t$$

$$\frac{\partial n(z,t)}{\partial z}\bigg]_{z=l} = 0 \quad 0 < t$$

$$n(z,t)_{t=0} \equiv 0 \quad 0 < z < l$$

Since the solution is proportional to q, this value was arbitrarily set at 1000.

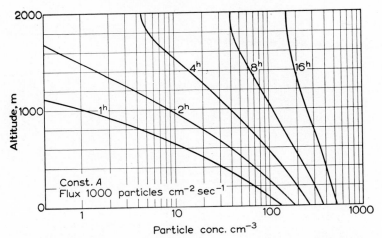

FIG. 4—Calculated particle concentration as a function of time and altitude with a constant austausch coefficient

Considerable difficulties in the numerical calculation are caused by the fact that the solution has a singularity at $z = -b$ [VERZUH, 1955]. The result is plotted in Fig. 3. In Fig. 4 the same calculation was performed with a constant $a = 255$, which represents a sort of average value between the surface and the inversion layer (Fig. 2).

Figures 3 and 4 do not show very much difference except for the layers near the sea surface, although the vertical distributions of A differ considerably. This surprising result is still better illustrated in Fig. 5 which compares the average slope of the curves of Figures 3 and 4 between 200 and 1600 m, and also the absolute values for an arbitrary level, that is, for 200 m, and shows how well the two solutions match. This result immediately indicates that detailed knowledge of our variable A is by no means important.

Fig. 3 (also 4) shows that the particle concentration decrease with altitude is approximately exponential. As time increases, the slope increases, and after one day the concentration at the inversion layer is less than half the value at the sea surface.

This result satisfies the observational results labelled (b) and (c). But it can also be shown that this model is not in disagreement with (a). To demonstrate this, we plotted the time dependence of the concentration for various altitudes in Fig. 6. We see that after about one day the increase in most levels becomes slow, and the difference in concentration between the various levels decreases rapidly. This would be more readily apparent if the calculations were extended to time intervals of one or two days, which can be expected especially in the trade winds.

We conclude from our model that the observed interrelationship between particle concentration and wind force is only approximately valid, representing some sort of 'saturation' value after the first period in which the vertical distribution is established.

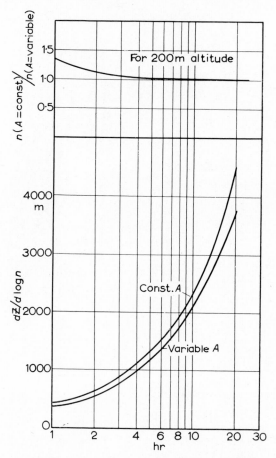

FIG. 5—(Upper part) Ratio of particle concentration of Fig. 4 to that of Fig. 3 as a function of time for an altitude of 200 meters; the ratio of almost unity indicates that the solutions differ only slightly; (lower part) comparison of the absolute slopes of the curves in Fig. 3 and 4; again indicating the similarity of both solutions

The fact that Woodcock, Moore, and Fournier d'Albe found no values below the dashed lines in Fig. 1 indicates that this early transition state is seldom encountered, probably only after heavy rainfalls or passage of fronts. This conclusion seems to be reasonable, especially in the trade winds. Our own measurements, however, showed this scattering to be very pronounced, probably due to the short trajectory of most of the air masses over sea.

Our model, of course, simplifies the natural conditions considerably. Most times there are clouds below the inversion layer, and once in a while rain showers eliminate particles locally. This clear air is laterally mixed with the undisturbed air masses, and the overall effect will be that of an uniformly distributed sink throughout the air mass. Indications of such disturbed layers were found by Lodge.

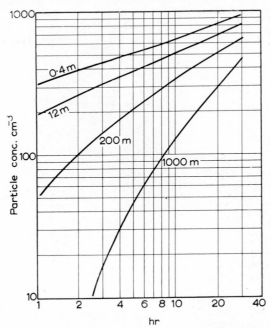

FIG. 6—Particle concentration as a function of time for various altitudes according to Fig. 3; after one day the increase in all altitudes is slow

Conclusions—The preceding consideration showed that the non-steady-state solution can well explain the observations about sea-spray particles. However, proof can only be obtained by combined measurements of the austausch co-efficient and particle concentration. Such measurements can finally result in data on the production rate, which is of interest for questions on the budget of sea-salt in the air. We can estimate from Fig. 3 that, under the assumed conditions the numerical value of the concentration, when saturation is reached after a few days, is approximately equal to the numerical value of the flux. We can conclude from this that the flux of particles with moderate winds is of the order of 0·1 particle per cm² per sec.

Acknowledgments—The writer is indebted to Fr. Verzuh, whose interest in the problem made it possible to solve the numerical calculations.

DISCUSSION

Mr. A. H. Woodcock—I wonder if it is useful to mention that aerosol sampling techniques such as yours, which require long sampling periods, determine average quantities during the

H

passage of thousands or sometimes tens of thousands of cubic meters of air? In speaking of turbulence elements, however, one usually thinks of their size in terms of tens or hundreds of meters. I am wondering if your sampling results might not have been significantly different if the mechanics of obtaining a sample had allowed you to obtain adequate quantities of aerosol in a much shorter time. Does this concept have any bearing upon your relationships between austausch and the vertical distribution of salt?

Dr. C. E. Junge—The few measurements available over the ocean are averages over such time and space intervals which can be considered large in the scale of austausch eddies. I think, therefore, that, in general, the results of our calculations represent a reasonable approach to natural conditions when applied to adequate dimensions in time and space. The results, however, cannot be applied to individual convective cells or any space and time intervals comparable to the dimensions of the turbulent elements.

The curves of Lodge obtained in Puerto Rico show detailed structure and I wonder about what time or space intervals they were averaged.

Dr. James P. Lodge, Jr.—Those sampling times ranged, depending on altitude, from ten to 30 minutes. Flight speeds were about 180 mph. So they will correspond to integration of the sample over some thirty to ninety miles. I would not be prepared to say just how real some of that fine structure is.

My feeling has been that where we have two points at a higher altitude where there is a definite increase shown by both of those and then two points lower which show a lesser value, I can generally believe them. I don't think two values in a row would be that far off.

The other case in which I feel fine structure can be given credence is when some particular feature is shown, perhaps only by a single point, but shown in a large number of samples such as the little tail that we always get, the decrease between five hundred and one hundred feet, over the sea. You almost invariably get a decrease in concentration there. I think that is real. I am not at all certain that I am happy about anybody's explanation for it.

Another real phenomenon is the very distinct sharp increase as you pass through the trade inversion. You get quite low concentration above it and relatively high ones immediately below it.

TIME VARIATIONS OF CHARGED ATMOSPHERIC NUCLEI

RITA C. SAGALYN AND GERARD A. FAUCHER

Geophysics Research Directorate, Air Force Cambridge Research Center, Bedford, Mass.

Abstract—An investigation of time variations in the vertical and horizontal distribution of charged atmospheric nuclei in fair weather has been carried out by means of aircraft. In the exchange layer, regular variations of nucleus concentration with time are observed from the vicinity of sunrise to early afternoon. Analysis of the meteorological data obtained simultaneously shows that this variation is caused primarily by the action of the daily turbulent cycle. During periods of low advection, regular variations of nucleus concentration with time are also observed in this region from early afternoon to the following sunrise, and are shown to be the result of coagulation and subsidence. The time variations at night are more complicated during periods of intense advection. Above the exchange layer, variations in nucleus content with time are not found to be regular. The effect of these daily variations in nucleus content on the electrical properties of the atmosphere is shown. An analysis of observed daily variations in the magnitude of the horizontal fluctuations of nucleus density is also given.

Introduction—The results of a systematic investigation of the variations with time in the vertical distribution of charged nuclei (large ions) and electrical conductivity of the atmosphere are presented. The experiments were carried out with instruments installed in a B-17 aircraft for measuring and recording the concentration and mobility distribution of charged particles with mobility between 7×10^{-1} and 2×10^{-4} cm²/sec volt. The corresponding particle size range is calculated from the Stokes-Millikan-Cunningham relation which can be expressed

$$r = \frac{e \pm \sqrt{e^2 + 24\pi\eta ekAL}}{12\pi\eta k} \tag{1}$$

where r is the particle radius, e the charge per particle; η is the coefficient of viscosity of the gas; A is a constant, and L the mean free path of the gas molecules. The solution of (1) for singly charged particles in the mobility range noted above, gives a particle size range of 8×10^{-8} to 6×10^{-6} cm radius. The measurement, therefore, includes the charged component of Aitken nuclei. Since the mobility distribution is measured, the total nucleus concentration can be easily calculated from the theory of BRICARD [1949] for the collision process between small ions and nuclei. Electrical conductivity, temperature, pressure, humidity, and airspeed were also recorded. The apparatus and method of measurement have been described in an earlier paper [SAGALYN and FAUCHER, 1954].

The discussion presented here is limited primarily to results obtained in fair weather in the altitude range 700 to 15,000 ft above the surface. These experiments are a continuation of experiments described in an earlier paper [SAGALYN and FAUCHER, 1954] where the results of an investigation of the vertical distribution of charged nuclei and electrical conductivity during the daylight hours were presented. The results of approximately fifty flights, although showing considerable variation in the profile and magnitude of the charged nucleus concentration and conductivity at a given level, also showed certain general characteristics which could be understood in terms of known meteorological

97

phenomena. For example, these flights showed that in the exchange or friction layer familiar to meteorologists, varying in depth from 1000 to 10,000 ft above the surface, the concentration and distribution of nuclei were determined largely by the intensity of atmospheric turbulence. In this region, collisions between small ions and nuclei had a dominant influence on the electrical conductivity of the atmosphere. At the top of this layer there was a sharp decrease in the nucleus concentration which generally resulted in an abrupt termination of their influence on the electrical properties of the atmosphere. Knowledge of the time variations of electrical conductivity and nucleus concentration is of importance in understanding the factors controlling the atmospheric electric current system over continents and also the introduction, motion and disappearance of nuclei in the atmosphere.

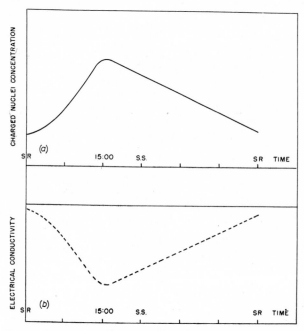

Fig. 1—Time variation of charged nucleus concentration and electrical conductivity at constant altitude in the exchange layer during periods of low advection

Method—Approximately 25 series of flights were carried out in fair weather. Each series consisted of three to seven flights over an 8- to 24-hour period. The average time interval between flights was four hours. All measurements in a given series were made in the same air mass. Most of the measurements were carried out over a fixed flight path, 25 miles long in southern New Hampshire. A few were carried out in Texas and in the vicinity of Mount Palomar in Southern California. On each flight, constant altitude measurements were made between 700 and 15,000 ft above the surface (1000 to 15,300 ft above sea level) at altitude intervals of 1000 ft up to 10,000 ft and at intervals of 2000 ft above this level. Measurements were carried out in all seasons of the year. Days on which there were no unbroken cloud layers in the immediate vicinity of the flight path are referred to as fair weather days. The mean values of the recorded parameters at a given level are used in plotting the vertical distributions shown in Figures 2, 3, 4 and 7, shown later. Altitudes above sea level are given in these figures. The nature of the horizontal variations in space and time will be discussed later.

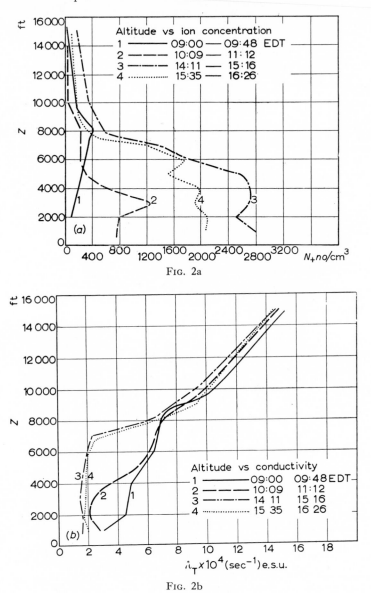

FIG. 2a

FIG. 2b

Charged-nuclei results—From shortly after sunrise to early afternoon, all fair-weather flights show a regular variation of the charged nucleus concentration with time from approximately 700 ft, the lower limit of measurement, up to the level where turbulent and convective mixing ceases (upper boundary of the exchange layer). This variation

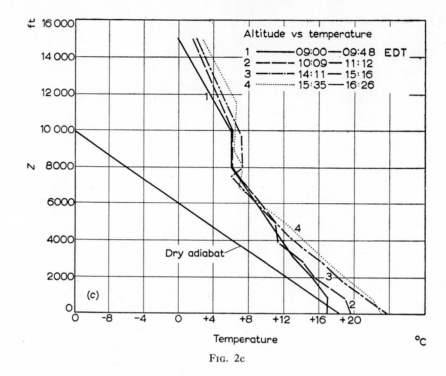

Fig. 2c

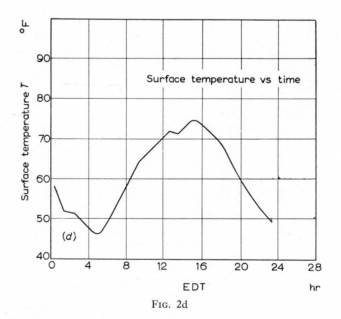

Fig. 2d

Fig. 2—Altitude and time variation of (a) charged nucleus concentration N_+, (b) total electrical conductivity (λ_T), and (c)
temperature T in southern New Hampshire, August 20, 1953;
(d) ground temperature vs time

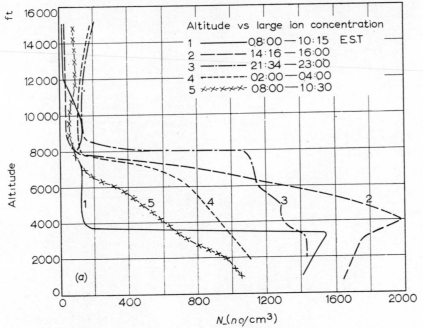

FIG. 3a

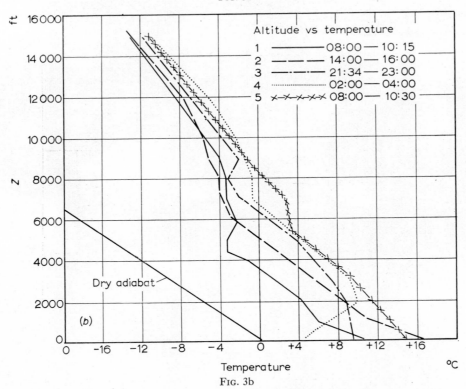

FIG. 3b

FIG. 3—Altitude and time variation of (a) charged nucleus concentration N_-, and (b) temperature T in southern New Hampshire, May 13–14, 1954

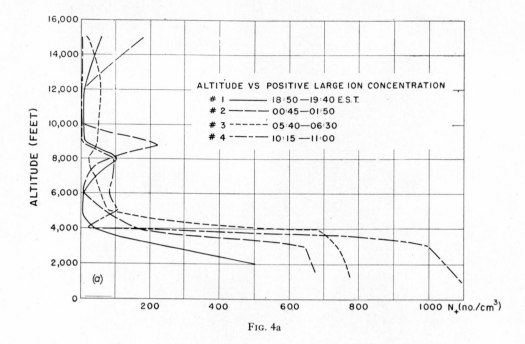

FIG. 4a

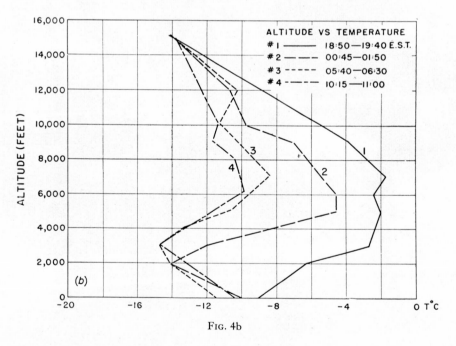

FIG. 4b

FIG. 4—Altitude and time variation (a) of charged nucleus concentration N_+, (b) temperature T in southern New Hampshire, January 21–22, 1954

consists of a continuous increase in the charged nucleus concentration with time at a given level, reaching a maximum at approximately 15h 00m Local Standard Time, as shown in Fig. 1a. The height of the exchange layer generally reaches a maximum at the time of maximum nucleus concentration. Illustrations of this type of variation are shown in the results of August 20, 1953 and May 13–14, 1954 in Figs. 2a and 3a.

The late afternoon and night results were more complicated. Approximately 65 per cent of the results show an essentially continuous decrease with time at a given level until shortly after sunrise (Fig. 1a). The magnitude of the decrease varied considerably on the nights examined, and was found to be dependent on the value of the charged nucleus concentration. The percentage decrease over a given period was greater for days with greater nucleus content. An example of this type of variation during the late afternoon and night hours is shown in the results of May 13–14, 1954 in Fig. 3a.

Thirty-five per cent of the results show a different type of variation between 15h 00m and sunrise which usually consisted of an increase in large ion content for at least several hours, sometimes at all altitudes in the exchange layer, sometimes in only a limited altitude range. The time of increase was not found to be associated with a definite local time on the days investigated. In Fig. 4a, showing the results of January 21–22, 1954 an example of this type of variation is given.

Above the exchange layer the variations in large ion concentration with time were not found to be regular. Note the variations in large ion concentration with time above the exchange layer in Figs. 2a through 4a. The maximum and minimum daily variations of the charged-nucleus density measured during the period of these experiments, in and above the exchange layer, are given in Table 1.

Table 1. *Maximum and minimum daily change in charged nucleus concentration measured at various altitudes*

| Altitude | $\Delta N_\pm (no/cm^3)$ | | | |
| | In exchange layer | | Above exchange layer | |
	Minimum	Maximum	Minimum	Maximum
ft				
1000	1000	7100	...	...
2000	880	4300	...	...
3000	350	3200	...	...
4000	250	2900	...	...
5000	280	2800	110	...
6000	300	...	95	...
7000	...	...	75	...
8000	...	...	90	300
9000	...	...	80	350
10,000	...	...	125	640
12,000	...	...	120	500
15,000	...	...	210	450

Discussion of charged-nuclei results—With regard to the interval from sunrise to 15h 00m, application of present knowledge of the effect of turbulence on the

distribution of water vapor and temperature to the meteorological data obtained simultaneously in flight shows that the variation of the charged-nucleus concentration with
time in the exchange layer from the vicinity of sunrise to early afternoon is due primarily
to the daily turbulent cycle. Analysis of the results shows that the daily variations in the
charged-nucleus concentration at a given level follow closely the daily variation in the
temperature gradient and also follow the well-known variation with time in temperature
and wind velocity at the surface [BRUNT, 1952, p.22] which reaches a maximum at
approximately 14h 00m and a minimum in the vicinity of sunrise. This is clearly illustrated, for example, in the results of August 20, in Figs. 2acd which show the temperature gradient becomes less stable between Flights 1 (09h 00m) and 2 (10h 00m) up to
4000 ft, corresponding to a considerable increase in nuclei in the same altitude range.
On Flight 3 at 14h 11m we see that the time of maximum nucleus concentration corresponds to the time of maximum temperature gradient. These features are also illustrated
in the time variations of May 13 in Figs. 3ab.

A quantitative check on the theory of mixing by atmospheric turbulence cannot be
carried out directly because the austausch coefficient as a function of time and height is
not known with sufficient accuracy for a nonadiabatic atmosphere. However, the equation of continuity is now being applied to these results to obtain information about the
height variations of the austausch coefficient with time and with varying meteorological
conditions.

With regard to the regular variation from 15h 00m to sunrise, it should be noted that
the time of the initial decrease in nuclei at approximately 15h 00m observed on 65 per
cent of the series also corresponds to the initial decrease in temperature, and change to a
more stable temperature gradient. The effect is most intense in the immediate vicinity
of the surface. The surface wind data also shows this corresponds approximately to the
time of initial decrease of wind velocity. The initial decrease in nuclei thus occurs when
the rate of transport of nuclei and other physical properties from the surface is being cut
off or gradually reduced.

Several possible contributing factors were considered in attempting to explain this
decrease in charged-nucleus concentration with time, such as diffusion through the top
of the exchange layer, advection, fall due to gravity, movement due to the electric field
of the atmosphere, nucleus coagulation, and subsidence. These processes will be considered in order.

(i) As indicated in the results for individual series, there was no experimental evidence
of diffusion through the top of the exchange layer during the late afternoon and night
hours.

(ii) Air-mass trajectories were determined from surface and upper air weather maps
up to fortyeight hours before the time of measurement. As illustrated in the 700 mb
trajectories for nine series given in Fig. 5, the results showed that during the period of
these experiments the variation in air-mass direction was over 180°. This indicates that
changes in nucleus concentration with time due to advection should not be systematic.

(iii) Application of the modified Stokes relation [MILLIKAN, 1947, p.101] showed that
the fall of particles of radius $2 \cdot 3 \times 10^{-6}$ cm due to gravity is negligible over a fifteen-hour
period. This is the average radius of maximum nucleus concentration obtained from
our measurements of the mobility distribution of atmospheric ions.

(iv) Calculations show that the effect of the vertical movement of these charged nuclei in the atmospheric electric field over a fifteen-hour period is also negligible. The velocity of a charged nucleus of either sign is given by $v = kE$, where k is the average mobility of the particle and E is the vertical component of the electric field.

(v) The theoretical expression for the coagulation process for uniformly sized spherical particles derived by SMOLUCHOWSKI [1918] can be written

$$-dZ/dt = \gamma Z^2 \qquad (2)$$

where Z is the total nucleus concentration and t is time. When the radius of the particles is less than or approximately equal to the mean free path of the molecules of the gas the coagulation coefficient is

$$\gamma = \frac{4RT}{3N_n\eta}(1+AL/r) \qquad (3)$$

where R is the gas constant, T the absolute temperature, N_n is Avagadro's number, η the viscosity of the gas, A is a constant, L the mean free path of the gas molecules and r is the particle radius.

FIG. 5—Air mass trajectories at 700 mb for nine time variation series

Eq. (2) was solved for Z as a function of time using a value of the coagulation coefficient $\gamma = 1\cdot6 \times 10^{-9}$ cm^3 sec^{-1} computed from (3) for particles with mean radius $2\cdot3 \times 10^{-6}$ cm at 20°C and 760 mm Hg. The variation in γ due to density variations is negligible between the surface and 4000 ft, the altitude region we will consider. In Fig. 6 the solid lines represent the computed variation of Z with time over the time interval in which coagulation is being considered as the most important process modifying the concentration of nuclei. These show that an initial concentration of 9600 per cc is reduced by coagulation 45 per cent in fourteen hours, while an initial nucleus concentration of 1200 per cc is reduced by only eight per cent over the same period. Examples of nucleus variations with time obtained experimentally are indicated by the dashed curves in the same figure. The theory of BRICARD [1949] was applied to obtain the total nucleus concentration from our measurements of charged nuclei. From this theory the ratio of uncharged to charged nuclei of either sign $N_0/N_\pm$ was calculated for particles with mean radius $2{\cdot}3\times10^{-6}$ cm. Assuming the concentrations of positive and negative large ions are approximately equal, $Z = N_\pm(2+N_0/N_\pm)$. The value of the ratio $N_0/N_\pm$ computed for particles of radius $2{\cdot}3\times10^{-6}$ cm is in good agreement with that obtained from the

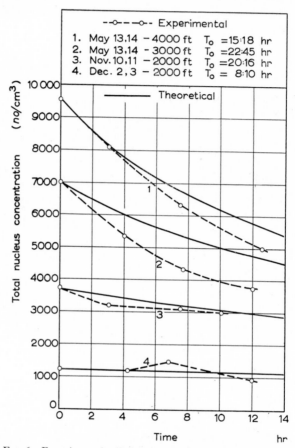

FIG. 6—Experimental and theoretical variation of total nucleus concentration with time; the theoretical values were computed assuming Smoluchowski's law

experimental results of NOLAN and KENNAN [1949] relating radius and the ratio of total to uncharged nuclei.

The influence of particle-size distribution and the variation of the coagulation coefficient with varying mean radius as coagulation proceeds have not been considered in these computations. Assuming that the product Zr^3 is approximately constant in the range of nucleus concentrations normally found in the atmosphere, the variation in radius will not have a significant effect on the coagulation rate over a fourteen-hour period. The analysis of the effect of heterogeneity by WHYTLAW-GRAY and PATTERSON

[1932, chap.11] for various size ranges indicates that heterogeneity has a small effect on the coagulation rate for atmospheric nuclei. These two corrections will also tend to cancel one another.

Away from the vicinity of the upper boundary of the exchange layer the experimental results, as illustrated in Fig. 6, generally show a decrease of nuclei with time slightly greater than would be expected from coagulation alone. However, taking into account the limitations of the assumptions made in carrying out these calculations and the possibility of inhomogeneities in the air mass, the results show that coagulation is often the most important mechanism reducing the nucleus concentration during the night hours. The rate of decrease of nuclei with time in the vicinity of the upper boundary of the exchange layer was usually much greater than that given by the coagulation theory and will be discussed later.

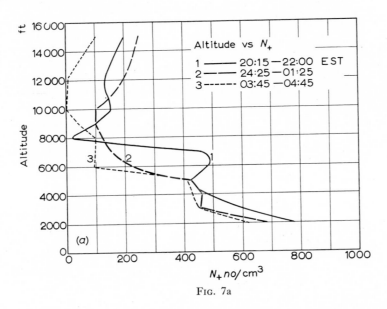

Fig. 7a

(vi) The surface and upper air weather maps and the wind magnitude and direction as a function of height, obtained from local balloon soundings were also examined to determine to what extent changes in the temperature and water vapor profiles during each series of measurements were due to advection, subsidence, or lifting. After taking into account changes in temperature and humidity due to advection, this examination showed that subsidence occurred on approximately 85 per cent of the nights where systematic changes in nucleus concentration with time were observed. This result is not surprising, since fair weather measurements are prejudiced toward high-pressure areas. The sinking of atmospheric layers had the greatest effect on the nuclei distribution in the vicinity of the upper boundary of the exchange layer. During the period covered by these experiments, the height of the exchange layer was lowered by subsidence, at varying rates, from a few hundred to 2500 ft. The influence of subsidence is most easily seen on nights when the nucleus concentration is low, so that loss due to coagulation is small. Consider, for example, the results of November 10 and 11, 1953, shown in Fig. 7. Examination of

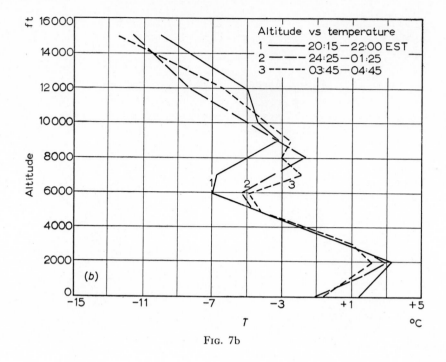

FIG. 7b

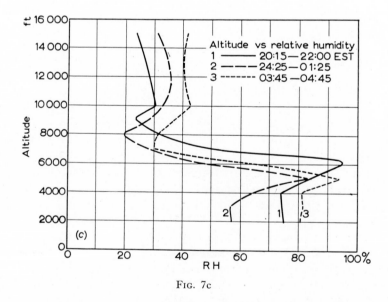

FIG. 7c

FIG. 7—Altitude and time variation of (a) charged nucleus concentration N_+, (b) temperature T, and (c) relative humidity in southern New Hampshire, November 10–11, 1953

the upper air maps showed that between Flights 1 and 2 the changes in temperature between 5000 and 9000 ft in the vicinity of the top of the exchange layer were due to subsidence which produces warming and drying as indicated in the temperature and humidity profiles of Figures 7b and 7c, and a lowering of the exchange layer by approximately 2000 ft (Fig. 7a). Between Flight 2 at 00h 25m and Flight 3 at 03h 45m, subsidence is negligible, and also there is essentially no change in the nucleus distribution in the exchange layer during this period. The influence of subsidence can also be seen in the results of May 13 and 14 (Figs. 3a and 3b) between 21h 00m and 08h 00m. The very large decrease in nucleus concentration with time at altitudes in the vicinity of the upper boundary of the exchange layer, mentioned in the discussion of coagulation, is therefore largely caused by the sinking of this layer. Further, since in general, the nucleus concentration decreases with increasing height, subsidence is also effective at all altitudes in the exchange layer in producing a rate of decrease slightly greater than would be expected from coagulation alone.

The analysis shows, therefore, that the systematic decrease of nucleus concentration with time in the exchange layer observed on 65 per cent of the night flights is largely the result of coagulation and subsidence; the relative importance of each at a given altitude during a series of flights being dependent on the pressure system in the immediate vicinity of the flight path and upon the magnitude of the nucleus concentration.

With regard to the irregular variation from 15h 00m to the following sunrise, examination of the available meteorological data showed that the most striking difference between the majority of the nights when regular variations with time were observed and the remaining 35 per cent of the flights was the intensity of advection. This can be seen in Table 2.

Table 2. Comparison of wind velocities for nights when regular and irregular variations of nucleus concentration with time occurred

| Altitude | Regular | | Irregular | |
| | Wind velocity | | Wind velocity | |
	Limits of variation	Average	Limits of variation	Average
ft	knots	knots	knots	knots
Surface	Calm–26	11	3–36	14
5,000	3–24	13	12–45	24
10,000	3–25	15	24–57	38
15,000	3–29	21	30–86	53

The differences in the intensity of advection are especially evident above 5000 ft where the frictional influences of the surface have a negligible influence on the wind velocity. At 10,000 ft, for example, the average wind velocity for the periods when systematic changes with time occurred was 15 knots with a maximum velocity of 25 knots, while in the nonsystematic cases the average velocity was 38 knots, with a minimum of 24 knots. Most of the nights with irregular variations in nucleus content also showed a departure from the normal daily wind cycle at the surface. In many cases the temperature gradient, fluctuations in the airspeed records, and random motion of the aircraft showed that the increase in nucleus concentration with time was due to the fact that stability did not develop in the surface layers, so that vertical transport from the surface remained the dominant influence. This is illustrated in the results of January 21–22, 1954, given in Fig. 4a, where a continued increase in nucleus concentration with time is observed in the exchange layer during the night hours. The temperature profiles in Fig. 4b show that stability is not developed near the surface and that there is intense temperature advection; the average wind velocity at 10,000 ft was 40 knots and the surface velocity showed a secondary maximum at 23h 00m. During two series, unstable temperature gradients were produced by advection at higher levels, resulting in mixing and modification of the nucleus distribution. This resulted in an extension of the height of the exchange layer. The analysis of individual series indicates that during periods of intense advection, the frictional effects of high winds and temperature advection are largely responsible for the increase in nucleus concentration at night at a given level; however, the increased possibility of inhomogeneities in the air mass during such periods can not be excluded. It should be noted that the average winds for the nonsystematic series given in Table 2 are approximately equal to the average values of the horizontal winds in the northeast in winter. Nonsystematic variations in nucleus concentration are, therefore, expected to occur most frequently during the winter months.

Above the exchange layer in fair weather, the nucleus content of the atmosphere is low above the exchange layer as shown in Figs. 2, 3, 4, and 7 and reported by Sagalyn and Faucher [1954]. The time variations in charged nucleus concentration which occur at a given level in this region do not show a regular daily variation. The experimental results show that the vertical transport of nuclei through the top of the exchange layer is negligible. Above the exchange layer no correlation has been found between the magnitude of the daily variation in nucleus content and the intensity of advection.

During the course of the investigation, two mechanisms were found important in introducing large numbers of nuclei into altitudes above the exchange layer: (1) While the discussion of results has been limited to results in fair weather, experiments were also carried out when fronts approached or thunderstorms developed. In such cases, measurements were continued as long as possible, and the results show with the close approach of the disturbance that the stable temperature gradient at the top of the exchange layer is broken up and large numbers of nuclei penetrate to higher levels. (2) If the exchange layer penetrates to height X on a given day, and on the following day because of lower winds, change in temperature gradient, wind direction, and other factors, mixing penetrates to a lower height Y, in the altitude interval $X-Y$ some of the characteristics of the distribution of the previous day will still be evident, and can persist for several days. The nucleus concentration is quickly reduced by coagulation, and there is no sharp concentration gradient in the vicinity of level X, so that the electrical properties in this region are not much affected. This influence of the previous history can also be seen in the morning flights before the exchange layer is fully developed, as shown for example, in the first and second flights of August 20, 1953 in Fig. 2.

Electrical conductivity, results and discussion—The changes in electrical conductivity at a given level in the exchange layer are the inverse of changes taking place in nucleus concentration; an increase in large-ion concentration is accompanied by a decrease in conductivity and vice versa. Thus, at a given level the conductivity begins to decrease in the vicinity of sunrise, reaching a minimum at approximately 15h 00m (Fig. 1b). On approximately 65 per cent of the series the conductivity increased up to the vicinity of the following sunrise, while a much more complicated time variation occurred during periods of intense advection. An example of the time variations obtained on individual series is shown in the curves of Fig. 2b. Above the exchange layer, the variations in electrical conductivity with time do not show a systematic daily variation.

A detailed presentation of the results of the electrical conductivity measurements and an analysis of the effect of changes in nucleus density on the electrical conductivity of the atmosphere is given elsewhere [SAGALYN and FAUCHER, 1956].

The influence of the daily changes in electrical conductivity on the atmospheric electric current system over continents can be summarized in terms of the columnar resistance of the atmosphere. The columnar resistance R of a vertical column one cm^2 in cross section from the surface to 15,000 ft, $R = \int_{0}^{15,000} 1/(\lambda_{+}+\lambda_{-})\ dh$, was computed from the conductivity measurements for all flights over the New Hampshire flight path. The experimental curves were extrapolated to obtain the conductivity at the surface.

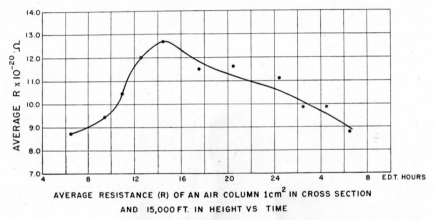

AVERAGE RESISTANCE (R) OF AN AIR COLUMN 1cm^2 IN CROSS SECTION
AND 15,000 FT. IN HEIGHT VS TIME

FIG. 8—Average resistance R of an air column one cm^2 in cross section and 15,000 ft in height versus time

Simultaneous surface and free-air measurements have shown that this will not introduce a serious error, and could not change the nature of the resulting columnar resistance variations to 15,000 ft. The average columnar resistance as a function of time was then computed, and the results are given in Fig. 8. The general nature of the local daily variations is clearly evident in this average curve; the columnar resistance starts to increase with time in the vicinity of sunrise, reaches a maximum at approximately 15h 00m, then decreases with time to the following sunrise. It thus closely parallels the diurnal variation in nucleus content with time at a given level in the exchange layer during periods of low advection. The regular variation in conductivity with time from sunrise to 15h 00m and the more complicated nature of the variation through the late afternoon and night, which was found to depend on the intensity of advection, is also indicated in the scatter of the individual points of Fig. 8.

I

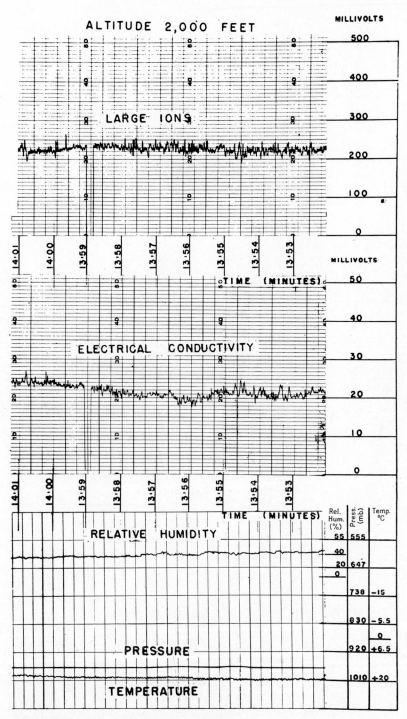

Fig. 9—Horizontal variation of charged nucleus concentration, electrical conductivity, relative humidity, temperature and pressure in the exchange layer, May 27, 1954

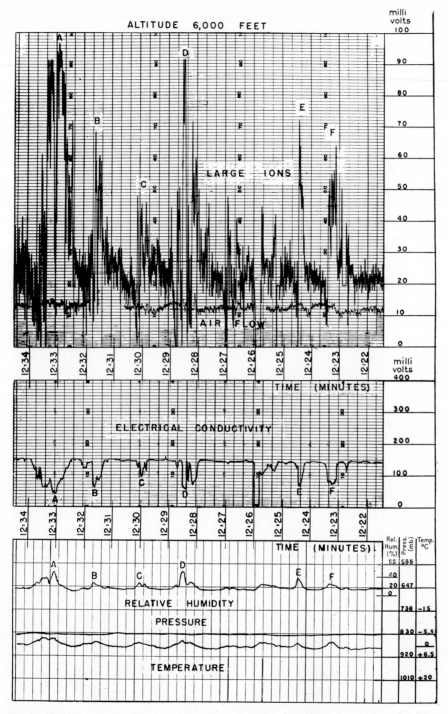

Fig. 10—Horizontal variation of charged nucleus concentration, electrical conductivity, relative humidity, temperature and pressure at the upper boundary of the exchange layer, May 27, 1954

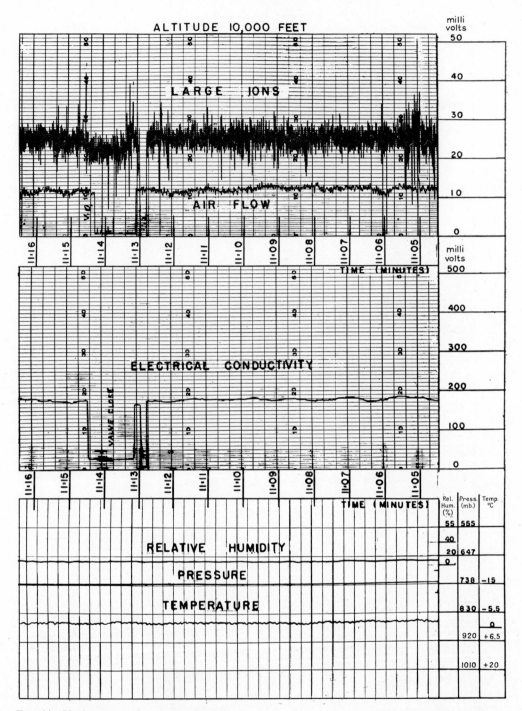

FIG. 11—Horizontal variation of charged nucleus concentration, electrical conductivity, relative humidity, temperature and pressure above the exchange layer, May 27, 1954

The daily variation in the total columnar resistance of the atmosphere varied from 13 to 60 per cent with respect to the average on individual series with a mean value of 30 per cent. The columnar resistance above 15,000 ft was assumed to have no diurnal variation. The daily changes in the columnar resistance of the atmosphere in southern New Hampshire due to local changes in nucleus concentration are, therefore, of the same order of magnitude as the universal daily variation in the potential between the earth and upper conducting layers deduced from potential gradient and conductivity measurements over oceans [GISH, 1951, p.112].

Time variations in the horizontal, results—Further support for the interpretation of the daily variation in the nucleus distribution just presented is given by the nature of the changes with time in the horizontal variations of nuclei, electrical conductivity, humidity, and the instantaneous fluctuations about the mean in the aerograph airspeed records. Our earlier measurements [SAGALYN and FAUCHER, 1954] obtained during the daylight hours have shown that above the exchange layer in a given air mass in fair weather these parameters vary slowly in the horizontal. Over a fixed flight path approximately 25 miles long, the magnitude of the variation at a given level usually amounted to less than 100 charged nuclei per cm³ and to less than ten per cent of the mean value of conductivity. In the exchange layer, in addition to the gradual variations observed at higher altitudes, large rapid fluctuations were observed, often amounting to a more than 100 per cent change in the mean value at a given level. These localized variations generally decreased with height in the lowest few thousand feet, then increased, reaching a maximum in the vicinity of the top of the exchange layer. Maximum horizontal fluctuations usually occur at, or slightly below the altitude where a change to a more stable temperature gradient is observed. The region of large, rapid fluctuations is approximately 2500 ft in depth. Examples of the horizontal variations of these parameters at low levels, in the vicinity of the upper boundary and above the exchange layer are given in Figs. 9, 10, and 11 which show the records obtained May 27, 1954 at 2000, 5000 and 10,000 ft, respectively. One minute of record corresponds to approximately $2\frac{3}{4}$ miles.

Extension of these measurements over 24-hour periods has shown that the magnitude of the fluctuations and the altitude region where maximum fluctuations occur, vary with time. The height of the altitude region of maximum nucleus, conductivity and water vapor variations, and the magnitude of these fluctuations increase from the vicinity of sunrise to approximately 15h 00m. During periods of low advection, the magnitude of the fluctuations then decreases from 15h 00m to the following sunrise, while the height of the altitude region of maximum disturbance remains constant or is lowered. Also, in the early morning hours, the upper boundary of the exchange layer is no longer always distinguished by a change to a more stable temperature gradient. This is illustrated in Fig. 12, which gives the magnitude of the short period horizontal variations in nucleus concentration, conductivity, humidity and the instantaneous fluctuations about the mean in the airspeed records for May 13, 14, 1954, a period of low advection, as a function of altitude and time over a 24-hour interval. The values given in Fig. 12 for the nucleus, conductivity and humidity fluctuations represent the maximum fluctuations over $1\frac{1}{4}$ mile of flight path. The instantaneous air speed fluctuations are given as a qualitative indication of the existence of turbulence. Since we only wish to point out the nature of the horizontal variations with time, the record deflections have not been converted to absolute units.

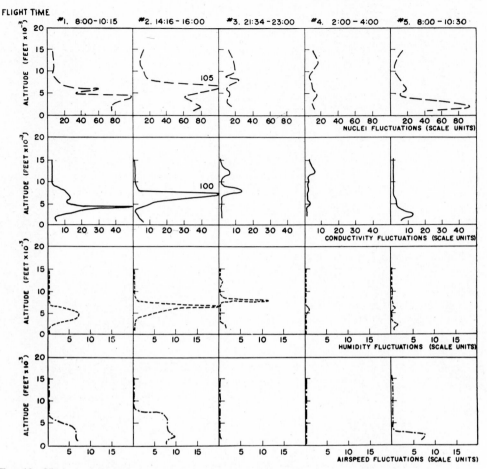

FIG. 12—Horizontal fluctuations of nuclei, conductivity, humidity and air speed as a function of time, May 13–14, 1954

During periods of intense advection, the horizontal fluctuations were not found to vary regularly with time. An example of the nature of the horizontal fluctuations during a period of intense advection is shown in Fig. 13, which gives the results of January 21–22, 1954.

Above the exchange layer the time variations in the horizontal fluctuations of these properties are not found to be regular. In this region the largest and most rapid variations in the horizontal occur at scattered cloud levels. The large horizontal fluctuations observed in the vicinity of 12,000 ft on the third and fourth flights of January 21–22, 1954, shown in Fig. 13, occur at a scattered cloud level.

Time variations in the horizontal, discussion—Regarding variation in height with time, the increase in the height of the exchange layer (the region of maximum horizontal fluctuations) from the vicinity of sunrise to early afternoon follows the well-known daily increase in the intensity of atmospheric turbulence [SUTTON, 1951, chap.2]. As

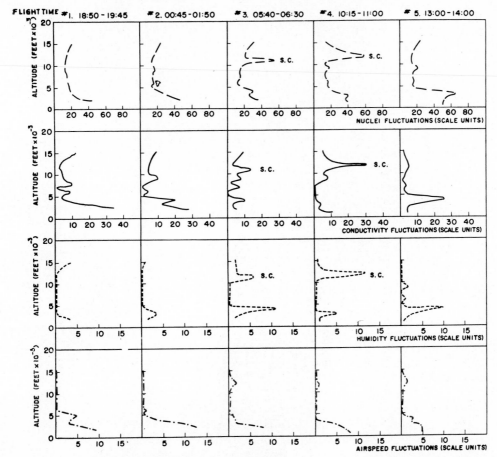

FIG. 13—Horizontal fluctuations of nuclei, conductivity, humidity and air speed as a function of time,
January 21–22, 1954

illustrated in the results of May 13–14, 1954, shown in Fig. 12, individual series show
that the variations in the height of the exchange layer during this period follow closely
the variations in the height to which turbulent mixing extends, as obtained from the airspeed records.

When the intensity of turbulence decreases, the atmospheric pressure system in the
area becomes important in determining any further changes in the height of the layer.
As pointed out under 'Discussion of charged-nuclei—results', above, these experiments
show that the exchange layer is often lowered by subsidence from late afternoon to the
following sunrise.

Regarding variation in nucleus fluctuations with time, from sunrise to approximately
15h 00m, the horizontal nucleus fluctuations are large at all altitudes in the exchange
layer. The horizontal fluctuations and their variations with time are greatest, however,
in the vicinity of the upper boundary of the exchange layer. This can be considered as
a region of very incomplete mixing, the boundary between two areas with very different
nucleus properties. The increase in the intensity of turbulence during this period causes

an increase in the vertical transport of nuclei which results in greater concentration gradients in the boundary region. When turbulence decreases in the afternoon, the inhomogeneities at all altitudes in the exchange layer also decrease, probably by diffusion. The time variations in the horizontal fluctuations of the electrical conductivity are discussed in another paper [SAGALYN and FAUCHER, 1956].

During periods of intense advection, these experiments show that during the late afternoon and night hours, mechanical turbulence and temperature instability are often great enough to maintain essentially daytime conditions.

Relation to suface measurements—The daily variation of nucleus concentration at constant altitude described in this paper differs, in some respects, from the most commonly reported daily variation measured at low elevation surface stations in fair weather. The latter shows a maximum in the morning, a minimum early in the afternoon, an evening maximum, followed by a steady decrease in nucleus concentration until sunrise.

The present investigation shows that the decrease in nucleus concentration in the middle of the day has been correctly attributed to the vertical transport of nuclei by turbulence from regions where the supply of nuclei is limited. The results also indicate that at some altitude between the surface and approximately 700 ft there is a change from a decrease of nucleus concentration with time in the middle of the day to a variation of the type described in Fig. 1. The decrease with time from late evening to sunrise has been attributed to the settling of nuclei by gravity [BRADBURY and MEURON, 1938], to a decrease in the production of nuclei [LANDSBERG, 1938], and to an increase in the austausch coefficient during the night hours [FRANKE, 1949]. While the last process may at times contribute to the decrease, comparison of available surface data with the theoretical coagulation curves indicates that coagulation is often the most important process causing the decrease in concentration during the night hours.

The reported daily variation of nucleus concentration at mountain stations in fair weather is essentially the same as that reported here for altitudes above 700 ft in the exchange layer and the same explanation should be applicable [LANDSBERG, 1938].

The daily variation of nucleus concentration at surface stations is thus the result of the action of several competing processes. The principle ones in fair weather are: the nature of the source of nuclei, vertical transport of nuclei by turbulence and convection, nucleus coagulation. Each of these is the controlling influence at different times of day. It should also be pointed out that the loss of nuclei by coagulation must be included in any explanation of variations of small ion density, electrical conductivity or electric field at surface stations during the night hours.

Air mass—These measurements, representing over one hundred flights, were carried out in maritime tropical, continental arctic, and continental polar air masses. No direct relation has been observed between air-mass type and the concentration or vertical distribution of nuclei between 1000 and 15,000 ft. The nucleus concentration has been found to be a non-conservative property of the air mass, being greatly modified daily by local influences and by changes in the physical properties of the nuclei.

Summary—An investigation of the time variations of charged nuclei in the altitude range 700 to 15,000 ft above the surface has shown:

(1) In the exchange layer at a given level the nucleus concentration increases with time from the vicinity of sunrise to approximately 15h 00m. During periods of low advection the concentration decreases from 15h 00m to the following sunrise. Analysis shows that the increase in nucleus concentration to 15h 00m is due to the transport of nuclei from the lowest levels by turbulent and convective mixing and the following decrease is due primarily to nucleus coagulation and subsidence. During periods of intense advection, the nucleus concentration does not vary in a regular manner from 15h 00m to the following sunrise. The frictional influence of high winds prevents the cutting off of nuclei from the lowest levels, and in some cases temperature advection produces unstable temperature gradients at higher levels in the atmosphere. Above the exchange layer the nucleus variation with time is greatly reduced and is not found to be regular.

(2) The variations with time in the electrical conductivity are the inverse of the changes in nucleus concentration. The columnar resistance of the atmosphere computed from the conductivity data is found to have a simple local daily variation during periods of low advection with a maximum at approximately 15h 00m. The amplitude of the daily variation in the columnar resistance of the atmosphere is of the same magnitude as the universal daily variation in the potential between the earth and upper conducting layers in fair weather, and therefore is an important factor contributing to variations in the atmospheric electric current system over continents.

(3) In the exchange layer, over a fixed flight path the horizontal inhomogeneities in nuclei, conductivity and water vapor have a regular daily variation during periods of low advection.

(4) The height of the exchange layer increases with time from sunrise to 15h 00m, and during periods of low advection; then remains constant or is gradually reduced depending on the pressure system in the vicinity of the flight path, until the following sunrise.

(5) The upper boundary of the exchange layer also corresponds to the upper limit of the scattered fair weather cumulus cloud layer. Above the exchange layer, an increase in nucleus concentration and large horizontal variations of nuclei, conductivity and water vapor are found at scattered cloud levels. Then, as at lower levels, an increase in nucleus concentration corresponds to an increase in water vapor.

(6) The magnitude of the nucleus concentration is not found to be a conservative air mass property.

Acknowledgments—The authors gratefully acknowledge the work of Maria Mahoney and Roland Matson, who assisted in the analysis of the data and in carrying out the experiments, and that of W. Mount, who gave invaluable assistance in the analysis of the surface and upper air weather maps. We also thank the personnel of the 6520th Flight Test Squadron, Hansom Air Force Base, Bedford, Massachusetts, who flew and maintained the aircraft.

REFERENCES

BRADBURY, N. E. and H. J. MEURON, The diurnal variation of atmospheric condensation-nuclei, *Terr. Mag.*, v.43, pp.231–240, 1938.

BRICARD, J., L'equilibre ionique de la basse atmosphere, *J. Geophys. Res.*, v.54, pp.39–52, 1949.

Brunt, D., *Physical and Dynamical Meteorology*, Cambridge Univ. Press, pp.22–24, 1952.

Franke, M., Der Doppelperiodische Tagesgang des luftelektrischen Potentialgefälles als Folge des Austausches, *Geofis. Pura e Applicata*, v.14, pp.120–131, 1949.

Gish, O. H., Universal aspects of atmospheric electricity, *in Compendium of Meteorology*, Amer. Met. Soc., pp.112–113, 1951.

Landsberg, H., Atmospheric condensation nuclei, *Erg. der Kosm. Phys.*, v.3, pp.155–241, 1938.

Millikan, R. A., *Electrons (+ and −)*, Univ. Chicago Press, pp.98–101, 1947.

Nolan, P. J. and E. L. Kennan, Condensation nuclei from hot platinum: size, coagulation coefficient and charge distribution, *Proc. R. Irish Acad.*, v.52, Sec. A, pp.171–190, 1949.

Sagalyn, R. C. and G. A. Faucher, Aircraft investigation of the large ion content and conductivity of the atmosphere and their relation to meteorological factors, *J. Atmos. Terr. Phys.*, v.5, pp.253–272, 1954.

Sagalyn, R. C. and G. A. Faucher, Space and time variation of charged nuclei and electrical conductivity of the atmosphere, *Q. J. R. Met. Soc.*, v.82, pp.428–445, 1956.

Smoluchowski, M., Versuch einer mathematischen Theorie der Koagulationskinetik kolloider Losungen, *Zs. Physikal Chem.*, v.92, pp.129–168, 1918.

Sutton, O. G., *Atmospheric Turbulence*, Methuen and Co., Ltd., London, pp.14–28, 1951.

Whytlaw-Gray, R. and H. S. Patterson, *Smoke*, E. Arnold and Co., London, pp.109–119, 1932.

DISCUSSION

Mr. Charles E. Anderson—I was interested to notice on your last figure that the nuclei fluctuation seemed to vary in the same manner as the humidity. Do you have an explanation for this?

Mrs. Rita C. Sagalyn—This relation is undoubtedly due to the turbulent and convective transport of parcels of air in non-uniform regions of the atmosphere where water vapor and nuclei are subject to the same laws of vertical transport. This is evident upon examination of the horizontal fluctuations of these variables in the vicinity of the upper boundary of the exchange layer as shown for example, in Fig. 10.

Dr. James E. McDonald—My question was going to be on that same point. The nuclei concentrations change very markedly at what you define to be the height of the exchange layer but it wasn't clear what your working definition of that layer really was. Did you define the height of the layer before you took the counts?

Mrs. Sagalyn—No. We first made many measurements of the vertical distribution of the charged nuclei concentration, electrical conductivity, temperature and humidity. In all fair weather flights, at a certain altitude, usually below 10,000 ft, there was found a sharp change in the nuclei and small-ion density, a change to a more stable temperature gradient, usually a sharp change in absolute humidity and in the middle of the day a sharp decrease in the random motion of the aircraft as it climbed through this region. These results, together with data obtained subsequently on the wind variation with height during the flight time, showed that the lower layer could be identified with the layer found in many sounding records which meteorologists refer to variously as the exchange, friction, turbulent and boundary layer. This has been discussed in detail in our paper cited [Sagalyn and Faucher, 1954].

Dr. McDonald—I thought about that because on one of your curves the height of the exchange layer is at around 6000 ft. and in another the height was taken as half way through a very deep inversion. It didn't appear the temperature lapse was the determining criterion for defining the top of your exchange layers.

Mrs. Sagalyn—In some cases, for example during periods of intense temperature advection as on Jan. 21–22, 1954 in Fig. 4, it is impossible to determine the upper boundary of the exchange layer from the temperature gradient alone. I think this will be clarified by the text.

Dr. David Atlas—It seems quite reasonable that the nuclei fluctuations should correlate well with the vapour fluctuations as noted in your observations. Our own radar observations of 'angel' echoes (which are primarily echoes from bubbles of moist air different in vapor pressure from their environment), show such 'angel' or bubble activity to be restricted to what you call the exchange layer, and their frequency is at a maximum at the hottest part of the day in the manner of your nuclei fluctuations. In addition, the 'angel' echoes frequently congregate at the top of the exchange layer indicating that this is the region of maximum fluctuation in vapor pressure. In other words, bubble type convection seems to be responsible for both the distribution of nuclei and water vapor.

Mrs. Sagalyn—This point is illustrated in Fig. 10.

Dr. Vincent J. Schaefer—I wonder if any of these runs were made under conditions in which there was a strong jet stream in the vicinity.

Mrs. Sagalyn—I don't think so.

DETERMINING THE CONCENTRATION OF FOGS AND OTHER AEROSOLS BY A SPACE-CHARGE MEASURING INSTRUMENT

B. VONNEGUT, C. B. MOORE, JOHN EHRENFELD AND C. R. SMALLMAN

Arthur D. Little, Inc., Cambridge 42, Mass.

Abstract—A newly-developed apparatus measures aerosol particles by first charging them by point discharge and then using a Faraday cage to measure the resulting space-charge density. For particles with diameters of more than a few tenths of a micron this apparatus gives a response that is proportional to the surface area of the particles per unit volume.

Introduction—Investigations into the properties of atmospheric fogs have led to the development of an instrument for directly measuring the surface area concentrations of fogs and other spherical aerosols. The instrument was developed under Contract DA–36–039–SC–42585 with the Signal Corps, U.S. Army, supervised by the Meteorological Branch, Evans Signal Laboratory, Belmar, New Jersey. It is based on the fact that the amount of electric charge spherical particles more than one micron in diameter will accept is a function of their surface area.

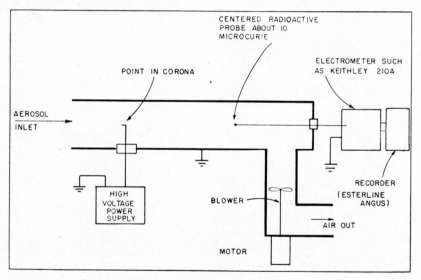

FIG. 1—Schematic diagram of aerosol surface-area meter

Principles of operation—The aerosol to be measured is drawn through a cylindrical tube (Fig. 1) with a pointed electrode maintained at a high voltage in its axis. Under the influence of the electric field and the current of fast ions produced by the electrode the aerosol particles become electrically charged with the same polarity as the

122

electrode. A blower then pulls the charged aerosol out of the electric field and into a cylindrical chamber, which is used as a Faraday cage. The potential produced at the center of the 'cage' by the charge concentration is a measure of the aerosol concentration.

According to LADENBURG [1930], the maximum charge acquired by spherical particles more than one micron in diameter is a function of the radius squared (or the surface area), the electric-field strength, and the particle dielectric constant. Poisson's equation [PENNEY and HEWITT, 1949] shows that the potential is proportional to the charge density. These two principles are combined to measure the surface-area concentration of the aerosol. This parameter is equivalent to ΣCr^2, where C is the population density of particles per unit volume of aerosol, and r is the mean effective particle radius. The aerosol mass concentration is $\Sigma Cr^3\rho$, where ρ is the effective density of the particles. If C and r are determined for a given aerosol, many of its properties can be characterized.

Derivation of performance relationships—The relationships defining the performance of the instrument are derived below. Although the proof is developed for a monodisperse aerosol, it can be extended to a polydisperse system. The Ladenburg equation which has been verified by PAUTHENIER [1932] and FUCHS [1936] gives for the acceptance of charge by a spherical particle more than one micron in diameter,

$$q = E_0 r^2 \left(1 + 2\frac{D-1}{D+2}\right)\left(1 + \frac{1}{\pi Nekt}\right)^{-1} \tag{1}$$

where

$q =$ charge acquired by a particle
$D =$ dielectric constant of particle
$E_0 =$ field strength (in electrostatic units)
$r =$ particle radius
$N =$ ion density
$e =$ charge on an electron
$K =$ ion mobility, and
$t =$ time

The factors in the rate-determining part of (1) are large enough for the particles to assume a maximum charge in a very short time. The equation can then be simplified to (Fig. 2)

$$q_{max} = E_0 r^2 \left(1 + 2\frac{D-1}{D+2}\right) \tag{2}$$

$q_{max} =$ maximum charge possible per particle in the field E_0.

The field produced by a uniformly charged cloud in a cylindrical cage is given by Poisson's equation

$$V = \pi(R^2 - A^2)J \tag{3}$$

where

$V =$ potential at a distance 'A' from the center (in stat volts)
$R =$ over-all radius of cylinder
$J =$ charge density (in esu)

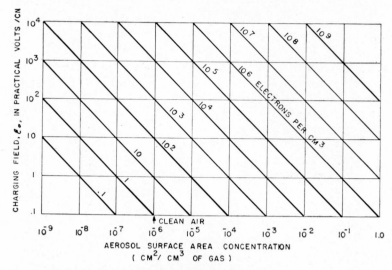

FIG. 2—Solution of Ladenburg's equation for a particle with a dielectric constant
of two

The maximum found at the center, is

$$V_{center} = \pi R^2 J \qquad (4)$$

If we now assume that the charged particles are very small, compared with the radius of the cylinder, and are uniformly dispersed, the charge density will be equal to the concentration of the particles times the charge per particle, or

$$J = C_q \qquad (5)$$

where

C = number or concentration of aerosol particles/cc.

If we assume that the particles acquire the maximum charge in the ionizing section, (6) defines the potential V developed by the charged cloud at the center of the Faraday cage

$$V = R^2\left(1+2\frac{D-1}{D-2}\right)E_0 r^2 C \pi \qquad (6)$$

Since the aerosol surface-area concentration, S_0, is given by $S_0 = 4\pi r^2 C$, (6) can be written in a form relating the measured potential directly to the surface-area concentration.

$$V = \frac{R^2 E_0}{4}\left(1+2\frac{D-1}{D+2}\right)S_0 \qquad (7)$$

Eq. (7) appears valid for systems that are not extremely polydisperse, since the potential depends only on specific surface. Fig. 3 shows the relationship (for spherical particles) between aerosol surface-area concentration, mass concentration, and mean particle diameter.

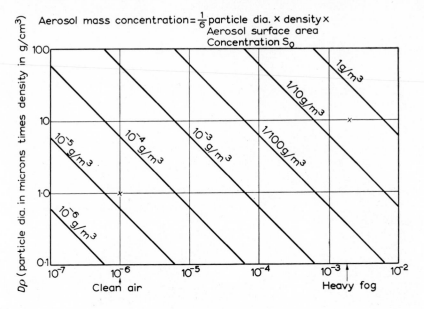

FIG. 3—Relationship (for spherical particles) of surface-area concentration to the mass concentration particle diameter and the effective density in metric units

Calibration procedure—Experiments designed to compare the actual performance with the theoretical performance of a prototype instrument involved recording the following data simultaneously: corona current and voltage, probe voltage, and aerosol diameter and mass concentration. The voltage for the corona was supplied by a stabilized high-voltage source capable of producing a controlled potential of four to 20 kV. The corona current was measured with a microammeter, which was protected against surges due to arcing by a series resistance, and by a neon tube and a one-microfarad condenser, both in parallel with the meter-resistance combination. This circuit raised the potential of the chassis of the high-voltage supply to about 75 volts. The chassis was insulated from the ground, so that the ammeter would not be short-circuited. The potential in the cylindrical cage was measured with a radio-active probe having about ten microcuries of radium.

The probe potential was measured with a wide-range electrometer. The lead from the probe to the electrometer was well-shielded, because the electrometer was sensitive enough to record stray fields. A vacuum-tube voltmeter indicated the electrometer reading. When it was found that the readings fluctuated, a recorder was used in conjunction with the electrometer. The probe voltage for each run was thus continuously recorded. A standard aerosol for test measurements was obtained from a dioctylphthalate (DOP) aerosol generator, which was directly connected to the inlet of the instrument. (Means for diluting the aerosol are included in the generator.) The concentration of the aerosol was obtained gravimetrically, by placing a weighed, all-glass 'Absolute' Filter in the exhaust of the instrument, and then collecting and weighing the aerosol. Weight and air-flow rate could then be used to compute concentration.

Laboratory calibration results and discussion—Fig. 4 shows a typical calibration of the laboratory instrument. Calibration data for test aerosols having diameters of 0·2 to 0·5 of a micron indicate that the potential in the cage is linearly dependent on the

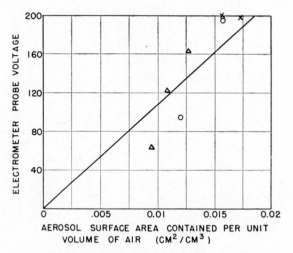

Fig. 4—Calibration plot of measured aerosol surface area vs probe voltage (5000 V applied to corona point)

specific surface. These data do not, however, exactly fit the theoretical equation. When the constants of the system studied are substituted in (7), it becomes

$$V/P = 1\cdot1 S_0 \tag{8}$$

where

P = corona potential
V = electrometer potential

In the laboratory tests, the values of the dielectric constant, D, and the radius, R, were $D = 5\cdot2$ for DOP, and $R = 2$ cm, where it was assumed for the sake of simplification, that the mean field

$$E_{0,} = P/R \tag{9}$$

When the calibration data is reduced, it is better represented by

$$V = 3\cdot52 \times 10^{-8} E^{3.1} S_0 \tag{10}$$

Eq. (10) shows that the theory is correct, for a particle 0·2 to 0·5 micron in diameter, in stating that the resulting electrometer potential is linearly dependent upon the surface area concentration. But the equation also shows that maximum charge per particle is a function of the mean field, E_0, to a power higher than unity. The same effect has been observed in Cottrell electrostatic precipitators, [White, 1941, 1952] where the particle mobility has been determined to be a function of the applied voltage to a power higher than unity. This variation might be due to the non-linear changes of the actual local-charging field when the voltage applied to the point in corona is increased.

While indicating its great sensitivity to voltage, the results of the experiment also show that the instrument can directly measure aerosol surface-area concentration. Data obtained for corona voltages below 4000 volts show a great deal of scatter with no evident correlation. These data were discarded because it was felt that the scatter was due to erratic behavior in the corona. At 4000 volts and below the corona just began to be evident, and fluctuated erratically. At 4000 volts and above, it was well-formed, and did not fluctuate significantly.

The charge concentration of test aerosols was still closely proportional to the surface area of particles 0·2 of a micron in diameter. It was stated in the introduction that the Ladenburg relationship is usually applied only to particles more than one micron in diameter. For particles smaller than one micron the thermal diffusion charging mechanism is usually considered to apply. TOWNSEND [1915] has shown that with this mechanism the number of elemental charges, H_0, acquired particle is given by the following empirical expression

$$N_0 = 3 \cdot 4 \times 10^3 DT \tag{11}$$

where D is the particle diameter, and T is the temperature in degrees Kelvin.

Even smaller particles such as condensation nuclei, may perhaps acquire only single charges. Accordingly, the apparatus may be non-linear in its response to the surface-area concentration of these aerosols. We therefore plan to modify the instrument so as to classify particles according to their mobility, and thus achieve a simultaneous and continuous measure of the particle-size distribution.

Some limitations of the electrostatic technique—The application of the instrument to spherical aerosols of uniform composition is limited in two ways. One has to do with the linearity of the charging field. A ten-micron water droplet passing near the outer circumference of the charging field receives a lower charge than a similar droplet passing very near the corona point. This difficulty can be minimized by calibrating the instrument. It appears desirable to redesign the instrument to make the charging field uniform between the parallel plates in order to overcome the difficulty.

A second limitation of the present apparatus is a background signal produced by a small concentration of aerosol particles generated by the corona discharge. The local high temperature at the corona point oxidizes and disintegrates the electrode with the resultant production of aerosol particles probably in the size range of Aitken nuclei. The concentration of these particles is so small that they cause appreciable error only when the apparatus is used with very low aerosol concentrations. The spurious signal resulting from this source can probably be eliminated by drawing off these particles through a tube at the corona point or by using radioactivity instead of corona as a fast ion source.

Description of a portable aerosol surface-area concentration meter—Fig. 5 shows a portable instrument (operated by a six-volt automobile battery) for measuring aerosol surface-area concentrations. In the laboratory we used the instrument to monitor water-fog concentration; it gave readings consistent with the fog concentrations. We have not used it as yet on natural fogs. In its present form it is applicable to clouds: it has a readable range of from 5×10^{-4} to about 5×10^{-3} cm²/cm³, while heavy fogs reach only 2×10^{-3} cm²/cm³ (see Fig. 4). We have also used it for suspended-oil fogs and other particles in natural-gas pipelines in Texas.

K

Design data for an aerosol surface-area meter—Dust loading in quiet air measured at Cambridge is 50 micrograms/m³. The particles have a mean diameter of about one micron, or in other words, a specific surface of about $3\cdot0\times10^{-6}$ cm²/cm³ (we assume a density of $1\cdot0$). The heaviest fog concentrations desired is $0\cdot5$ m/m³. If we assume that these particles have unit density and a mean diameter of 10 microns, the equivalent surface area is 3×10^{-3} cm²/cm³.

Application of the instrument to heterogeneous aerosols is limited in three ways. (1) The foregoing derivation has been for spherical aerosols, since the Ladenburg relationship is based on the field at the particle surface. For non-spherical particles the charge acquired per particle may be a very complicated function of the particle shape. Therefore, such particles will require a calibration, which might consist of a simultaneous measurement of surface area, mass concentration, and mean effective particle diameter. (2) The dielectric constant of heterogeneous aerosols consisting of water, oil, and solid particles will vary. This function will change the number of accepted electrons by a factor of some $1:3$ over-all possible ranges of dielectric constant. We do not believe that this is a serious limitation. If one knows the mean aerosol concentrations to within $\frac{1}{2}$ an order of magnitude, one has probably as much data as is significant. (3) As we have said, the size, too, of aerosol particles affects the number of charges accepted. However, our experimental data shows that the Ladenburg relationship applies to particles $0\cdot2$ of a micron in diameter and larger.

For a dielectric constant of 80, the charge, q, accepted per particle is:

$$q = 3E_0 r^2 \qquad (12)$$

where

$E_0 =$ true electric field
$r =$ particle radius

The charge concentration J is the product of the particle concentration C and the maximum charge accepted by each particle q

$$J = Cq \qquad (5)$$

The surface area concentration S_0, is $4\pi r^2 C$ and C, the particle concentration, equals $S_0/4\pi r^2$. Therefore the charge concentration

$$J = Cq = 3E_0 S_0/4\pi \qquad (13)$$

In a cylindrical Faraday cage, the potential V in the center of the radius R is

$$V = \pi R^2 J \qquad (4)$$

Accordingly, $V = (\frac{3}{4})E_0 S_0 R_0^2$ (in electrostatic units), or

$$V/S_0 = (3/4)E_0 R^2 \qquad (11)$$

The design problem is to vary the cylindrical cage radius R so as to give ratios of V/S_0 practicable for the aerosol surface-area concentrations to be measured, and for available electrometers.

The parameters—V (in practical units) is limited to values between $0\cdot2$ of a volt and 80 volts, when commercial electrometers, such as the Keithley 210A, are used.

FIG. 5—Portable model of apparatus for operation with six-volt automobile battery

S_0 should fall between 3×10^{-6} and 3×10^{-3} cm²/cm³. The corona potential which produces the field E_0 should be constant between 5000 and 6000 practical volts in a 2-cm radius tube.

Let $E_0 = 3000$ volts/cm $= 10$ esu/cm

For this case the relation between cylinder radius R and the ratio V/S_0, is given by the following equation in consistent electrostatic and cgs units

$$V/S_0 = 7 \cdot 5\, R^2 \tag{15}$$

The parameters show that the limits of V/S_0 should be $6 \cdot 67 \times 10^4$ cm and $2 \cdot 67 \times 10^4$ volt cm. We then vary R to obtain a usable ratio of V/S_0. When V/S_0 is $6 \cdot 67 \times 10^4$ volt cm, with S_0 at 3×10^{-6} cm²/cm³ and $0 \cdot 2$-volt electrometer reading, R is $5 \cdot 45$ cm. When V/S_0 is $2 \cdot 6 \times 10^4$ volt cm, with S_0 at 3×10^{-3} cm²/cm³ and an 80-volt electrometer reading, R is 3·45 cm. The surface-area concentration equivalent to the minimum usable electrometer voltage of 0·2 of a volt in a cylinder with a radius 3·45, is 6×10^{-6} cm²/cm³, or twice the concentration found in relatively clean air.

It is desirable to calibrate the instrument with known concentrations of uniform aerosols, so that the data obtained will be usable. This need arises in part from the fact that the particles pass through a non-linear charging field around the point in corona. The mean field might be better approximated by an inverse square or cube relationship; we have not done this as yet. Space-charge and geometric considerations also make a direct calibration desirable. The validity of the various assumptions underlying the finished aerosol monitor would thus be insured.

Acknowledgment—The support of the Pipeline Research Committee of the American Gas Association under Research Project NFX-12, in the construction, calibration and field testing of an instrument is gratefully acknowledged.

REFERENCES

Fuchs, N., and others, Rate of charging a droplet by an ionic current, *Trans. Faraday Soc.*, v.32, pp.1131–1138, 1939.

Ladenburg, R., Untersuchungen über die physikalischen Vorgänge bei der sogenannten elektrischen Gas Reinigung, *Ann. Physik*, v.4, pp.5863–5897, 1930.

Pauthenier, M. and M. Moreau-Hanot, La charge des particules spheriques dans un champ ionise, *J. Phys. Radoim.*, ser.7, v.3, p.590, 1932.

Penney, G. W. and G. W. Hewitt, Electrically charged dust in rooms, *Proc. Amer. Inst. Elec. Eng.*, v.168, p.974, 1949.

Townsend, J. J., *Electricity in Gases*, Oxford, pp.214, 215, 1915.

White, H. J., Particle charging in electrostatic precipitation, *Trans. Amer. Inst. Elec. Eng.*, v.70, pt.2, pp.1186–1191, 1941.

White, H. J., The role of corora discharge in the electrical precipitation process, *Elec. Eng.*, v.71, pp.67–73, 1952.

DISCUSSION

Dr. Richard Schotland—I have two questions concerning the design of the charging chamber of this instrument. The first concerns the potential and ion distribution about the corona point. Since the amount of charge collected by the aerosols is a function of the potential gradient and ion concentration, it is important that these quantities be constant in the charging region. This is difficult to accomplish with a single point discharge. I wonder if this has been checked.

The second question is: with only 6000 volts between the outer cylinder and corona point, do charges existing initially on the aerosol cause any trouble?

Mr. Charles Moore—It depends on the range you're interested in. We are putting possibly ten thousand charges per cubic centimeter on the aerosols compared to possibly ten natural charges per cc naturally on the air pollution aerosols.

Mr. Vernon G. Plank—I wonder if you could give me an estimate of the relative difference in strength between pulses from large ions, which you say are thrown off from the charging probe under excess voltage conditions, and pulses from ten micron diameter water droplets.

Mr. Moore—We do not measure individual pulses but the integrated 'signal'. The error here depends on the range of aerosol concentration in which you are interested. If you are interested, as we are, in areas where ordinary air may not be very dirty, the effect is extremely important. This is when one is concerned with aerosol surface area concentrations of 10^{-7} or 10^{-8} cm^{-1}. Here one uses a Faraday cage one foot or more in diameter. With such a cage dimension, one could filter all the particulate matter from the air with an 'absolute' filter and still pick up an appreciable reading from these artificial large ions.

On droplets, fog droplets of ten microns in the range mentioned, I think the error would be negligible.

PRELIMINARY INVESTIGATION OF THE DISTRIBUTION OF SPACE CHARGE IN THE LOWER ATMOSPHERE

B. VONNEGUT, C. B. MOORE AND M. BLUME

Arthur D. Little, Inc., Cambridge 42, Mass.

Abstract—Measurements from a small airplane have been made of the vertical distribution of the fair-weather atmospheric electrical potential gradient. The measurements, the majority of which were made over eastern Massachusetts, show large departures from the classical picture of the variation of the electric field with altitude. Usually there are one or more regions in the lower atmosphere in which the potential gradient increases rather than decreases with increasing altitude. These regions usually are found at inversions and at haze levels that probably mark discontinuities in the atmospheric conductivity. These measurements show that frequently there are regions of negative as well as positive space charge in the lower atmosphere.

Introduction—One of the authors [VONNEGUT, 1955] has suggested a theory of thunderstorm electrification based on the idea that electrification is initiated by the small space charge found in the lower atmosphere. According to this idea, space charge in the lower atmosphere is drawn into clouds, thus causing them to have a weak electric field. Under the influence of this field, a current of oppositely charged fast ions flows from the surrounding air to the surface of the cloud and these ions are then trapped upon the cloud droplets. The down drafts on the surface of the clouds remove this screening layer of space charge as fast as they form and carry them to lower altitudes. This results in the accumulation of a negative region of charge at intermediate levels in the clouds, which subsequently lead to a regenerative charging mechanism.

If this theory of thunderstorm electrification is correct, then the development of the electric charge in a cloud depends to a very great extent on the distribution of fair-weather space charge in the lower atmosphere. Accordingly, a program of investigation is being carried out to determine how space charge is distributed in the lower atmosphere, and how this distribution is affected by different meteorological conditions.

Before considering the results of the investigations which have been carried out it is interesting to examine the classical view [GISH, 1952] of distribution of space charge in the atmosphere. According to this picture, the ionosphere is maintained at a potential of around 300 or 400 kV by the activity of thunderstorms over the Earth. Because of this potential a continuous current of positive electricity flows from the ionosphere to the Earth. It has been found that the conductivity of the atmosphere increases with altitude, so that this fair weather current which is flowing from the ionosphere to the earth results in a distribution of field with very small fields at high altitudes and larger fields near the surface of the earth. The potential gradient corresponds to the voltage drop of the current flowing through the atmosphere. Since the resistance of the atmosphere is greatest at low levels, this region has the highest field. From Poisson's equation we have

$$dF/dZ = 4\pi\sigma \tag{1}$$

131

where F is the electric field, Z is the height, and σ is the space-charge density. We can see that the space charge can be determined from the rate of change of potential gradient with altitude. An average picture of the variation of the gradient with altitude can be

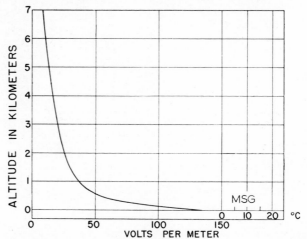

Fig. 1—Electric field as a function of altitude according to Schweidler

obtained from the empirical expression of Schweidler [1929] who found that the results of a large number of balloon measurements in Central Europe could be approximated by the relation (Fig. 1)

$$dV/dZ = 90 \exp(-3 \cdot 5 Z) + 40 \exp(-0 \cdot 23 Z) \tag{2}$$

where dV/dZ is gradient in volts per meter and Z is in kilometers.

From this classical picture of the distribution of the field in the atmosphere, we can

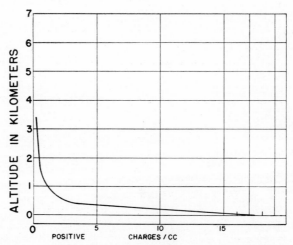

Fig. 2—Space charge densities computed from Schweidler's equation

compute the space charge is as a function of altitude. By differentiating the potential gradient with altitude, we obtain an expression for the space charge as a function of altitude, and this distribution is given in Fig. 2. It was the purpose of this investigation to determine how well the distribution of space charge in the atmosphere corresponds to that computed on the basis of the foregoing theory.

Instrumentation—There are several possible methods for measuring space charge [KELVIN, 1862; OBOLENSKI, 1925] such as those involving a Faraday cage or filters. However, these schemes are not readily adapted to measurements from small aircraft, so it was decided to make the initial measurements of the space distribution in the atmosphere by first measuring the potential gradient in the atmosphere as a function of altitude and then obtaining the space charge by differentiation. The observations that are reported in this paper were carried out from a small Beechcraft Bonanza airplane.

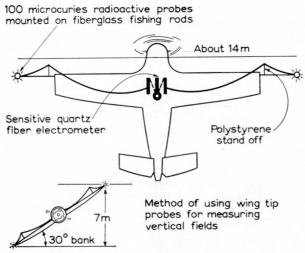

FIG. 3—First method for measuring vertical electric field from an aircraft

The measurements of potential gradient were carried out by the use of radioactive probes that were attached to the airplane. In the first measurements that were made the radioactive probes were installed on the airplane as is shown in Fig. 3. Here we have the two radioactive probes supported on fishpoles at a distance of about four feet past the wing tips of the airplane. These radioactive probes were connected by fine lead-in wires to a fiber electrometer that was read in the cockpit of the airplane.

Through this arrangement it was possible to measure the electric field by putting the airplane in various orientations and determining the potential difference between the two probes on the wings. In normal straight and level flight the potential difference between the probes was a measure of the horizontal component of the gradient. In fair weather this was almost invariably found to be negligible. The vertical component of the gradient was obtained by banking the airplane, thus causing the probes to have a vertical separation. From the observed potential difference, it was possible to compute the vertical

component of the field. Measurements were made with this apparatus by flying the airplane in a 20° spiral to the maximum altitude and then descending again in a similar
spiral, either with a 20° or sometimes 30° bank. From a knowledge of a separation of the
electrodes, the bank of the airplane, and the sensitivity of the electrometer, it was possible to compute the vertical gradient. This method of measuring potential gradient as a
function of altitude worked out quite well. However, it suffered from the disadvantage
that it was not possible to make continuous measurements of the vertical gradient in
straight and level flight. Therefore, this arrangement of the probes on the wing tips was
supplemented by another set of probes above and below the airplane, as shown in Fig. 4.

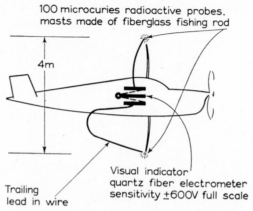

FIG. 4—Second method for measuring vertical electric
field from an aircraft

A fiber-glass fish pole was attached to the top of the airplane and another fish pole was
attached to the bottom of the airplane. The lower fish pole was affixed to the landing
gear so that while the plane was on the ground this pole, with its electrode, was in a
horizontal position. However, after take off, when the landing gear was retracted and
the wheel folded under the wing, this pole was oriented vertically and the two electrodes
above and below the plane were separated by a distance of approximately four meters.
The difference in potential between these two electrodes was measured similarly by
the use of a fiber electrometer.

   Results—The results of the soundings that have been made thus far frequently show
a very considerable departure from the idealized average picture of the distribution of
space charge and fields shown in Fig. 2. The results typical of the soundings made thus
far are shown in Figures 5–13. There are several interesting characteristics: First of all,
as we can see from the sounding in Figures 8 and 9, when we have two soundings in the
same region of air, even though they may be separated by as much as 50 miles as was the
case with these, they are very similar. In other words, under fair-weather conditions the
distribution of space charge is fairly uniform over appreciable distances. The second
feature, immediately obvious from the majority of the soundings shown, is the stratification in the distribution of field and space charge in the atmosphere. A very ragged
structure indicates that under many conditions not much mixing of the air is taking place,

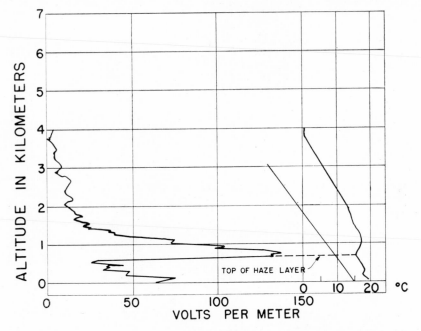

FIG. 5—Vertical field distribution over ocean near Provincetown, Mass., June 28, 1955

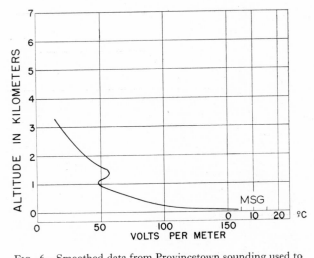

FIG. 6—Smoothed data from Provincetown sounding used to compute space-charge density

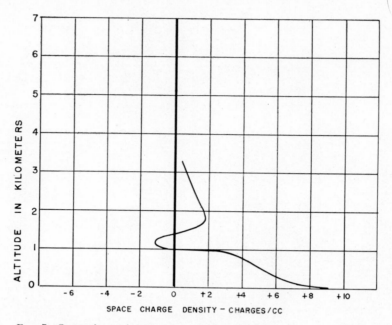

Fig. 7—Space-charge densities computed from field distribution, Provincetown, June 28, 1955

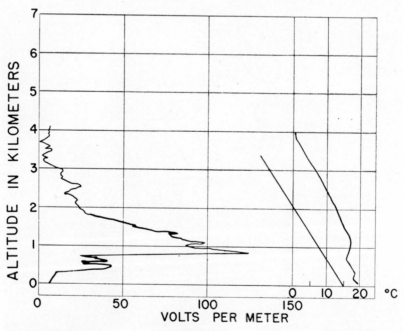

Fig. 8—Electric field measuring during descent over ocean near Marshfield, Mass.,
May 28, 1955

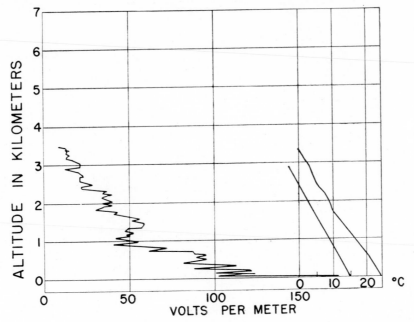

FIG. 9—Electric field measured during Ascent over land near Marshfield, Mass., May 28, 1955

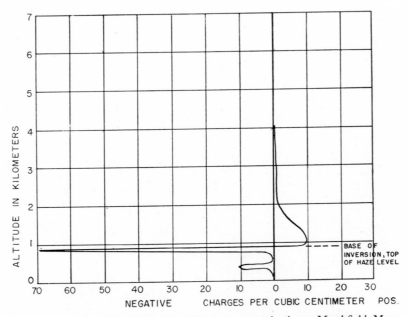

FIG. 10—Space charge distribution during ascent over land near Marshfield, Mass., May 28, 1955

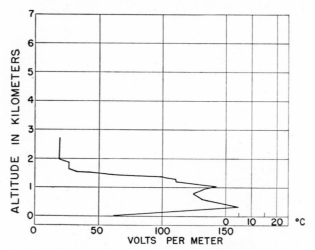

Fig. 11—Field measurements made during flight from Bedford
to South Weymouth, Mass., July, 11, 1955

and that we have numerous layers of space charge. Another effect which is quite marked is that of inversion. We frequently find, as is shown in Figures 8, 9 and 11, at the inversion level a very abrupt change in the field, and therefore we have considerable amounts of space charge. This is exactly what classical theory would predict at a discontinuity in the conductivity of the air. Under practically all conditions a haze layer is found to terminate at the inversion.

A rather interesting feature of many of the soundings is the fact that in the lower levels of the atmosphere frequently an increase occurs in the potential gradient with increase in height. This is shown in Figures 7, 10, and 11. In other cases, such as the one shown in Fig. 13, there is practically no change in the gradient in the first kilometer above the

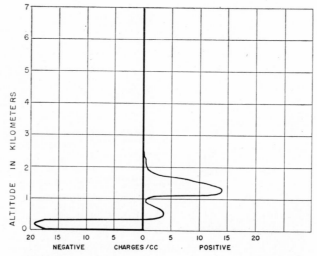

Fig. 12—Computed space charged distribution, July 11, 1955

ground. An increase in electric field with increasing altitude over the Earth's surface, means that there must be a region of negative space charge, rather than the normal positive space charge. These results are quite similar to some of the observations reported by KOENIGSFELD [1953] which he made with balloon soundings over the Belgian Congo. The exact reason for the existence of this region of negative space charge in the lower atmosphere is not clear. It must mean that the conductivity of the atmosphere in the lower levels is higher than that in the air above it. This will give a distribution of potential gradient which will correspond to one caused by a region of negative space charge.

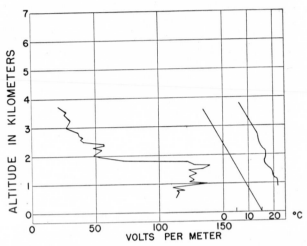

FIG. 13—Field measurements made in the evening near Dubuque, Iowa, July 23, 1955

There appear to be several alternative explanations as to why this region should exist. First of all, such a region may be produced when the concentration of aerosols in the lower levels of the atmosphere is less than in the region of air above it. Such a distribution of suspended particles would give a higher resistivity at some region above the Earth than at the Earth's surface, and therefore result in a region of negative space charge. Another possible explanation for this peculiar distribution of charge is that such a redistribution may somehow be brought about by convective activity. However, this seems rather doubtful because a region of negative space charge has frequently been observed on days when the air appears to be quite stable. A third possible explanation is that radioactivity at the Earth's surface produces ionization which increases the conductivity of the air. The fact that KOENIGSFELD'S [1953] observations of the electric field in the Belgian Congo over what is probably a fairly radioactive land mass show this effect most markedly, suggests rather strongly the possibility that this region of high conductivity and negative space charge near the Earth's surface may well be the result of radioactivity. On the few soundings made over water and away from land masses, we have found that the potential gradient has a more normal structure. If further flights over maritime regions confirm these findings, it will suggest rather strongly that this is caused by the radioactivity associated with land masses.

Conclusions—On the basis of the investigations thus far, it is concluded that the distribution of space charge in the lower atmosphere is highly variable and depends quite markedly on such factors as atmospheric pollution, the radioactivity of the Earth's crust and the convective activity at the time. If the space charge in the lower atmosphere is responsible for the initiation of electrification in cumulus clouds, it follows from the foregoing observations that the initiation of electrification may vary quite widely from one place to another, depending on the distribution of space charge. The data presented indicate that under some conditions a growing cloud may inhale air which is rather highly charged with either a positive or negative sign, and that under other conditions the air entering the clouds may be substantially neutral. We may therefore expect that the initiation of electrification in clouds is quite variable. Furthermore, the sign of the electricity in the clouds may be of either polarity, depending upon whether the space charge which enters is predominently positive or negative.

Acknowledgments—The authors wish to acknowledge the invaluable help of Le Kerivan in planning the flights and piloting the aircraft. Also we wish to thank the following staff members of Arthur D. Little, Inc. for their large part in constructing instrumentation and in making the measurements: Lawrence Baxter, C. K. Harris, John Kidder, Kiah Maynard, and Wendell G. Sykes. We wish to acknowledge, with thanks, the support of the office of Naval Research, whose help made this work possible under Contract No. Nonr 1684(00).

REFERENCES

Gish, O., Universal aspects of atmospheric electricity, *in* Compendium of Meteorology, *Amer. Met. Soc.* pp.101–119, 1952.

Thompson, William, Convective equilibrium of temperature in the atmosphere, *Manchester Lit. Phil. Soc. Mem.*, v.2, 1865.

Koenigsfeld, L., *Investigations of the Potential Gradient at the Earth's Ground Surface and within the Free Atmosphere in Thunderstorm Electricity*, Univ. Chicago Press, pp.24–45, 1953.

Obolensky, W. N., Über elektrische Ladungen in der Atmosphäre, *Ann. Phys.*, v.77, pp.644–666, 1925.

Schweidler, E., *Luftelektrizität, Einführung in die Geophysik*, v.2, pp.291–375, J. Springer, Berlin, 1922.

Vonnegut, B., Possible mechanism for the electrification of cumulus clouds, *in Proceedings on the Conference on Atmospheric Electricity*, Geophys. Res. Pap. 42, A. F. Cambridge Res. Cent., pp. 169–181, 1955,

DISCUSSION

Dr. James E. McDonald—How large are these areas which have an anomalous potential gradient? Presumably they must be rather limited, since the average picture certainly is based on a large space. Did you have an opportunity to fly over a large enough distance horizontally to find the limits between the areas that have a negative space charge?

Dr. Bernard Vonnegut—Each determination of space charge distribution by this technique requires making a sounding in which the potential gradient is measured as a function of altitude. Because only a few soundings can be made during each flight, we are unable to obtain a detailed picture of the instantaneous horizontal distribution of space charge. In measurements made in the mid-western United States, we have found very similar distributions of negative space charge in soundings made several hours apart at locations separated by several hundred miles. The soundings shown in Figures 9 and 10 were made approximately 60 mi in distance and one hour in time apart. The similarity of the space charge distribution in the two soundings above 500 m is quite noticeable. In both soundings, there was an intense layer of space charge at the top of the haze level where concentrations of more than 70 charges per cc were computed. On other occasions, measurements made near Boston have shown marked differences in space distribution between locations only a few miles apart. As the space charge distribution depends in turn on the distribution of electrical resistance in the atmosphere, variations in air pollution, stratification, mixing and ionization processes will affect the space charge.

Dr. David Atlas—Could you tell us whether the vertical variation of field strength approaches the standard variation in a well-mixed adiabatic atmosphere?

Dr. Vonnegut—When there is an adiabatic lapse rate, the soundings do not show the layers of intense space charge which usually characterize non-convective situations. In a well-mixed atmosphere we most frequently find that there is little change of potential gradient with altitude and that its vertical distribution departs considerably from Schweidler's classical picture.

Mrs. Rita C. Sagalyn—In all our measurements, the greatest departure from the idealized picture occurs in the middle of days of intense convection. The sharpest change in conductivity with altitude occurs at the upper boundary of a well-mixed adiabatic layer. The variation with altitude of electrical conductivity and therefore potential gradient, is closest to the idealized distribution before sunrise.

CONDENSATION AND COAGULATION;
MEASUREMENT OF CLOUD- AND RAIN-DROP SIZE;
RAIN FROM WATER CLOUDS

THE ROLE OF ADSORPTION IN WATER CONDENSATION

S. J. BIRSTEIN

Geophysics Research Directorate, Air Force Cambridge Research Center, Bedford, Mass.

Abstract—The work of various investigators is discussed in an attempt to determine what effect, if any, the chemical composition of condensation nuclei has on the supersaturation ratio necessary for water droplet formation. Gendron, using a diffusion cloud chamber, found that various nuclei became active at different supersaturation ratios. Anderson, using a kinetic system, has found a marked difference in the saturations at which sodium chloride and silver iodide will cause water droplet formation. Birstein, in a study of the adsorption isotherms of water vapor on various salts, has found that different materials take up water vapor in different ways. It is concluded that chemical composition of the nuclei plays an important part in water droplet formation.

WORK on the nucleation of water droplets from the supersaturated vapor does not ordinarily take into account the nature of the solid material involved in the nucleation; only the particle size is usually considered. This paper will explore, generally, the effect of the nature of a solid material on water droplet formation. A great deal of this material is taken from reports of Professor Pierre Gendron, of work done on Air Force contracts AF19(122)–380 and AF19(604)–1201.

Gendron employed a modified Langsdorf diffusion cloud chamber (Fig. 1) in his work. Vapor was supplied from evaporator E by heating water to a constant temperature with a nichrome heater H_2 wound on the outside of the evaporator. The level of the evaporator was maintained by reservoir R. Thermocouple T_1 was used to measure the temperature at the top of the chamber. The bottom of the chamber was cooled by immersing a six-inch brass tube rod B in a dry-ice acetone mixture. The condensate could be removed from the chamber bottom through drain D. The actual portion of the chamber in which the temperature gradient was maintained K consisted of two glass cylinders, the outer one L 25 cm long and 60 mm in diameter. The inner cylinder was constructed of Corning electrically conducting glass, through which a constant current was passed to produce a uniform temperature. The volume between inner and outer cylinders was filled with a clear white oil. The temperature at any point in the chamber could be obtained by lowering thermocouple T_2 to any height.

In making a run, oil, at a temperature of 60° was allowed to flow between the inner and outer jackets. By regulating the oil flow and the current through the conducting glass, the oil temperature at the top of the chamber was maintained at 90°. The brass rod was immersed one-half inch into the freezing mixture. These conditions were held constant for about four hours until a steady state was reached. By this time, all foreign particles in the chamber had settled out and the temperature gradient was constant; a cloud, caused by self-nucleation, appeared about two cm from the floor of the chamber. After the steady state had been reached, nuclei were injected into the top of the chamber by means of a heated syringe. The nuclei were invisible in the cloud chamber; when nucleation took place, however, the droplets could be readily seen if the chamber was illuminated with a beam of parallel light. The height of the cloud remained constant for

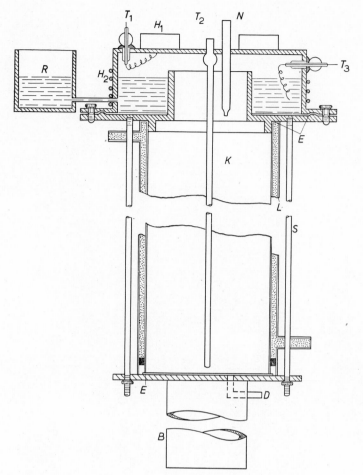

FIG. 1—Diffusion cloud chamber

about ten minutes, and the temperature at the cloud top was measured with T_2. The vapor pressure at any point in the chamber was calculated by modifying Langsdorf's original equations in order to eliminate the energy flux and thermal conductivity coefficient and add a term including the experimentally obtained temperature. Saturation vapor pressure was obtained from the temperature measured with T_2.

Table 1. *Test results for six salts*

Material	Supersaturation
Li Cl	$1 \cdot 02 \pm 0 \cdot 01$
Na Cl	$1 \cdot 06 \pm 0 \cdot 02$
Ca Cl$_2$	$1 \cdot 06 \pm 0 \cdot 02$
Mn Cl$_2$	$1 \cdot 07 \pm 0 \cdot 01$
Cu SO$_4$	$1 \cdot 11 \pm 0 \cdot 02$
Ag I	$1 \cdot 12 \pm 0 \cdot 02$

Gendron tested six salts in his diffusion cloud chamber, lithium chloride, sodium chloride, calcium chloride, manganese chloride, copper sulfate, and silver iodide. The results shown in Table 1 were obtained.

In these experiments, the difference in supersaturation tolerated was found to be independent of particle size. The minimum diameter of each nucleus was above 10^{-6} cm. According to Pound's theory of heterogeneous nucleation, nucleation rate is not affected by particle size when the particles are larger than 10^{-7} cm.

When Gendron's results were examined in terms of physical and chemical properties of the substances such as solubility, hygroscopicity, crystal structure, molecular weight and other properties, no relation could be found between the supersaturations tolerated and any of the above properties.

Another experiment, run at GRD by Anderson, used the apparatus shown in Fig. 2 to measure the supersaturations necessary for water droplet formation. Nuclei from hot-wire nuclei generator N were passed over saturator S, filled with distilled water for

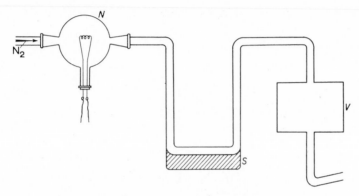

FIG. 2—Droplet growth apparatus

100 per cent relative humidity or an appropriate saturated salt solution for other relative humidities. The nuclei, after passing over the saturator, were viewed in viewing chamber V illuminated with a beam of parallel light, to monitor the formation of water droplets.

When sodium chloride nuclei, with a mean diameter of approximately 0.06μ, were used in the above apparatus, it was found that water droplets were visible in the viewing chamber when the relative humidity in the saturator was 85 per cent. When silver iodide was used instead, no water droplets were seen until the relative humidity was approximately 100 per cent. These results are at variance with theory which shows that it is impossible for water droplets to be formed at relative humidities of under 100 per cent (Fig. 3), and also with Gendron's work in the diffusion cloud chamber. Let us not now consider classical theory which essentially neglects the influence of the composition of the material on droplet growth, and consider Gendron's and Anderson's work solely in terms of the physical process involved in water droplet formation. When a solid soluble substance is exposed to water vapor, the first thing that occurs is adsorption of water vapor on the particle surface. The vapor, after adsorption on the surface, diffuses into the crystal lattice and solution begins. Both the initial rate of adsorption on the surface and the rate of solution depend on the nature of the particle, not only on its size.

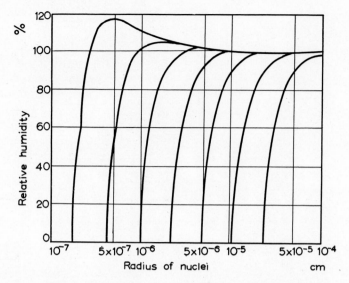

FIG. 3—Theoretical growth of sodium chloride nuclei

In Anderson's experiment, the particles were allowed to grow at a constant relative humidity, and thence form sodium chloride nuclei droplets at a relative humidity of 85 per cent. In Gendron's experiment, because the relative humidity in the cloud chamber varied with distance from the top, and because a finite time was necessary for his falling nuclei to grow in his chamber, all of his supersaturation values would appear to

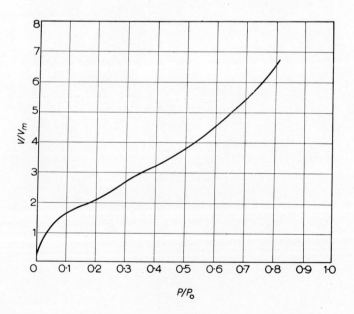

FIG. 4—Adsorption of water vapor on sodium chloride, 20°C

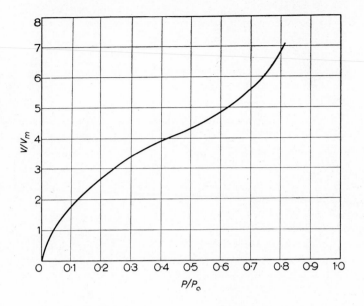

FIG. 5—Adsorption of water vapor on manganese chloride, 20°C

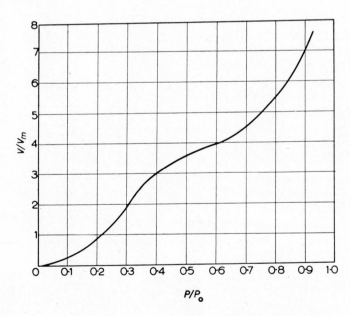

FIG. 6—Adsorption of water vapor on magnesium sulfate, 20°C

be high. The differences between the values for the various substances, however, appear real; hence the qualitative agreement between Anderson's results for sodium chloride and silver iodide and those of Gendron.

In a further study of the differences among various soluble nuclei, we measured the adsorption isotherms of water vapor on sodium chloride, manganese chloride, and magnesium sulfate. While generally the isotherms are of the same shape, the great differences among them are quite apparent as shown by Figures 4–6.

A calorimetric study of the shape of the adsorption isotherm, and also the heat of adsorption of water vapor on solids is now being conducted at the University of Ottawa by Dr. Gendron. The instrument employed is an extremely sensitive Calvet type microcalorimeter, developed and built in France and now set up in Ottawa. This calorimeter is sensitive enough to detect heat changes of the order of 25 microcalories, and is stable enough to measure heat changes of the order of 0·001 calories over a period of one hour. Experiments can be conducted over a period of several weeks, and the results are recorded automatically. The actual instrument is set in an aluminium can about $1\frac{1}{2}$ inches thick. This can is enclosed in three more cans about $\frac{1}{4}$ inch thick with a three-inch air space between cans. The apparatus is set up in a specially temperature-controlled room set at 25° and a relative humidity of five per cent. For an idea of the temperature control in the instrument, the second largest can is controlled within $+0·01°$.

In making an actual run, water vapor is placed in one cell and the adsorbent in another. One curve is plotted of the difference between the heat of evaporation of the water and the heat of condensation; this gives the heat of adsorption of the water vapor on the solid. The second plot is a direct measure of the heat of evaporation of the water in the first cell and gives a measure of the amount of water being used in the experiment and the amount of water vapor being adsorbed.

The instrument was calibrated by the adsorption of water vapor on the rutile form of titanium dioxide, a system which has been measured with extreme precision, and adsorption measurements have been made on a uniform-surface-area, finely divided, extremely pure sodium chloride sample prepared by Morrison in Ottawa. So far, very interesting results have been obtained. It has been possible to measure the heat of adsorption of water vapor on sodium chloride layer by layer. It has been found that the heat of adsorption increases rapidly at first, begins levelling off, and then there is a sharp break as the first layer is completed. After the abrupt break, the heat of adsorption again increases as the second layer begins building up, and a break is noticeable when this layer has been completed. Studies have been made on the first four layers adsorbed, and it is planned to continue measurements to the point where the particles dissolve, in order to measure accurately the rate at which nuclei take up water vapor and the energies involved. It is also hoped to make measurements at temperatures below 0°C in order to obtain an insight into ice crystal formation.

These experiments are all being used to gain an insight on the role of particle composition and particle surface on water droplet formation. Since the relative humidities necessary for water droplet formation seem to bear no relation to known properties, we feel that measurements of the initial rate of the taking up of water vapor on a surface, and the amount of water taken up on the surfaces will be directly translatable into valuable information regarding the role of chemical composition of nuclei in water droplet formation.

DISCUSSION

Dr. David Turnbull—Did you measure or calculate the supersaturation ratio at which droplets formed in the absence of foreign nuclei?

Mr. S. J. Birstein—I did not mention what the supersaturation was where droplets formed without nuclei. However, Gendron assumed that the supersaturation ratio where a pure water cloud formed in the chamber was 4·2. He used diffusion theory to calculate the supersaturation at various heights in the chamber.

Dr. Helmut Weickmann—I am interested in this case. It seems the role adsorption plays

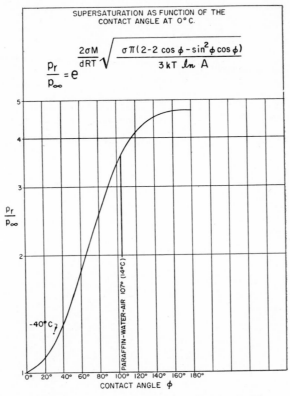

SUPERSATURATION AS FUNCTION OF THE
CONTACT ANGLE AT 0° C.

$$\frac{p_r}{p_\infty} = e^{\frac{2\sigma M}{dRT}\sqrt{\frac{\sigma\pi(2-2\cos\phi-\sin^2\phi\cos\phi)}{3kT\,\ln A}}}$$

FIG. 7—Condensation on unsoluble surfaces according to
Volmer

in the condensation process is an important one; and it is still more important in connection with ice nucleation.

As we know there are many solid and liquid substances which may act as condensation nuclei; and of the solid substances some are wettable and others are unwettable. Theoretically a completely unwettable substance would not act as a condensation nucleus. This can be shown by means of Volmer's nucleation theory if the interface energy between the nucleus and the water is expressed by means of the contact angle at the interface. The supersaturation $p_r/p\infty$ needed for condensation as a function of the contact angle is given through the equation which is shown in the graph of Fig. 7) where

p_r = vapor pressure over solid substance with contact angle larger than 0
p_∞ = vapor pressure over solid and wettable substance (contact angle = 0)
σ = surface energy over water

M = molecular weight
φ = contact angle
d = density of water
R = gas constant
T = absolute temperature
k = Boltzmann constant
A = constant about 10^{25}

In this case Volmer's theory does not hold true. Condensation experiments carried out by Ch. Junge in 1938 with nuclei freshly generated from paraffin did not require the supersaturation shown in the figure. Paraffin acted as condensation nucleus just as any other solid and wettable substance does. The discrepancy can be resolved since it was found that the contact angle of a water droplet with a solid depends on the relative humidity and decreases toward zero if the humidity approaches saturation. The reason for this behaviour must be that even on unwettable substances adsorption of H_2O molecules takes place. An adsorption film forms which masks the specific surface properties of the solid and facilitates condensation. Thus, adsorption plays an important role during the process of condensation on solids. The H_2O molecule being a dipole is especially favored to be absorbed.

DIFFUSIONAL GROWTH PROBLEMS IN CLOUD PHYSICS

CHARLES E. ANDERSON

Geophysics Research Directorate, Air Force Cambridge Research Center, Bedford, Mass.

Abstract—The growth of cloud droplets by diffusion is examined with the new theory of Frisch and Collins and the proper form of the steady-state growth law is shown to be $\gamma[R(t)-R_0]$ $+\frac{1}{2}[R^2(t)-R_0^2] = kDat$ instead of $R^2-R_0^2 = 2kaDt$ as normally used in meteorology. Using experimentally determined growth rates, the condensation coefficient of water on a water droplet is found to be $0\cdot5$ when the Frisch and Collins theory is applied. Finally the question of the heat balance of growing drops is discussed and it is shown that unreasonably high temperature rises are found in the cases of rapid growth.

The steady-state diffusion equation—Since 1950 several important papers concerning the growth by diffusion of aerosol particles have appeared in the non-meteorological literature. Inasmuch as it is believed that these treatments are now well known among meteorologists, I would like to review this progress and point out its significance to cloud physics.

The starting point for this discussion might as well commence with the basic equations governing heat and mass diffusion on the molecular scale. Thus for mass diffusion

$$\frac{\partial c}{\partial t} = D\nabla^2 C \tag{1}$$

sometimes called Fick's second law of diffusion, and for heat transfer

$$\frac{\partial T}{\partial t} = K\nabla^2 T \tag{2}$$

which is the familiar equation for heat conduction. C is concentration of the diffusing material, D is the diffusion coefficient, T is the temperature, and K is the coefficient of heat conduction.

The solutions of these two equations with appropriate initial and boundary conditions give the distribution of concentration and temperature around the growing particle at any point in the field at any time. We are interested in what the flux of heat and water vapor will be under the patterns our particular solutions yield, for we make the assumption that the particle grows by absorbing through its physical boundaries material which has diffused up to the boundary because of the concentration gradient. Likewise, we assume that heat released by the condensation process at the growing drop is conducted away to the ambient air at a rate which is proportional to the temperature gradient.

Therefore, the flux of water vapor for the case of spherical symmetry is

$$\text{Flux, } \Phi_{\text{vapor}} = 4\pi R^2 D \left(\frac{\partial c}{\partial r}\right)_R \tag{3}$$

153

where R is the radius of the drop and $(\partial c/\partial r)_R$ is the concentration gradient in the vapor evaluated at R. The flux of heat is likewise

$$\text{Flux, } \Phi_{\text{heat}} = 4\pi R^2 K \left(\frac{\partial T}{\partial r}\right)_R \tag{4}$$

where we assume the flux is the total flow through a spherical shell of surface area $4\pi R^2$.

The derivatives of the solutions of (1) and (2) with respect to r evaluated at R will specify the gradients $(\partial c/\partial r)_R$ and $(\partial T/\partial r)_R$ in (3) and (4).

Returning to (1), this is a well-known parabolic differential equation whose solution depends on the particular initial and boundary conditions employed. The usual conditions are

$$c(r, o) \quad = a \ R_0 \leqslant R < \infty$$
$$c(\infty, t) \quad = a$$

where a is the excess concentration which assumes the loss of vapor to the condensed phase is negligible on the ambient vapor density. The appropriate condition to use at the drop boundary has been shown by FRISCH and COLLINS [1953] to be

$$C(R, t) = \gamma(\nabla C)_R$$

where γ is a transmission coefficient, although previous investigators assumed for a boundary condition at the drop

$$C(R, t) = b, \text{ or } C(R, t) = 0$$

This latter condition imposes complete absorption of all diffusing vapor molecules.

Both FRISCH and COLLINS [1953] and REISS and LA MER [1950] solved (1) in the complete form although not for the same boundary conditions and determined the form of the corresponding flux equation. However, both papers point out that much mathematical difficulty is avoided if in the beginning the steady-state is assumed, thus reducing the diffusion equation to a variation of La Place's equation

$$\nabla^2 C = 0$$

The transient term of the solution which is neglected in this case was shown by Frisch and Collins to be important during the first microsecond of the growth period, and therefore, is of little consequence on the solutions at later times.

The fact that the droplet grows in time means that its boundary is moving, and account must be taken of this. The usual procedure consists of invoking the continuity condition that all diffusing molecules are absorbed and contribute to the particle growth. Thus

$$\frac{dV}{dt} = k\Phi$$

where V is volume of droplet, or

$$4\pi R^2 \frac{dR}{dt} = k4\pi R^2 D \left(\frac{\partial c}{\partial r}\right)_R \tag{5}$$

where k is a growth constant.

Under the Smoluchowski boundary condition, $C(R, t) = 0$, solution of (5) yields the familiar parabolic growth equation

$$R^2(t) = R_0^2 + 2kaDt \qquad (6)$$

where

$$k = \frac{M}{Ad}$$

M = molecular weight
d = density of bulk water
A = Avogadro's Number.

This law is perhaps more familiar in the form

$$R^2 = R_0^2 + \frac{2D}{d}(d_w - d_{ow})t \qquad (7)$$

d_w = ambient vapor density, d_{ow} = vapor density at drop, as used by meteorologists.

From the restriction under which this law is derived, we should expect experimental confirmation for the following types of systems: (1) where supersaturation remains constant during process, and (2) where all the diffusing molecules are absorbed. Thus, the case of droplets growing in a Wilson chamber experiment during its sensitive time and for ice crystals growing in a supercooled water cloud should be governed by this law. Furthermore, if we let a represent the sub-saturation, (6) or (7) will define the evaporation of particles under steady-state conditions. HOUGHTON [1933] verified this latter case, while REYNOLDS [1952] presented ice crystal growth data, which confirms the correctness of the general form of HOUGHTON's [1950] equation for planar crystals, a modification of (7).

However, Wilson cloud chamber data does not seem to be satisfied by this law particularly during the early stages of growth. HOWELL [1949] pointed out possible difficulties when the particle size is quite small, and Frisch and Collins explored this problem thoroughly, and present the equation correcting for this problem.

The difficulty resides in the fact that molecules are evaporating from the surface of the growing droplet, as well as condensing. Thus, the Smoluchowski condition, $C(R, t) = 0$ must be modified to allow for this. Frisch and Collins take this into account by using the 'radiation' boundary condition, $C(R, t) = \gamma(\nabla C)_R$ where γ is a parameter defined

$$\gamma = \frac{\rho}{\alpha}, \ \rho = \frac{\langle s^2 \rangle}{\langle s \rangle}$$

where $\langle s^2 \rangle$ is the mean square free path of the diffusing molecules; $\langle s \rangle$ is the mean free path, and α is the probability that a molecule striking the droplet is absorbed.

Using this radiation boundary condition, Frisch and Collins solve the diffusion equation to find

$$\frac{dR}{dt} = \frac{kDa}{\gamma}\left[1 - \frac{R}{\gamma + R}\right] \qquad (8)$$

which on integration gives

$$\gamma\{R(t) - R_0\} + \tfrac{1}{2}\{R^2(t) - R_0^2\} = kDat \qquad (9)$$

It is seen that this solution contains an additional term to that of (6). Thus, when R is small this additional term will be important and govern the growth until R becomes larger, since when $R \ll \gamma$, (8) becomes

$$\frac{dR}{dt} = \frac{kDa}{\gamma} \tag{10}$$

and integrating

$$R(t) = R_0 + \frac{kDat}{\gamma} \tag{11}$$

Eq. (11) predicts a linear variation of radius with time in contrast with the parabolic growth (6). Typical values of γ may be computed. By definition

$$\langle s^n \rangle = \int_0^\infty s^n \phi(s)\ ds$$

where $\phi(s)$ is a jump density function of the form

$$\phi(s) = \frac{1}{\langle s \rangle} \exp(-s/\langle s \rangle)$$

For air at standard conditions

$$\rho = \frac{\langle s^2 \rangle}{\langle s \rangle} \simeq 10^{-5}$$

It is presumed that ρ for water vapor will be of the same magnitude.

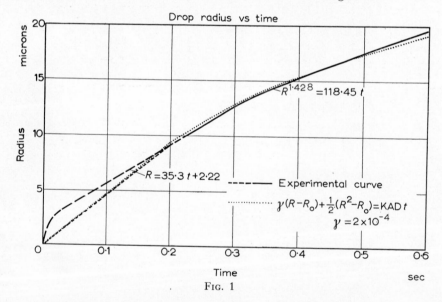

Drop radius vs time

FIG. 1

The condensation coefficient for water—The absorption probability a according to Frisch and Collins, varies with the radius of the drop, being subject to the temperature of the droplet and to the surface tension of the droplet. However, COLLINS [1950] argues that a is important only when R is small such that $aR \ll \rho$.

ALTY and MACKAY [1935] experimentally determined evaporation coefficients for water to be about 4×10^{-2}. Thus, it is possible for a to vary between unity and 0·04, with a corresponding effect on γ. Not knowing what value to assign a, we turned to some experimental cloud chamber data by BARRETT and GERMAIN [1947]. The published graph showing the relationships of the square of the radius to the time was drawn for actual measured points after 0·2 second but evidently extrapolated between zero and 0·2 second. The resulting relationship of radius to time as shown in Fig. 1 contains an anomalous departure near zero time. We argue that a better extrapolation would be to continue the measured portion at the same slope to zero time. The revised relationship is seen in Fig. 1 to be linear over the early portion of growth to about 0·3 second, as predicted by Frisch and Collins, and thence becoming parabolic during later times. From the above ranges of a, we find $10^{-5} \leqslant \gamma < 10^{-3}$, depending whether a equalled 1 or 0·04.

The Barrett and Germain data were best fitted by (9) using a value of $\gamma = 2 \times 10^{-4}$ which would give a value for the condensation coefficient, or absorption probability of water vapor on a water droplet of 0·5.

The growth of cloud droplets—The Barrett and Germain data further confirm the linear growth rate until the $(R^2 - R_0^2)$ term becomes larger than $\gamma(R - R_0)$ term, since with a value of γ of 2×10^{-4} a linear rate would be predicted until the radius was of several microns. The significance of this finding on the problem of the size distribution of cloud drops may be considerable. Although both the linear law and the parabolic law minimize the influence of initial size distribution of nuclei on the size distribution of the cloud droplets, especially if $R(t) \gg R_0$, the effect is not as great with the linear as with the parabolic. This result, coupled with a time lag for various nuclei to start growth, may very well account for cloud drop size distribution before coalescence effects commence. Computations are being carried out now by me to determine this consequence.

In the meteorologically important case of cloud formation by adiabatic lifting, several additional factors complicate the treatment described above, for we are faced with a number of droplets growing simultaneously, and thus reducing the ambient excess concentration to the extent that a constant value of a can be no longer assumed. Likewise, the lifting process brings about cooling of the system, which certainly means a change in its heat transfer characteristics with time, which acts also to cause a change in the excess concentration. Our approach to this more complicated problem has been through the simultaneous solution of adjusted steady-state mass and heat flux equations at chosen time intervals. The method will not be detailed here, since it is the subject of current investigation by us and will be reported later.

The heating effect during growth—The heat-transfer aspect deserves mention because of some interesting results one gets for the Barrett and Germain data mentioned earlier. If the usual assumption of steady-state drop temperature is made: Flux of heat from drop = heat generated by condensation; we can write

$$4\pi R^2 K \left(\frac{\partial T}{\partial r}\right)_R = \frac{4\pi R^2 \mathrm{d} \Delta H_v}{M} \frac{\mathrm{d}R}{\mathrm{d}t} \tag{12}$$

where ΔH_v is the molar heat of vaporization for water. The gradient $(\partial T/\partial r)_R$ may be obtained by solving equation (2) to find $T(r)$ and differentiating at R. Frisch and Collins employed the steady-state form of (2) and solved under the boundary conditions

$$\lim_{r \to \infty} T(r) = T\infty(t)$$

$$\text{and } T_s = T(R)$$

where $T(R)$ would be the temperature of the surface of the droplet if the gradient were continuous up to the surface and T_s is the actual surface temperature. This leads to a heat flux of the form

$$\text{Flux, } \Phi_{\text{heat}} = \frac{4\pi R^2 K(T_s - T\infty)}{g + R} \tag{13}$$

where g is a temperature jump distance of value $2 \cdot 7\langle s \rangle$. When $g + R \approx R$, (12) and (13) yield

$$T_s - T_\infty = \Delta T = \frac{\mathrm{d}\Delta H_v}{2KM} \frac{\mathrm{d}(R^2)}{\mathrm{d}t} \tag{14}$$

ΔT thus is the temperature difference between drop and ambient air. Computations of ΔT for droplet growth rates encountered under ordinary atmospheric conditions give temperature rises of less than one degree. However, in the case of the Wilson cloud chamber growth rates of Barrett and Germain, the computed (Table 1) temperature rise was some 35°C.

Table 1. *Temperature rise on growth**

Time	dR^2/dt	T
sec.	cm²/sec.	°C
0·025	2·44 × 10⁻⁶	11·98
0·05	2·88 × 10⁻⁶	14·14
0·075	3·19 × 10⁻⁶	15·66
0·10	3·5 × 10⁻⁶	17·185
0·15	5·38 × 10⁻⁶	26·416
0·20	6·37 × 10⁻⁶	31·27
0·30	7·28 × 10⁻⁶	35·6
↓	7·28 × 10⁻⁶	35·6

* Data taken from BARRETT and GERMAIN (1947)

The drops in this experiment were growing in a vapor with about a 400 per cent relative humidity, and thus had a very high rate of growth. However, the sensitive time of the chamber was less than one second; therefore, the drops grew from practically zero size to some 20 microns in about 0·6 second. It can be questioned whether in this short space of time the droplet had time to acquire a steady state temperature. If the transient time is of the same magnitude as for establishing the steady-state diffusion flux, 0·6 second is more than adequate. From the expansion ratios employed in the experiment, a reasonable value of $T\infty$ would be at -1°C if a starting temperature of $+20$°C was used. However, a 30°C rise means that the droplet was growing with a saturation vapor density at a temperature 10° higher than the ambient saturation vapor density. This obviously is an impossible situation, since growth would cease just as soon as the vapor densities at the drop surface and in the ambient air became equal.

One might be tempted to assume that the difficulty resided in the use of steady-state conditions for the temperature flux and drop temperature. However, high drop temperatures are distinctly possible under high supersaturation maintained over times greater than one second, since steady-state conditions should certainly prevail after this lapse of time. NAKAYA, TODA and MARUYAMA [1938] reported an interesting example of this fact during his experiments on the growth of snow crystals on rabbit hairs under controlled conditions. He found that under high supersaturations, instead of snow crystals, frozen drops were formed which he attributed roughly to the inability of the growing particle to lose heat quickly enough to avoid large temperature rises. This same type of factor may be responsible for the reported icing conditions at −50°C in tops of thunderstorms by BUNDGAARD and DOWNIE [1953].

Acknowledgment—The help of Richard Sampson in the preparation of material in this manuscript is cheerfully acknowledged.

REFERENCES

ALTY, T. and C. A. MACKAY, The accommodation coefficient and the evaporation coefficient of water *Proc. R. Soc.* A, v.149, pp.104–116, 1935.

BARRETT, E. O. and L. S. GERMAIN, Growth of drops formed in a Wilson cloud chamber, *Rev. Sci. Instr.*, v.18, pp.84–86, 1947.

BUNDGAARD, R. C. and C. S. DOWNIE, Thunderstorm icing and precipitation, *Bul. Amer. Met. Soc.*, v.34, p.427, 1953.

COLLINS, F. C., Diffusion in chemical reaction processes and the growth of colloid particles, *J. Colloid Sci.*, v.5, pp.499–505, 1950.

FRISH, H. L. and F. C. COLLINS, Diffusional processes in the growth of aerosol particles, II, *J. Chem. Physics*, v.21, pp. 2158–2165, 1953.

HOUGHTON, H. G., A study of the evaporation of small water drops, *Physics*, v.4, pp.419–424, 1933.

HOUGHTON, H. G., A preliminary quantitative analysis of precipitation mechanisms, *J.Met.*, v. 7, pp.363–369, 1950.

HOWELL, W. E., The growth of cloud drops in uniformly cooled air, *J. Met.*, v.6, pp.134–149, 1949.

NAKAYA, U., Y. TODA and S. MARUYAMA, Further experiments on the artificial production of snow crystals, *J. Faculty of Science, Hokkaido Univ.*, ser.2, v.2, pp.13–57, 1938.

REISS, H. and V. K. LAMER, Diffusional boundary value problems involving moving boundaries, connected with the growth of colloidal particles, *J. Chem. Physics*, v.18, pp.1–12, 1950.

REYNOLDS, S. E., Ice-crystal growth, *J. Met.*, v.9, pp.36–40, 1952.

DISCUSSION

Dr. Raymond Wexler—Can you tell me in what size ranges it is safe to apply the equation in the usual form?

Mr. Chas. E. Anderson—The Barrett and Germaine data confirmed the theoretical expectation for a linear change of radius with time to about four microns. I would say that the usual form is applicable above four microns radius.

Dr. G. A. Wolff—I would like to refer to the condensation coefficient of water. This coefficient was found to be about 0·04 by Alty and Mackay, as was mentioned by Mr. Anderson. Another very careful determination was made by W. Prueger in 1940, by a very careful investigation. His value of 0·02 is, therefore, in the same range, that is, a value much higher than 0·04 is not acceptable. It is very possible, however, that there is a slight change in the value for very small droplets.

M

Dr. Vincent J. Schaefer—I would like to mention an experimental observation which probably bears on some of your suggestions.

In the diffusion chamber at the critical temperature of about minus forty degrees, with air in the chamber with slight supersaturation with respect to water, large particles fall through this zone and crystalize, giving birth to large numbers of small crystals. These newly formed crystals rise two mm against the strong inversion which exists in the chamber. This effect is apparently due to the heat of condensation and is probably related to the effects you suggest occur in rapidly rising air. These particles are originally probably not more than a hundredth of a micron in diameter and yet the heat generated in their formation is enough to be easily observed.

I certainly think that we have to worry about how these very very small particles get rid of the heat when they are formed almost instantaneously in a supersaturated field.

I remember an observation by Professor Nakaya, in which he found that when he increased the supersaturation in the chamber where he grew his snow crystals, instead of the snow crystals growing larger he produced frozen droplets. This would further indicate the importance of understanding the problems involved in getting rid of the heat in rapidly growing clouds.

A NOMOGRAM FOR THE CALCULATION OF COLLISION EFFICIENCIES

HELMUT WEICKMANN

Evans Signal Laboratory, Belmar, N.J.

Abstract—Albrecht's formula of collision efficiency can be presented as nomogram. It is thus possible to obtain a qualitative picture for the collision efficiencies of different types of precipitation particles.

ALBRECHT'S [1931] theory gives differential equations for the movement of a spherical particle in the potential flow field around a cylinder. For collection efficiencies M'/M above 22 per cent the equations can be solved and yield a simple formula

$$\frac{M'}{M} = \frac{1}{1 + 0 \cdot 53 \ d/x}$$

Here d is the diameter of the body upon which the droplets are deposited, and x is the distance which droplets travel if they move according to Stokes' law and enter stagnant air with the velocity v.

$$X = \frac{\pi s \delta^2 v}{6c}$$

s is the density of the droplet, δ its diameter and $c = 3\pi \times 17 \cdot 3 \times 10^{-5}$ cgs is the constant of the Stokes' law.

Applied to precipitation particles, v is the fall velocity of the particle when the fall velocity of the droplet can be neglected; otherwise it is the difference between the fall velocity of the particle and the fall velocity of the droplet. The parameters to be concerned with are the droplet radius r, the radius of the precipitation particle R and its fall velocity v_R.

$$\frac{M'}{M} = \frac{1}{1 + CR/r^2 v^2}$$

The collection efficiency becomes a maximum for $R \to 0$ or $r^2 v_R \to \infty$; in other words, the collection efficiency decreases with increasing R and increases with increasing r or v_R. Since R and v_R are not independent of each other, it is not apparent how the collection efficiency changes with increasing R. Therefore, Fig. 1 presents collection efficiencies of different particles in form of a nomogram. The collection efficiency E'/E for spherical particles can be obtained if the square of the cylindrical collection efficiency is taken, $E'/E = (M'/M)^2$. The left columns of Fig. 1 are the collection efficiencies in per cent; the numbers on the left side are valid for the two-dimensional, cylindrical case, and the numbers on the right side for the three-dimensional spherical case. The middle column is the droplet radius in microns, and the right columns give the radii of different precipitation particles in millimeters. These radii are plotted in units of R/v_R. The values

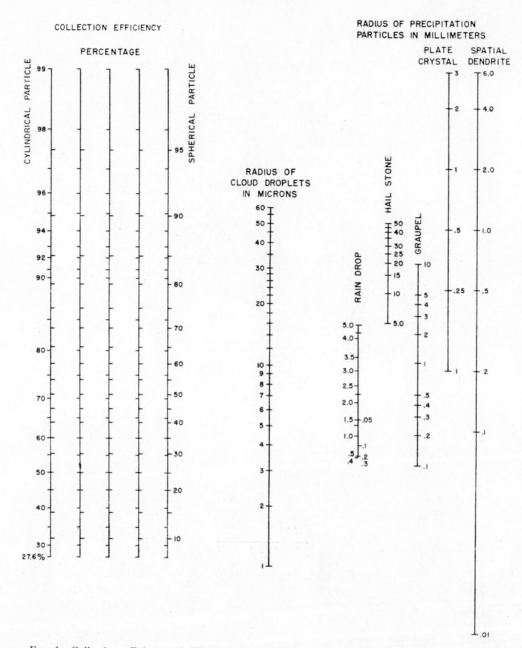

Fig. 1—Collection efficiency of different precipitation particles according to Albrecht's theory.

are based upon fall velocities which are presented in Fig. 2. A collection-efficiency column exists for each precipitation particle column. The cloud-droplet column is always in the center between a corresponding pair of columns for collection efficiency and for the precipitation particle considered.

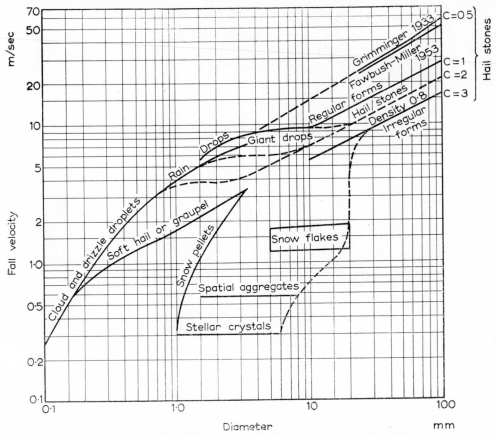

FIG. 2—Diagram of fall velocities for different precipitation particles

Collection efficiencies of raindrops, hailstones and soft hail (graupel)—For raindrops the GUNN–KINZER [1949] values of fall velocity have been adopted up to a size of 3·0 mm radius; for larger radii a constant value of 9·2 m/sec was taken.

For hailstones we have taken the values as listed in Fig. 2 for 'regular forms' with the formula

$$v_R = 4\sqrt{R_{\text{hail}}} \; \text{m/sec}$$

which is valid for R from 5 to 50 mm.

No observations exist for the shower-type graupel or soft hail particle, but since this particle originates from large cloud or drizzle droplets rather than from crystals, it was tentatively assumed that its fall velocity follows the dotted line for hailstones down to the intersection with the line for drizzle droplets. v_R was calculated according to the expression

$$v_R = 2·8\sqrt{R_{\text{graupel}}} \; \text{m/sec}$$

According to the nomogram, cloud droplets with radii larger than 20 microns are deposited on all raindrops with an efficiency of 80 per cent or more. Since for large cumuli most of the water content is contained in droplets larger than 20 microns (Fig. 3),

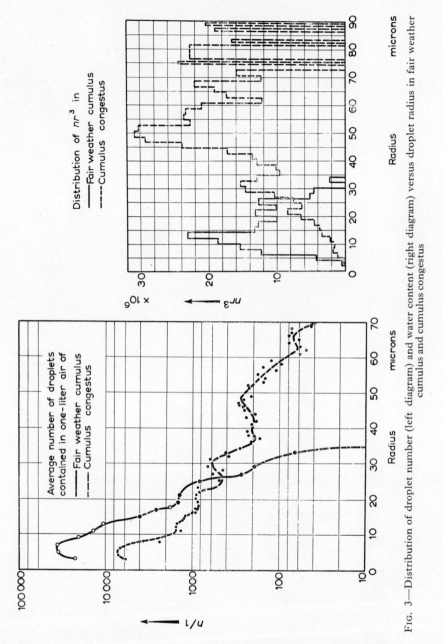

FIG. 3—Distribution of droplet number (left diagram) and water content (right diagram) versus droplet radius in fair weather cumulus and cumulus congestus

growth of shower droplets by accretion only is no problem once they have reached a certain size and the water content of the cloud is sufficiently large. It is favorable also that the collection efficiency is highest for smaller droplets, such as drizzle droplets. They collect even ten micron droplets with an efficiency of over 80 per cent. It may appear that drizzle droplets are rather unimportant particles whose collection efficiency does not matter. This may be true, if they would be considered to be precipitation particles. Actually, however, their most important role seems to be a 'trigger' particle for soft hail or hail formation.

Collection efficiency of snow crystals—Little attention has been given so far to collection efficiencies of particles other than rain drops, and yet it appears that the collection efficiency of snow crystals plays a very important role in any precipitation during the winter and in certain types of precipitation during the summer also. In 219 observations of forms of snow crystals, only 76 or one-third had no visible sign of riming. Kuettner (unpublished), and CUNNINGHAM [1952] have calculated the collection efficiency of snow crystals and have arrived at very low values by assuming that the airflow goes around the crystal as a whole and not in between the branches and rays of the crystal. Observations of rimed snow crystals indicate that this assumption is erroneous and that indeed a snow crystal, especially the dendritic spatial aggregate, act as a 'rake' for cloud droplets. This is more true as the transition from viscous to aerodynamic flow apparently does not occur at a Reynolds number of 60, as Langmuir states, but at numbers between 1 and 10. This has been shown experimentally for water droplets by GUNN and KINZER [1949]. In addition, Vierhout's thermodynamical theory of coalescence as well as Facy's observations concerning the growing crystal surface constitute mechanisms whose action furthers the collection efficiency of ice crystals.

Fig. 1 gives collection efficiencies for plate crystals (dendrites) and spatial dendrites. Their fall velocity was taken from NAKAYA [1954] as shown in Fig. 2. If the plate and stellar crystals, respectively, were considered as stellar disks, and the spatial plate aggregates or spatial dendrites as being spheres, their collection efficiencies would be very small for both, small and large, cloud droplets. The first mentioned particle would travel around the disk or sphere and the latter would fall too fast. It is most probable that stars and dendrites do not act as disks, but that their branches collect droplets individually. This may be concluded from several reasons: (1) Rimed stars have in most cases droplets homogeneously distributed all over their surface; if they would rime as disks, one would expect to find more droplets at the peripheries than in the center. According to DIEM [1948] the radii of cloud droplets deposited on plates or stars ranged between 8 and 25 microns. (2) Dendrites quite often have air bubbles irregularly lined up along the middle ridges of the six rays. Air bubbles form if water freezes. It is therefore likely that these dendrites have collected cloud droplets with their branches. Nakaya has shown that in the temperature interval between 0 and $-7°C$ such droplets merge with the wet surface film of the ice crystal. Consequently, the subsequent growth of the ice crystal after riming must proceed partly from the water phase. Needles are another excellent example of such a process of growth which in this case starts from prisms.

At low temperatures (below $-9°$ according to rime observations which we carried out on Mt. Hohenpeissenberg), each droplet collected freezes individually and starts to develop crystal planes. It is quite often the nucleus of a new branch or sector. Thus it is possible that such a crystal increases quickly its effective diameter. It is still far from being a graupel, but it is a large irregular spatial aggregate which is most probably an efficient reflector for radar. We are convinced that they are the particles which are sometimes considered to be a very fast growing graupel particle (see Dr. Atlas' contribution and note also the BROWNE-WEXLER [1953] on a similar subject). The nomogram shows how efficient these particles are as droplet collector. If a dendrite has branches which are

200 microns wide, and if such a branch is considered in a first approximation as being a cylindrical body, it will collect ten micron droplets with an efficiency of nearly 80 per cent, whereas the collection efficiency of a crystal as a whole would be much smaller.

Still more efficient collectors are plate or dendrite aggregates. They may fall with one edge forward, and, since the thickness of this edge may be of the order of 20 microns it would collect any size of cloud droplets with nearly 100 per cent efficiency. Small droplets will evaporate toward the ice surface before they hit; large ones will crystallize if the temperature is sufficiently low and form a new branch. If the shape of these crystals would be approximated by a circumscribed sphere, we feel that for theoretical computations a collection efficiency of 100 per cent was more real than the values given by CUNNINGHAM [1952]. This type of crystal forms at around −20°C, which is quite often the generating level of snow crystals in both, warm-front precipitation and winterly instability showers. Due to its high collection efficiency it will sweep out supercooled water clouds in levels where the concentration of freezing nuclei is insufficient.

REFERENCES

ALBRECHT, F., Theoretische Untersuchungen über die Ablagerung von Staub aus strömender Luft und ihre Anwendung auf die Theorie der Staubfilter, *Phys. Zs.*, v.32, pp.48–56, 1931.
BROWNE, I. C. and R. WEXLER, The collection efficiency of ice crystals, correspondence, *Q.J.R. Met. Soc.*, v.79, p.549, 1953.
CUNNINGHAM, R. M., The distribution and growth of hydrometeors around a deep cyclone, MIT T.R. 18, Contract DA36–039 SC–124, Signal Corps Eng. Labs., Ft. Monmouth, N.J., 1952.
DIEM, M., Messungen der Grösse von Wolkenelementen, II, *Met. Rundschau*, v.1, pp.261–273, 1948.
GUNN, R. and G. D. KINZER, The terminal velocity of fall for water droplets in stagnant air, *J. Met.*, v.6, pp.243–248, 1949.
NAKAYA, U., *Snow Crystals*, Harvard University Press, 510pp., 1954.

DISCUSSION

Mr. Duncan C. Blanchard—What would be the effect of using the raindrop fall velocities of Kinzer and Gunn instead of the older values of Lenard?

Dr. Helmut Weickmann—They would reduce the collection efficiency somewhat, but not much.

Mr. Charles E. Anderson—Why did you base the nomogram on Albrecht's theory when you have so many others since his?

Dr. Weickmann—Because it's easy. You have one equation.

Dr. Richard M. Schotland—Do you take each spoke of a snow crystal as a cylinder when you compute the collection efficiency?

Dr. Weickmann—Yes.

Dr. Schotland—I would think that this would be a good approximation near the outer end of the spoke but toward the center the crystal would behave somewhat more like a disk.

LABORATORY MEASUREMENTS OF THE GROWTH
AND OF THE COLLECTION EFFICIENCY
OF RAINDROPS

GILBERT D. KINZER AND WILLIAM E. COBB

U.S. Weather Bureau, Washington 25, D.C.

Abstract—The growth of raindrops produced by coalescence with cloud droplets was measured under laboratory controlled conditions. A telescope and scale and microphotographs were used to find the time rate of increase of drop radii when the drops were supported on an upward flow of cloud inside a vertical tapered glass tube. The cloud water content was measured and was used to evaluate the collection efficiency from the growth rate taking into account the ellipsoidal shape of the supported drops shown in the photographs. The cloud droplet radius distribution was determined and was used to calculate the collection efficiency by the method of Langmuir. The measured efficiency was 27·6 per cent for a drop 0·83 mm in radius and it decreased to 11·5 per cent at a drop radius of 1·40 mm. The corresponding theoretical values of the collection efficiency were 55·0 per cent and 49·5 per cent. The experimental results agree well with other laboratory measurements of the growth and collection efficiencies of both smaller and larger raindrops.

MEASUREMENTS of the growth of raindrops in a natural cloud cannot be made directly, but KINZER and COBB [in press] using a technique developed earlier by KINZER and GUNN [1951] supported a drop of water in a tapered glass tube on an upward flow of a cloud of known water content and droplet radius distribution, and measured the growth rate. They obtained results with drops whose radii ranged from 75 microns to 0·75 mm. However, they were unsure of the results for radii exceeding 0·50 mm.

The same apparatus has been used in an extension of the work, and the growth of raindrops has been measured for radii lying between 0·83 and 1·40 mm. A tapered glass tube of larger bore has been employed in order to decrease uncertainties caused by wall effects and instead of measuring the growing drop radius with a telescope and scale, photographs were made of the supported drop at one-minute intervals. Suitable calibration of the linear distances in the photograph was obtained from measurements of steel cylinders of known lengths and diameters suspended down into the tapered tube and photographed. The cloud which supported the drop had a droplet radius distribution with a single peak at 6·5 microns rather than at 5·2 microns as in the earlier experiment [KINZER and COBB, in press], but, as before, there were no droplets whose radii exceeded 16·8 microns.

The shape of the growing drops could be approximated closely by assuming them to be ellipsoids of revolution and their collection efficiencies were computed from the formula

$$E = 2Q(\mathrm{d}a/\mathrm{d}t)/wU$$

where Q is the ratio of the minor axis to the major axis, a is the major axis, w is the free water content of the cloud, U is the terminal velocity of the supported drop of water and E is the collection efficiency.

The experimental efficiencies were determined by inserting in the equation above

167

values of the growth rate of the major diameter obtained from the photographs and appropriate values of the other factors.

The theoretical collection efficiency, computed by the method devised by Langmuir for the cloud droplet radius distribution employed in this study, decreased from 55 per cent down to 49·5 per cent as the drops grew through the range of radius covered by the present study. The experimental values of the collection efficiency were found to be much less, starting at 27·6 per cent and decreasing steadily to 11·5 per cent. These are mean values obtained by averaging the results of five sets of growth measurements in clouds whose free water contents ranged between 6·2 and 4·1 g/m³. GUNN and HITSCHFELD [1951] measured experimentally the collection efficiency of a drop of water 1·60 mm in radius falling in a cloud that was similar to the one used in this investigation, and they found it to be 15 per cent. If their value of 15 per cent be modified by taking into account the ellipsoidal shape assumed by a falling drop of water 1·60 mm in radius, as has been done in the present study, it becomes 12·7 per cent. This agrees rather well with the results of the present study which in turn appear to be a reasonable extension of the earlier measurements [KINZER and COBB, in press]. Small discrepancies between the results of the three experiments are readily accounted for by small differences in the cloud droplet radius distributions.

REFERENCES

GUNN, K. L. S. and W. HITSCHFELD, A laboratory investigation of the coalescence between large and small waterdrops, *J. Met.*, v.8, pp.7–16, 1951.

KINZER, G. D. and R. GUNN, The evaporation, temperature, and thermal relaxation-time of freely falling waterdrops, *J. Met.*, v.8, pp.71–83, 1951.

KINZER, G. D. and W. E. COBB, Laboratory measurements of the growth and of the collection efficiency of raindrops, *J. Met.*, in press.

DISCUSSION

Mr. James D. Wilcox—I believe Langmuir's theory considered drops in still air. If I'm not mistaken, didn't your experimental conditions create quite a bit of disturbance on the surface of the drops?

Dr. Gilbert D. Kinzer—Yes. Watching them with a telescope you quickly realize that things going on around the drops are quite different from the theoretical picture.

I might mention another experiment. Sartor made a study of a droplet model, using an atmosphere of oil rather than air, to follow the path of a cloud droplet relative to a falling raindrop. Some condition of the experiment, perhaps some energy factor, permitted contact without coalescence. But I am particularly interested that he observed the droplets to follow a more devious path than that traced out by aerodynamic theory He felt that the collision efficiency was considerably greater than the aerodynamic theory prescribed.

Dr. Helmut Weickmann—I am amazed at the discrepancy between observation and theory. There is the question whether collection efficiency is equal to collision efficiency. Also, might it be that the cloud was not entirely saturated, and the droplets started to evaporate?

Dr. Kinzer—The best guarantee we had of saturation was maintaining a slight degree of cooling in the tube, with the temperature outside it two or three hundredths of a degree centigrade lower.

Dr. Ukichiro Nakaya—I am afraid the taper of the glass tube might disturb the streamlines so that collection efficiency might be different from that for free fall.

Dr. Kinzer—I agree with you. We have had constantly to consider in this experiment how truly the cloud and free fall are reproduced. However, let me repeat that the geometry provided a reasonable approach to free fall. The diameter of the growing drop never exceeded $\frac{1}{4}$ of the diameter of the tapered tube at the position of observation.

Dr. K. L. S. Gunn—Did you try the small drop in the large tube, and did everything check?

Dr. Kinzer—Yes, we did. We overlapped some of our sizes, and used larger tubes. The curves come parallel to one another, but shifted by a small amount due, I believe, to a slightly larger radius all the way along.

Dr. James W. Ford—In addition to Dr. Nakaya's comment, I think the shape of the drop front will influence the effect as against free fall. I'm not sure I know the diameter of your tubes.

Dr. Kinzer—I quite agree that there are wall effects. The size of the tube goes from about 2 mm diameter where the drop is small up to about 10 mm where the drop has grown tremendously.

Dr. J. S. Marshall—Isn't the change of size by a considerable factor from the small tube to the large one reassuring with regard to any wall effect?

Dr. Kinzer—I feel reassured.

Prof. Charles S. Hosler—Was there enough change of shape of the bottom of the drop to make it a predominant factor in the airflow around it?

Dr. Kinzer—There was a change of shape as the drop grew, the horizontal diameter becoming about 1·15 times the vertical diameter. This is another difficulty in comparing the Langmuir theory with what a drop actually does. The Langmuir theory assumes a sphere, while the flattening increases the frontal area by about 30 per cent.

Mr. D. C. Blanchard—Did you notice any bounce-off effects at all?

Dr. Kinzer—No, the relative velocity is too high. With small drops I have seen things that might be bounce-off, but I have no proof of it. That might be a reason for the low collection efficiency.

THE COLLISION EFFICIENCY OF CLOUD DROPLETS

R. M. SCHOTLAND

New York University, New York, N.Y.

Abstract—An experimental determination by a modelling technique has been made of the collision efficiencies of water cloud drops. Collision efficiency curves are presented for simulated 11, 14, 17 and 21μ diameter cloud drops with respect to a range of smaller cloud drops.

Introduction—In order to explain the observed time scale for the growth of rain drops in warm clouds, it has been necessary to assume that collisions occur between the cloud drops which result in coalescence. Theoretical work by Albrecht, Langmuir and others [JOHNSON, 1954] has been carried out on the problem of the collision efficiency between large and small drops falling in the gravitational field. In each of these treatments approximations were made which make the results questionable, particularly in the region where the drops are the size of cloud drops. It was thought, therefore, that an investigation of the collision efficiency of cloud drops would be desirable.

The basis for the experiment—It was realized at the outset that the problems of the generation and the trajectory control of charge-free drops in the micron range would be very difficult. Therefore, a modelling technique was sought which could allow the use of relatively larger drops.

The analysis of the modelling problem is as follows. The significant parameters involved in the collisions of two drops are the drop radii R and r, the drop density ρ_D, the relative co-ordinate distances x and y, the terminal velocities of the drops v_1 and v_2, the medium density ρ_M, and the medium viscosity μ. Thus there are nine secondary quantities and three primary quantities in this set. Application of the π theorem results in nine minus three or six independent dimensionless products. An equation relating these quantities may be written as follows

$$x = yf\left[\frac{R}{r}, \frac{r}{x}, \frac{\rho_M v_1 R}{\mu}, \frac{\rho_M v_2 R}{\mu}, \frac{\rho_M}{\rho_D}\right] \tag{1}$$

The first of the two quantities in the bracket represents a modelling of the geometry of the system. The second and third terms are Reynolds numbers which model the hydrodynamic forces, and the last term models the ratio of the medium density to that of the drop. The first four terms can be modelled easily [SARTOR, 1954]; however, the last term poses a problem. The density ratio of the prototype is 10^{-3}. The lightest fluid which gives a reasonably large scale factor has a density of $0\cdot9$, while the heaviest material suitable for modelling drops has a density of 11. Therefore the density ratio using such components would be too large by a factor of 100.

Since it was not possible to model the density ratio, a simplifying assumption had to be made. If the Reynolds numbers of the drops considered are limited to values of one or smaller, the fluid inertial forces are much smaller than the fluid viscous forces.

Consequently the fluid density is no longer a significant parameter. The significant terms remaining are (see Fig. 1)

$$x, y, \rho_D, \mu, R, r, g_e$$

where the terms have the same significance as before except that in place of v_1 and v_2 a term g_e which is gravity minus the buoyancy force is included. This is permissible since

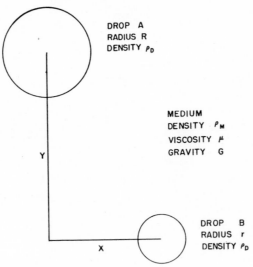

FIG. 1—Significant quantities in modeling of cloud drops

v_1 and v_2 are functions of R, r, ρ_D, μ, and g_0. An equation formed from the remaining terms is

$$x = yf\left[\frac{R}{r}, \frac{r}{x}, \frac{\rho_D g_e^{1/2} r^{3/2}}{\mu}\right] \tag{2}$$

The first two terms represent the geometry of the system; and the last term, called the viscosity term, represents the ratio of the fluid viscous force to the inertial force of the drop.

Fortunately, this approximation is not too serious, since the Reynolds numbers of cloud drops smaller than 60μ (microns) in diameter are less than unity.

Eq. (2), together with the auxiliary condition that the Reynolds number be less than unity, establishes the similarity requirements for the experiment.

Experimental apparatus—Apparatus was constructed for the purpose of obtaining stereoscopic photographs of pairs of simulated drops falling in a viscous medium.

A drop may be characterized by its radius and density. It can be shown by writing the viscous term of (2) in terms of the Reynolds number that the ratio of the drop density to medium density must be large, approaching 10^3, if the full range of cloud drops are to be modelled correctly. However, with a density ratio of the order of 7, drops 25μ in diameter and smaller are modelled correctly.

A length scale factor of 600 permits model sizes between 1·5 mm and 1·5 cm to correspond to cloud drops in the range 2·5μ to 25μ in diameter. These model sizes allow for easy visual and photographic observation. Steel ball bearings in this model range are readily available. These bearings have a density of 7·8.

The fluid medium may be characterized by its viscosity and density. From the discussion in the section above it follows that the fluid density should be as small as possible. The viscosity required of the fluid was determined from the viscous term of (2) by setting this term for the model (subscript M) equal to that of the prototype (subscript p).

$$\mu_M = \mu_p \times \frac{\rho_{DM}}{\rho_{D_p}} \times \frac{g_{eM}^{1/2}}{g_{ep}^{1/2}} \times K_L^{3/2} \tag{3}$$

where $K_L = r_M/r_p$. Substitution of the values given in the section above into (3) results in a viscosity value of approximately 15 poises. An aqueous invert sugar solution (donated by Refined Syrups and Sugar, Inc., Yonkers, N.Y.) containing 76 per cent by weight

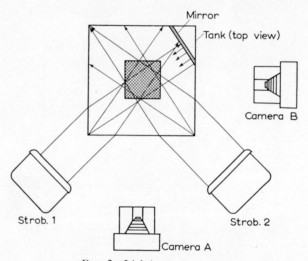

Fig. 2—Lighting arrangement

of sugar was found suitable. The fluid has a viscosity of 20 poises at 21°C and a density of 1·34 g/cm. Although the color of the fluid is pale yellow, it is sufficiently clear for photographic purposes.

A dropping mechanism was constructed so that the bearings could be accurately dropped, one at a time, with respect to each other.

A transparent tank was constructed of $\frac{1}{4}$-inch plexiglas. The tank was five feet high and eight inches square. When filled it contained approximately 18 gallons of fluid. The dropping mechanism was placed on top of the tank and a plumb bob hung from it, immersed in the fluid to serve as a photographic reference line.

The illumination of the bearing pairs was provided by two Type 1532A Strobolumes (Fig. 2). The Strobolumes were mounted on the tank in such a way that they could be moved to follow the freely falling bearings. The Strobolumes were flashed periodically by an adjustable tripping mechanism.

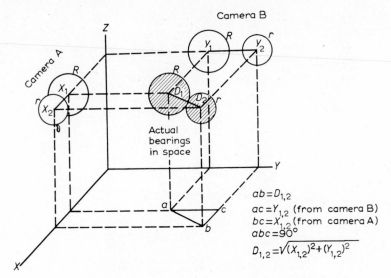

FIG. 3—Projection and computation of bearing position

Two Crown Graphic cameras were located at right angles to each other approximately four feet from the tank. In operation, the shutters of the cameras were opened during total fall of the drops. This provided a series of photographs, one at each flash, superimposed on each negative. These photographs determine the position of one drop with respect to the other at all times.

Calculations of the location of the center of the bearings with respect to each other were made by enlarging the negative $10\times$ on cross-section paper and using the relation (Fig. 3)

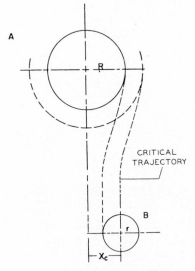

FIG. 4—Critical trajectory diagram

$$D_{12} = \sqrt{\bar{x}_{12}{}^2 + \bar{y}_{12}{}^2}$$

Collision was considered to have occurred when (see Fig. 4)

$$x_c \equiv D_{12} = R + r$$

Critical collision occurred when $D_{12} = R + r$ at the point of apposition.
Collision efficiency was defined as

$$\frac{x_c{}^2}{R^2} \times 100 \qquad\qquad (4)$$

where x_c is the initial separation of the bearings in space.

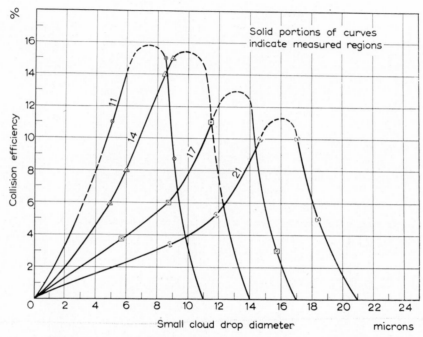

FIG. 5—Measured collection efficiencies for given cloud drops (microns) versus a range
of smaller cloud drops

Measurements were made with an accuracy of $\pm 0 \cdot 1$ mm. The majority of initial separation distances were greater than $2 \cdot 5$ mm so that the uncertainty of the computed efficiency may be written approximately $E(1 \pm \cdot 08)$.

Results—A total of 183 bearing pairs were photographed as described above. Calculations showed that 62 of these cases resulted in collisions; and, of the 62, 17 were critical collisions. The collision efficiencies corresponding to the critical collisions are presented graphically in Fig. 5. Note that small but important collision efficiencies were found over the total region considered. This is significant since most theoretical work suggests that the collision efficiency should be zero over a major portion of the graph.

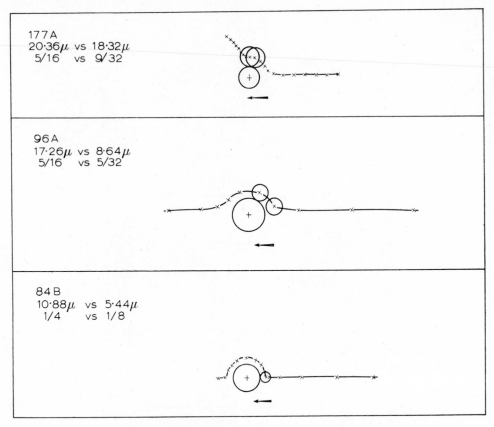

FIG 6—Relative trajectory of small drop about larger drop

One cause for the discrepancy between the theoretically and experimentally derived efficiencies is the modification of the flow pattern about the larger drop due to the presence of the smaller drop. Most theoretical treatments do not consider this effect. Fig. 6 shows examples of the relative motion of the smaller drop about the larger drop. It is seen that when the smaller drop is very small compared to the larger drop, a nearly symmetrical relative trajectory is obtained. As the smaller drop approaches the larger one in size, the trajectory becomes markedly asymmetrical, indicating the pronounced modification of the flow about the large drop.

Acknowledgment—The research for preparation of this paper has been sponsored by the Geophysics Research Directorate, Air Force Cambridge Research Center, under contract No. AF.19(604)–993.

REFERENCES

JOHNSON, J. C., *Physical Meteorology*, John Wiley and Sons, 393pp., 1954.
SARTOR, DOYNE, A laboratory investigation of collision efficiencies, coalescence, and electrical charging of simulated droplets, *J. Met.*, pp.91–103, 1954.

DISCUSSION

Prof. T. W. R. East—With the Chairman's permission, I would like to draw the Langmuir curves on the blackboard. The agreement with experimental results is very poor, and since I am one of the people who use the Langmuir equation, I'm not very happy.

Mr. Duncan C. Blanchard—It was interesting that your experiment showed separation of flow at the edge of the drop. Several years ago James E. McDonald worked backward from the shape of a drop to deduce the pressure profile and showed from this that there was flow separation at the edge of the drop. About a year ago, using smoke, I was able to take a photograph that showed indeed a separation point at the very edge of the drops.

Dr. Raymond Wexler—I would like to comment on Langmuir's collection efficiencies. His theory is pertinent where the large drop is large compared to the small drop. It does not apply and should not be used where the drops are of comparable size.

Prof. East—I would have thought the disparity of sizes in at least some of Dr. Schotland's experiments would make Langmuir's equation approximately valid, so that it should predict efficiencies of a few per cent for at least some of his droplet pairs. But according to the equation, if the diameter of the larger droplet is less than 28·6 microns (which was the case throughout the experiments, I think), its fall velocity is always too small to give other than zero efficiency.

Dr. W. E. Howell—Experiments on Mount Washington verified Langmuir's equations for ice collection of spheres, but the smallest spheres we used were about three-quarters of an inch in diameter.

Dr. Vincent J. Schaefer—To my knowledge Langmuir never intended his equations to handle this kind of problem. We were concerned with the collection efficiency of airfoils, and we dealt with small droplets but rather large collectors. As an afterthought, a few more points were obtained with the computer, and it is these data which are now being used.

Dr. Richard Schotland—This work wasn't meant as a general reflection on Langmuir's collision calculations. Rather, it is an experimental exploration of that phase of the calculations which has been generally recognized as deficient. The collision efficiency calculations to which I refer are those which were published in his article on the chain reaction process.

Dr. Schaefer—In that article he was mainly concerned with trying to build up a new approach to cloud physics. I think he probably based it on quite a lot of extrapolation from this tag-end of work. I think what is needed now is for some meteorologist to re-work the problem with a computer using a whole new set of criteria that realistically describe the problem we have here, of droplets colliding with droplets.

ISOKINETIC FLOW AND SAMPLING OF AIRBORNE PARTICULATES

JAMES D. WILCOX

Chemical Corps, Chemical and Radiological Laboratories, Army Chemical Center, Md.

Abstract—Isokinetic conditions prevail when there is no divergence of flow lines around the sampler inlet. The velocities of the sampled and the sampling streams must be equal, and the sampler inlet must face directly into the sampled stream in order to minimize or eliminate divergence of flow lines at the sampler inlet. When divergence of these flows is present there is the possibility of particle-size fractionation. Errors incurred by deviation from isokinetic conditions are discussed, and methods of estimating these errors are reviewed. Results of other investigators are reviewed. Recommendations and procedures for sampling isokinetically are presented.

THE sampling of airborne particulates by chemists, physicists, biologists, meteorologists, engineers, and investigators in the field of medicine is indicative of the many types of aerosol sampling being performed. Some of the investigators engaged in this field of sampling realize the importance of isokinetic sampling but are unfamiliar with the errors incurred by deviation from isokinetic conditions, others are confused by it, and it is completely overlooked by others. In most cases of sampling of airborne particulates, isokinetic sampling has not been stressed enough for investigators to become aware of its importance to test data.

Isokinetic conditions prevail when there is no divergence of flow lines around the sampler inlet. The velocities of the sampled and sampling streams must be equal, and the sampler must face directly into the sampled stream in order to minimize or eliminate divergence of the flow lines at the sampler inlet. When divergence of these flow lines is present, there is the possibility of particle size fractionation. Many investigators [entire list of References] have contributed to the practices now being used in isokinetic sampling.

Familiarity with isokinetic flow and sampling is necessary when determining the performance of sampling instruments, when evaluating aerosol and air polution data, and when obtaining information for the design of sampling equipment.

Obtaining a representative aerosol sample, often a primary factor in the intelligent selection of an aerosol dispersing apparatus or collecting device, is usually very difficult, and is subject to many errors. Special precautions must be taken when sampling to avoid segregation or classification of the particulate material. When the sampling velocity is too low, Fig. 1a, that is when the velocity in the sample tube is less than the velocity in the main stream, the particles in the stream will enter the sampling tube due to their greater inertia while the gas is diverted around the tube. This gives a higher particulate concentration in the sample tube than in the main stream, as can be visualized by studying Fig. 1a. Let us take the other case when the sampling velocity is too high, Fig. 1b, that is when the velocity in the sample tube is greater than the velocity in the main stream, the inertia of the particle will keep the particle from following the flow lines which converge into the sampling tube. This gives a lower concentration in the sampling

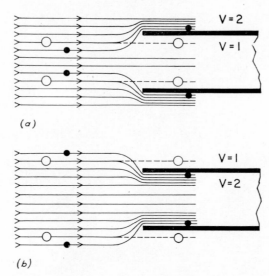

FIG. 1—The inertial effects of particles are shown resulting in non-isokinetic sampling; the flow lines depict non-isokinetic flow; the large hollow spheres represent particles of a relatively large mass, and the small solid spheres represent particles of a relatively small mass; (a) the sampling velocity is too low; the large particles in the stream enter the sample tube due to their greater inertia, while the small particles and the gas follow the flow lines; (b) the sampling velocity is too high; the inertia of the large particles will keep them from following the flow lines which converge into the sampling tube.

tube than in the main stream. A finer particulate sample is obtained where the sampling velocity is too high and a coarser particulate sample when the velocity is too low.

To understand this better, visualize a tube sealed at one end in an airstream containing particulate material. The dynamic pressure of the air current will set up a static or back pressure in the tube; this in turn, will split the air current so that it will pass on the outside of the tube. A particle in the position at which the airstream is beginning to deviate from a straight line, has a tendency, due to its momentum, to continue in a straight line into the tube, but it has also a force acting upon it tending to carry it around with the airstream. Its path is parallel to the resultant of these two forces. If the particle is small then its momentum is small, but a larger particle, with a correspondingly greater momentum, will deviate only slightly from the straight line and will enter the tube. The sample of particulate material which collects in the tube will consist only of the coarse particles, and, as no air has passed through the tube, the figures obtained by such an experiment would give infinite concentration.

Now let us consider the case of a tube containing a filter and fitted with an outlet tube for exhausting air behind the filter. If the air is exhausted at a rate such that the velocity in the tube is less than the velocity of the airstream, then the effect is similar to that of the first case, as there will still be a back pressure in the tube. The sample collected will contain all the coarse particles and some of the finer particles, but the finest particles will still be lost as in the first case.

Using the same apparatus as in the previous case, if the air is drawn through the tube at a velocity in excess of that in the airstream, this will produce a reduced pressure, or suction, instead of back pressure in the tube, and will tend to draw air into the tube, which would normally pass outside. The paths of the air are bent inwards, and on deviating from their straight path they will lose their coarse dust, which will continue in nearly a straight line, and so miss the inlet of the tube. The dust sample collected will contain a higher percentage of the finer dust than is actually in the dust carried by the air.

The location of the sampling tube in a system is an important part of the sampling operation. Usually samples should be taken at various points across a tube to obtain a representative sample. It is interesting to observe the velocity profile across a tube, as shown in Fig. 2. The reduced velocity at the edges of the tube is due to friction, roughness of surface, and turbulence. One of the best sampling points in a system is at the end of a long straight vertical section of tubing. Long horizontal tubing tends to yield

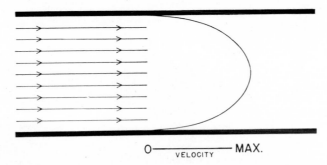

FIG. 2—Velocity profile across a tube; the reduced velocity at the edges of the tube is due to friction, roughness of surface, and turbulence

a higher and coarser particulate concentration near the bottom of the tube. However, in sampling from a vertical tube it is well to keep in mind that all particles in the tube may not be moving at a uniform rate and that the larger particles may be moving only along the tube axis. It is often desirable when conveying large particles to use a high degree of turbulence. Also, it is obvious that the shorter the tube length the lower the loss of particulate material on the tube walls. Bends will tend to concentrate the particulate material at the outside walls of the tubing. It is often a good idea to install a mixing device, such as a disk baffle or nozzle, in the tubing some distance upstream from the sampling location.

Detailed experiments of several investigators reported by HARDIE [1937] show that sampling accuracy is obtained only when isokinetic conditions prevail. Fig. 3 shows the case of velocity balancing. An accuracy of 100 per cent in sampling is obtained at a velocity ratio of unity. The sampling value is too low when the sampling velocity is too large, and the sampling value is too high when the sampling velocity is too low. The three curves a, b and c of Fig. 3 represent work of FAHRENBACK [1931], ZIMMERMAN [1931], and CALDWELL [1934], respectively. The disagreement of the three curves is caused by the difference in the particle size of particulate material used by the three investigators.

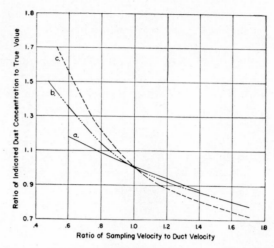

FIG. 3—Curves showing magnitude of the experimental
error caused by incorrect sampling [Hardie, 1937]

Table 1 shows some experimental effects [GRIFFITHS and JONES, 1939–1940] of velocity on the accuracy of sampling, in which tubes A and B sample from the same stream. Tube A and the sampling stream were always at the same velocity. Thus, the concentration of particulate material in Tube A represents the actual concentration in

Table 1. Effect of velocity on accuracy of sampling

	Tube A		Tube B
Steam velocity in tube	Concentration	Velocity	Concentration
ft/min	mg/ft³	ft/min	mg/ft³
300	4·4	400	3·9
300	5·9	225	6·2
120	31·6	60	47·3
220	8·3	120	9·2
120	19·5	180	17·6
220	8·3	320	7·8

the sampled. As depicted in Fig. 3, the data in Table 1 shows that when the sampling velocity is too great the concentration is too small.

There is a velocity profile across a tube (Fig. 2) caused by drag by the wall of the tube. If enough drag is present in the tube, the velocity will be lowered and the stream lines of flow will be effected. Knowing this, then there must be a minimum diameter of tube size to be used in sampling. Table 2 shows that the tube diameter does have an effect on the sampling accuracy.

GRIFFITHS and JONES [1939–1940] performed those tests maintaining a constant concentration. The stream and tube velocities were equal. The concentration checks obtained for the first two diameters of Tube B were fairly close and probably within experimental

Table 2. Effect of size of sampling tube

Stream and tube velocity	Tube diameter		Concentration	
	A	B	A	B
ft/min	inch	inch	mg/ft³	mg/ft³
300	1·125	0·6	5·24	5·19
275	1·125	0·6	2·78	3·10
300	1·125	0·4	5·25	5·40
310	1·125	0·4	4·14	4·22
340	1·125	0·25	4·54	7·30
275	1·125	0·25	3·39	6·50

error. However, the 0·25-inch tube diameter a concentration difference of 40 and 50 per cent is shown. Therefore, it can be seen that a point is reached where there is a large deviation in sampling accuracy rather than a small one.

What can one do if it is entirely impractical to use isokinetic sampling? Control tests can be run, calibrations can be made, and calculations can be made based on the inertia of the particles. Eq. (1) is LAPPLE and SHEPARD's [1940] formula for the estimation of sampling errors.

$$18\eta s/(\rho_s-\rho)D^2V_s = (Y-E)+\ln(Y/E)$$

where

E = fractional sampling error = C_s-C_d/C_d
Y = fractional velocity unbalancing = $(V_d-V_s)/V_s$
η = the viscosity of the medium
s = the net effective distance that the particle is affected by the velocity in the sampling nozzle
ρ_s = the particle density
ρ = the fluid density
D = the particle diameter
C_s and C_d = the concentrations of particles of size D airborne in the sampling nozzle and in the main stream
V_d and V_s = the average velocities in the main stream and in the sampling nozzle.

The formula gives the error in concentration of particles of size D in the sample obtained, expressed as a fraction of the true concentration of that size particle in the main stream. In the derivation of the equation, the velocity distribution around the sampling nozzle is neglected. In its place it is assumed that the average velocity V_s in the sampling nozzle acts on the particle over a net effective distance s. From flow pattern photographs, such as those presented by KOWALKE [1938], one might estimate s to be on the order of one to five times the nozzle diameter. Although the above formula is of little quantitative value, it does permit an insight as to what order of particle size would be appreciable affected by a given velocity unbalancing.

When attempting to obtain a truly representative sample of airborne particulate material the following points should be considered: (1) Velocity balancing of the main and sampling streams. For minimum divergence of flow lines these velocities must be equal. The large particles which represent a large portion of the mass of the sample are difficult to sample because of their high inertia. A sharp edge on the sampling inlet aids in reducing divergence and turbulence. (2) Position of the sampling inlet relative to that of the main stream. Divergence of lines of flow is minimized: When the sampling inlet faces directly into the main stream. (3) Length of the sampling tube. Tube losses are reduced by using a shorter sampling tube. (4) Diameter of the sampling inlet. Investigations have shown that the selection of an appropriate sampling tube diameter is a source of error [GRIFFITHS and JONES, 1939–1940]. (5) Particle size distribution and density of the material. These factors aid in estimation of the inertial effects of the airborne particulate material.

REFERENCES

ANDERSON, EVALD, On the quantitative determination of industrial gas dispersoids, *Trans. Inst. Chem. Eng.*, v.34, pp.589–601, 1938.

CALDWELL, M. R., and others, Characteristics of large Hell Gate direct-fired boiler units, *Trans. Amer. Soc. Mech. Eng.*, v.56, pp.73–75, 1934.

DALLA VALLE, J. M., *Micromerities*, Pitman Publishing Corp., 1948, p.485.

DRINKER, PHILIP, AND THEODORE HATCH, *Industrial Dust*, McGraw-Hill Book Co., 1936, p.133.

FAHRENBACK, W., Die Dynamic des Staubes und ihr Einfluss auf die Staubgehaltmassungen, *Forschung Gebiete des Ingenieurwesens*, v.2, pp.395–407, 1931.

GRIFFITHS, J. H. and T. D. JONES, The determination of dust concentrations in mine atmosphere, *Inst. Min. Eng.*, v.98–99, pp.156–166, 1939–1940.

HARDIE, P. H., Resume of methods for measuring flue dust, *Trans. Amer. Soc. Mech. Eng.*, v.59, pp.355–358, 1937.

KOWALKE, O. L., Manner of liquid flow through a pipe line orifice, *Indust. Eng. Chem.*, v.30, pp.216–222, 1938.

LANDAHL, H. D. and R. G. HERRMAN, Calculation of the efficiency of impaction of airborne droplets in bent cylindrical tubes, *J. Colloid Sci.*, v.4, pp.133–135, 1949.

LAPPLE, C. E., Dust and mist collection, in *Air Pollution Abatement Manual*, Manufacturing Chemists Association, Washington, D.C., 1951, chap.9, p.5.

LAPPLE, C. E., Sampling of process and ventilation gases, *Heating, Piping and Air Conditioning*, v.16, 1944, p.578.

LAPPLE, C. E. and C. B. SHEPHERD, Calculation of particle trajectories, *Indust. Eng. Chem.*, v.32, pp.605–617, 1940.

MAY, K. R., The cascade impactor, *J. Scient. Instrum.*, v.22, pp.187–195, 1945.

ROBERTS, M. H. and H. F. JOHNSTONE, Deposition of aerosol particles from moving gas streams, *Indust. Eng. Chem.*, v.41, p.2417, 1949.

ZIMMERMAN, E., Messung von Flugstaub in Rauchgasen, *Zs. Vereins Deutscher Ing.*, v.75, pp.481–486, 1931.

DISCUSSION

Dr. E. M. Fournier d'Albe—I would like to ask Mr. Wilcox whether he thinks that, in the particular case of sampling in still air with the cascade impactor, any modification to the shape of the air intake would improve the accuracy of sampling.

Mr. James E. Wilcox—Still-air sampling has been a real problem with us. If the particles are small enough, then their inertia is small, so you get by very nicely. One of our investigators found 100 per cent efficiency for these particles of small inertia.

There have been two different groups attempting to make isokinetic sampling devices. One is the Battelle Memorial Institute, and the other was at the University of Delaware under C. E. Lapple.

Dr. James P. Lodge—In the Cloud Physics Project of the University of Chicago, we had a situation of extreme anisokineticity. We were running impactors, initially, and then the millipore collectors off the inlet assigned to us on the project aircraft, where a velocity mismatch of roughly a thousandfold existed. Then I heard a talk by H. H. Watson of Suffield Experiment Station who stressed the horrors of anisokinetic sampling, and I made an approximate computation from Langmuir's collection efficiencies, considering the intake tube as a disk of four inches diameter. Since the mismatch was so bad, the results were pretty discouraging. We were oversampling the larger sizes by about a thousandfold, by these calculations.

So to test that, I looked at the size distribution of some aerosol samples that had been taken on the ground, with a much closer velocity match, and by various means, including t-tests, could detect no difference whatsoever in the distributions. We also tried a one-quarter-inch intake with the same volume of flow through it to see what effect that would have. We should have changed our over-sampling by a hundredfold. Again we could detect no difference whatsoever.

So I think that isokinetic sampling is desirable, but that the sin of anisokinetic sampling is not so grievous as some workers have indicated.

Mr. Wilcox—In our sampling from a B–17 airplane, we used a six-foot probe ahead of the plane. We found that with even a five-foot probe, the air disturbence ahead of the nose actually affected sampling. The probe tapered with about a seven-degree angle into a plenum chamber.

DROPLET SIZE MEASUREMENTS IN
CONVECTIVE CLOUDS

LOUIS J. BATTAN AND CLAYTON H. REITAN[*]

Department of Meteorology, The University of Chicago, Chicago, Ill.

Abstract—Curves showing mean droplet size distributions in fair weather cumuli and cumulus congestus clouds over the central United States and in tropical cumuli are presented. The data are compared with measurements of other investigators. Droplet size distribution and liquid water content in fair weather cumuli are considered in some detail.

DURING the flight operations of the Cloud Physics Project, measurements of droplet size distribution were made in convective clouds over the ocean in the vicinity of Puerto Rico and over the central United States. The droplets were collected on oil-covered slides which were moved rapidly through the cloud air. In general, three slides were exposed on each cloud penetration and two photographs were taken of each slide, with each photograph representing the droplets in a volume of about 1·25 cm³. The practical lower limit of the sampling technique was about three to four microns diameter. For a more detailed discussion of the instrument, the reader is referred to a paper by BROWN and WILLETT [1955].

In the evaluation of the data, two corrections had to be made: the first corrected for evaporation of the droplets during the interval of time between their impaction on the slide and photography; the second took into account the differences of collection efficiency of the sampler at different droplet sizes. Both corrections were most important at the small droplet sizes.

During the period between the collection and photography of the droplets, there was a change in the droplet distribution because of evaporation of the droplets. It was found from a study of the changes of diameters of particular droplets that evaporation proceeded at a rate given approximately by

$$a^2 = a_0{}^2 - ct$$

where a is droplet diameter, t is time, and c is approximately constant and equal to 1·75 when units of microns and seconds are used. The effects of evaporation calculated from this equation are shown in Fig. 1. In making the calculations, it was assumed that the droplets were uniformly distributed over each five-micron size interval. It is obvious that the smallest drops are most seriously affected by evaporation. There is some uncertainty regarding the time during which evaporation is effective; however, the sampling procedure was such that the slides were exposed to the air for a period of about 20 to 25 sec prior to photography. All the data presented in this paper have been corrected for an evaporation time of 20 sec.

From the equations of LANGMUIR and BLODGETT [1946], calculations were made of the collection efficiency of the slides used in the droplet sampler. The results are given

---

[*] Present affiliation: Institute of Atmospheric Physics, University of Arizona, Tuscon, Arizona.

by BROWN and WILLETT [1955]. The correction for collection efficiency is small for droplets exceeding ten-microns diameter. It is to be noted that, because the slide was moving rapidly across the air stream when the sampling was accomplished, the actual collection efficiencies may have been higher than those given by the Langmuir and Blodgett equations.

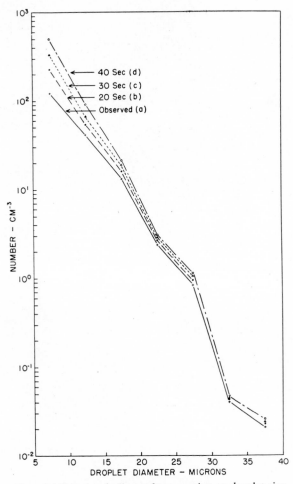

FIG. 1—Calculated effects of evaporation on droplet size
distribution

Average droplet size distribution curves—(Some of the data given in this paper is taken from a report entitled 'Artificial Nucleation of Cumulus Clouds' by R. R. Braham, Jr., L. J. Battan, and H. R. Byers to be published in the *Meteorological Monographs*. In this earlier report, the data were not corrected for evaporation.)

The average droplet size distribution in cumulus humilis clouds over the central United States found by the Cloud Physics Project is shown in Fig. 2 which also contains the data of DIEM [1948] and WEICKMANN and AUFM KAMPE [1953]. This new curve shows important differences from those given by other investigators. The range of the

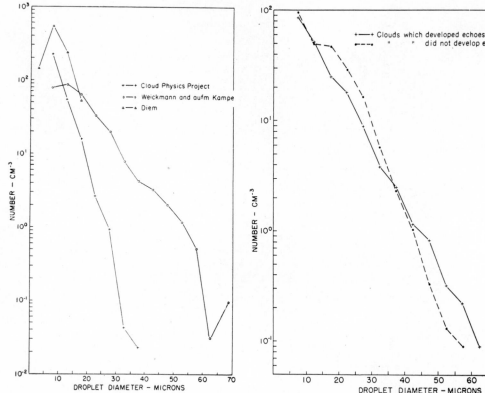

Fig. 2—Mean droplet size distribution in fair-weather cumulus; average droplet concentrations of 1000, 302, and 293 were found by Diem [1948], Weickmann and aufm Kampe [1953] and the Cloud Physics Project, respectively; one drop of 57 and one of 105 microns were collected in one of the 19 clouds sampled; these are not included in this figure; if used, they would be equivalent to 0.006 droplets cm^{-3}

Fig. 3—Mean droplet distribution in cumulus congestus over the central United States; the average concentration in ten clouds which developed precipitation echoes was 188 cm^{-3}, and in 21 clouds which did not develop echoes it was 247 cm^{-3}

distribution is smaller than that found by Weickmann and aufm Kampe. However, these authors point out that they studied clouds with 'extremely warm' cloud bases and thus clouds with higher liquid water contents than those involved in this paper. Note that the concentration of droplets reported by Diem was about three times that given by Weickmann and aufm Kampe and the Cloud Physics Project. In a later section of this paper, a more detailed discussion is given of the fair-weather cumulus.

The droplet size distributions in cumulus congestus clouds over the central United States (Fig. 3) were significantly different from those found in fair-weather cumulus. It can be seen that the distribution was broader in the former. However, it was narrower than that found by Weickmann and aufm Kampe in cumulus congestus.

None of the clouds represented in Fig. 3 contained echoes at the time of the sampling pass, although echoes subsequently developed in some of them. It is evident that there was a greater number of droplets greater than 35 microns in the clouds which later developed echoes. In these clouds one would expect to find even larger droplets than those observed, but the probability of capturing large, sparsely separated drops is quite small using the present sampling techniques.

The droplet size distribution in tropical cumulus clouds (Fig. 4) shows several interesting features which were not observed in the distributions in the clouds over the central United States. The first feature to be noted is that the concentration of droplets in the tropical clouds was much smaller than in the clouds over the continent. It is also observed that in the former there was a double maxima in the distribution curve, with the

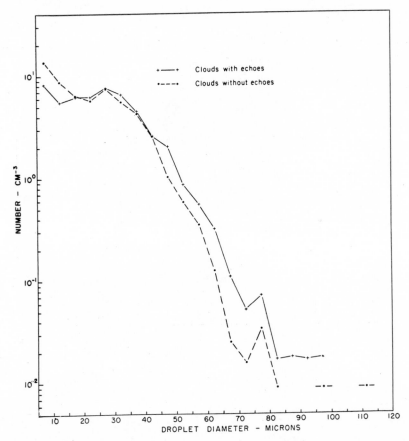

FIG. 4—Mean droplet size distribution in tropical cumuli; the average concentration in 11 clouds with echoes was 52 cm^{-3}, and in 26 clouds without echoes it was 58 cm^{-3}

first mode at the smallest size range and the other at 25 to 30 microns. This bimodality was found in many individual clouds and was not a result of the averaging process. Another important feature of the data was the large number of droplets observed at diameters greater than 75 microns. The concentration of these large droplets is sufficiently large that if a fraction grew by coalescence for a sufficient period of time, precipitation would result. In Fig. 4, the curves represent observations in clouds which did or did not contain precipitation echoes at the time of observation. It can be seen that those with echoes had a greater number of large droplets. However, the presence or absence of an echo cannot be explained by the observed differences. Calculations of radar reflectivity show that neither distribution would cause a detectable echo. This must mean that the echo is produced mainly by the much larger droplets which have not been detected because of their low concentrations.

In summary, it can be stated that the cloud droplet distributions, in the classes of clouds considered, differ significantly from one another. In the small cumulus humilis clouds, the width of the distribution is fairly narrow. Since these clouds did not develop precipitation, it is expected that with time there was little change. In the cumulus congestus and tropical cumulus clouds, droplets greater than 50 microns were frequently observed. These droplets can grow rapidly by coalescence and given sufficient time, the clouds could develop precipitation.

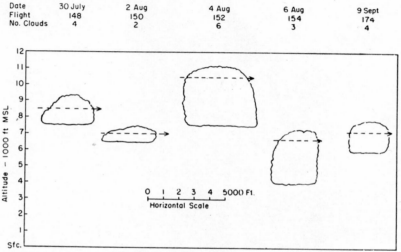

FIG. 5—Sketches of fair-weather cumuli on different days and the altitudes at which droplet samples were obtained

The results presented in this section represent the initial examination of the droplet data collected. There are obviously many important aspects of the problem of cloud and precipitation development which can be studied using these observations. Analyses of this type are currently in progress.

Detailed analysis of cumulus humilis—The cloud-droplet measurements in cumulus humilis clouds summarized in Fig. 2 were obtained on five days and represent a total of 19 clouds. The clouds on each day were very similar. Fig. 5 shows the approximate dimensions of the clouds as measured or estimated from the airplane which took the samples. The clouds were small, ranging in thickness from 1000 to 4000 ft. They were all true fair-weather cumuli in the sense that they did not develop into larger or more active cumuliform clouds.

The droplet measurements obtained on each day were grouped and mean distribution curves were calculated, Fig. 6. Values of liquid water computed from the droplet data are also shown. It can be seen that in general these curves are similar to the curve

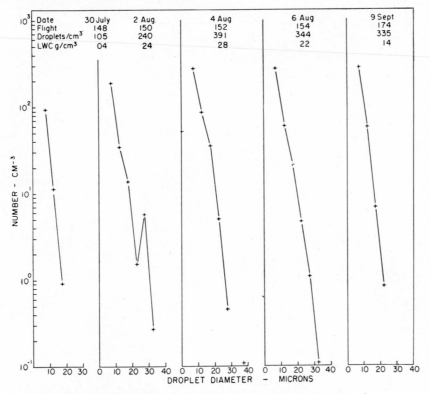

FIG. 6—Mean droplet size distributions for clouds on each of five days

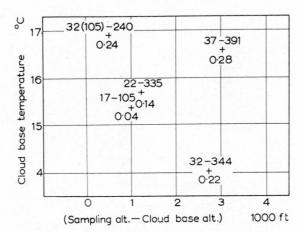

FIG. 7—Variation of cloud parameters as a function of cloud
base temperature and altitude above the cloud base at which
sample was taken; the upper right number gives the average
droplet concentration on that day, the upper left number
gives the diameter of the largest drop, and the lower number
gives the average liquid water content in g/m³

given in Fig. 2 which combines all the data. As might be expected, the values of maximum droplet size, droplet concentration and liquid water content depend on the temperature of the cloud base and height above the cloud base at which the samples were taken, Fig. 7. With increasing values of these two variables, there appears to be an increase of the three-cloud droplet parameters.

Because of the importance of liquid-water content, it is of interest to consider how well the droplet observations can measure this parameter. During the Cloud Physics Project flight operations, liquid-water content was measured directly using an instrument developed by Warner and Newnham [1952]. This device measures variations of the conductivity of a paper tape as it is wetted by impinging droplets. Data were obtained during penetrations through the clouds observed on Flights 150, 152, 154 and 174. Table 1 presents maximum and average values of liquid water taken from the records as well as those calculated from the droplet data.

Table 1. *Observed and calculated values of liquid-water contents* (g/m^3)
in fair-weather cumuli

Flight	Calculated from droplets	Measured		Calculated assuming moist adiabatic ascent
		Mean*	Maximum	
148	0·04	...	...	0·61
150	0·24	0·33	0·91	0·70
152	0·28	0·29	0·57	1·59
154	0·22	0·37	0·77	1·58
174	0·14	0·32	0·66	0·87

* Mean values represent upper limits of the true means because the liquid water content meter has a lower limit of measurement of approximately 0·25 g/m³. Zero readings during cloud penetrations were taken to correspond to actual lower limit of the instrument.

It can be seen that, in general, the mean measured values and those calculated from the droplet data are in fairly good agreement considering the small droplet samples involved. The maximum measured values are about twice the mean value.

A question which frequently arises is one which deals with the validity of the assumption of moist adiabatic conditions within convective clouds. Table 1 shows that, except for the clouds on Flight 150, the liquid water, calculated under the assumption of moist adiabatic ascent from the base to the sampling level, was larger than the maximum observed values. On every flight the liquid water calculated from parcel method considerations exceeded the mean values by significant amounts. These results indicate that entrainment and mixing have important effects on the growth of droplets in small fair-weather cumuli.

Acknowledgment—The authors wish to thank Edward N. Brown and Bernice Ackerman for their assistance in the analysis of the data used in this paper. The research reported in this paper has been sponsored by the Geophysics Research Directorate of the Air Force Cambridge Research Center, Air Research and Development Command, under Contract AF19(604)–618.

REFERENCES

BROWN, E. N. and J. H. WILLETT, A three-slide cloud droplet sampler, *Bull. Amer. Met. Soc.*, v.36, pp.123–127, 1955.

DIEM, M., Messungen der Grosse von Wolkenelementen, II, *Met. Rundschau*, v.1, pp.261–273, 1948.

LANGMUIR, I. and K. B. BLODGETT, A mathematical investigation of water droplet trajectories, *AAF Technical Rep. no. 5418*, 1946.

WARNER, J. and T. D. NEWNHAM, A new method of measurement of cloud water content, *Q. J. R. Met. Soc.*, v.78, pp.47–52, 1952.

WEICKMANN, H. K. and H. J. AUFM KAMPE, Physical properties of cumulus clouds, *J. Met.*, v.10, pp.204–211, 1953.

DISCUSSION

Dr. E. J. Workman—I recall oral information from Pat Squires to the effect that in making liquid-water content measurements of clouds, the gradient of this quantity as you go in from the edge of the cloud is relatively sharp discontinuity at the boundary. This observation would seem to indicate that in such clouds entrainment of dry air at the boundary is negligible. Also, the fact that calculations for the liquid-water content of towering cumulus clouds yield values close to the theoretical maximum would seem to indicate a relatively small amount of mixing at the edges.

Dr. L. J. Battan—It certainly looks as if the mixing isn't complete. On entry into some clouds the liquid-water content increases rather abruptly. There are marked variations in water content over distances of the order of hundreds of feet. In some clouds the maximum value approaches closely that which would be calculated from the parcel method. In several clouds, the maximum values exceeded 3 g/m³. The relation of the liquid-water content to other cloud parameters is being pursued.

Dr. Helmut Weickmann—It would be good to avoid evaporation loss from the slide before photographing it. In our work, one man exposed the slide and another photographed it; with teamwork we got the time interval down to about five seconds. Even so, we were sometimes able to see that droplets evaporated as soon as the slide was out of the cloud. Finally, we placed the slides in a water-filled cell and photographed them in the water.

Dr. Battan—With our apparatus, the slides could not be photographed until all three were exposed, and the slide exposure required five or six seconds. Even with teamwork we have trouble pushing the time interval for droplet collection and photography below ten seconds. Photographing them in water or using an evaporation-inhibiting oil should help. We have made tests on silicone oils, looking for one giving minimum evaporation but not too viscous.

Dr. Hans J. aufm Kampe—We found that the thinner the oil the more one must watch out for splash. How viscous was your oil, compared, let us say, to castor oil?

Dr. Battan—More nearly like molasses in January.

Dr. David Atlas—It seems to me that the small difference in drop size distribution that you show between clouds having echoes and those not having echoes is too small to be significant; certainly it is too small to explain differences of reflectivity of a factor of four or more which must separate truly detectable from undetectable clouds.

Dr. Battan—The droplets we sampled are not the ones that give an echo, and the large ones that make the echo are too few to be sampled this way. What I maintain is that these distributions, within their limitations, characterize these clouds; and if they were extended over the whole range of drop sizes, they would explain the differences in radar reflectivity completely.

Dr. Raymond Wexler—Couldn't you conclude from these distributions that it is not for lack of large drops that these clouds fail to precipitate? The failure must be due to wind shear or some other reason not stated, since all these clouds contain fairly large drops.

Dr. Battan—This question keeps coming up. Why don't they all rain? Certainly there are many other factors involved.

O

PRECIPITATION OF CONVECTIVE WATER CLOUDS

T. W. R. EAST

McGill University, Montreal, Canada

Abstract—The measured characteristics of cumulus clouds show that both condensation and coalescence are taking place as the cloud develops. If the applicability of Langmuir's equation for coalescence or some such law is assumed, it is possible to account by these two processes for the observed changes in the droplet size distributions, for the appearance of the radar echo, and for the production of rain without assuming the presence of giant nuclei or ice. The critical parameter which decides the presence or absence of precipitation would then be the liquid water content.

Introduction—The problem under study is the development of rain by some process which is possible in warm cumulus clouds, where the Bergeron process is impossible. Once a sufficient population of drops of 50 microns radius is present, their fall velocity is sufficient to ensure rapid growth by collision with smaller drops. The initial formation of cloud droplets by condensation on to hygroscopic nuclei is also well understood [HOWELL, 1949; also others]. The present work was concentrated on the processes occurring in the intermediate stage, in which the radii of the droplets increase from values in the neighborhood of ten microns to a broad range extending through 50 microns. Specifically a limit was set to the investigation at 50 microns, somewhat arbitrarily.

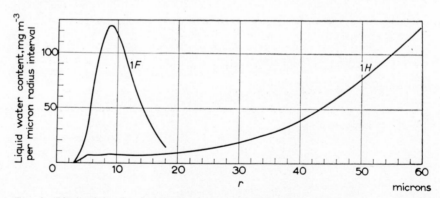

FIG. 1—Idealised droplet size distributions; I.F., fairweather; I.H., heavy cumulus; the upper end of the I.H. curve, which depends on observations of few droplets, is approximate only

A survey of droplet size distributions measured in clouds by DIEM [1942, 1948] and by aufm Kampe and Weickmann, showed [EAST and MARSHALL, 1954] that fair-weather cumulus clouds (classified as Cumulus Humilis and Cumulus) have distributions which typically resemble the idealised curve of Fig. 1 (marked IF). An important feature is the observed lack of droplets of radii greater than 18 microns. BATTAN and REITAN [1957] confirm this feature in fair-weather clouds, though they found liquid-water contents considerably smaller than the one g/m^{-3} shown by the IF curve. The curve IH in Fig. 1 represents the spectrum of heavy cumulus (Cumulus Congestus and Cumulonimbus). This idealised heavy-cumulus spectrum has a maximum of water content between 50 and 100 microns radius. The cloud air which contains these droplets must have risen through the condensation level originally and acquired a fair-weather type of spectrum first. ZAITSEV [1950] found a progressive change of spectrum with increasing altitude inside one cloud, from a fair-weather type spectrum towards the IH distribution.

Curve IH shows four times the liquid-water content of IF, a typical ratio between measured water contents, which can only be accounted for at this stage in the life-history of the cloud by the condensing of extra liquid water on to the droplets. Measurements also show that heavy cumulus have several times fewer drops per cm³ than fair-weather.

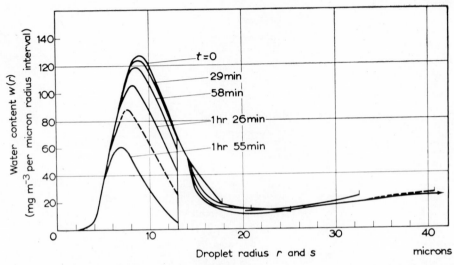

FIG. 2—Modification of distribution with time by coalescence in the absence of condensation; the LWC remains at 1 g/kg (= 1 g/m³ approx.); the final curve extends to 50 microns radius

Though some spreading-out must occur through the increase in specific volume of the air with altitude, it would not usually exceed a 1·5 to 1 change of volume, and leaves a large change in population which must be due to coalescence between droplets. It will be shown that the combination of condensation and coalescence can readily account for the observed change of the spectrum and that it provides a likely mechanism for rain formation.

Coalescence—It was assumed as a basis for calculation that LANGMUIR'S [1948] equation for collision efficiency applies to small droplets of comparable size; the experimental evidence, some of which conflicts with the theory, is not yet comprehensive enough to replace it. [GUNN and HITSCHFELD, 1951; ADDERLEY, 1953; SARTOR, 1954; TELFORD and others, 1955; SCHOTLAND, 1957; KINZER and COBB, 1957].

The curve IF of Fig. 1 was taken to represent the droplet size distribution of a parcel of cloud-filled air in the early stages of its life in a heavy cumulus. This was considered to be a more realistic procedure than attempting to reproduce (by calculation) the generation of cloud droplets at the cloud base by condensation on to some assumed distribution of nuclei.

To find the effect of differential settling by gravity on the IF distribution, the rate of collisions between five sizes of larger drops and five sizes of smaller droplets were calculated. From them the change of drop size distribution with time was calculated step-by-step, assuming the water content to remain at one g/m^3. Fig. 2 shows that the change in the spectrum is of the right nature but the process would take two hours, which is much too slow to occur in the life-time of a parcel of air in cumulus, though it might occur in thick stratus [MASON, 1952].

Coalescence by turbulence has been considered as an alternative way of inducing precipitation. Random motion of the air must be followed to different extents by different sized droplets, and the relative motion can lead to collisions in the same way that differential settling does. In fact, calculations showed that if the root mean square acceleration of the air were three times the acceleration due to gravity, it would speed up the coalescence process at $M=1$ g/m^3 by a factor of nine, approximately. Measurements of turbulent velocities have mainly been made in clear air near the ground, but there are some published results of airborne accelerometer records of gusts in growing cumuli [BRAHAM, 1952; MALKUS, 1954]. Calculations based on such data give a root mean square acceleration of roughly one quarter of gravity, which would have negligible effect on coalescence. The calculations have been reported in part [EAST and MARSHALL, 1954] and will be completed shortly.

It has been suggested that droplets of sea spray [LUDLAM, 1951] or exceptionally large droplets produced by condensation on to giant hygroscopic nuclei [WOODCOCK, 1952], are present in all clouds in sufficient number to grow by coalescence into drizzle or rain drops. The concentration of such droplets, while greater than that of raindrops may well be low enough to have escaped detection in fair-weather cumuli. But if this were so, they would also escape detection in heavy cumulus clouds. It is possible that the droplets which formed from giant nuclei or sea spray do indeed grow to raindrop size by coalescence, but it is obvious from Fig. 2 that coalescence alone would not convert a typical fair-weather to a heavy cumulus distribution in a reasonable time.

Condensation—As the cloud-filled saturated air ascends in the updraft of a growing cumulus, vapor condenses. No new droplets are formed; the existing droplets all grow, the smallest showing the greatest increase in radius. The drop size distributions which result from this process were calculated and are shown in Fig. 3. Starting from the IF spectrum of Fig. 1, water vapor has been condensed on to the droplets already there, until there are 2, 4, or 10 grams of liquid water for every gram originally present. In an updraft of 3 m/sec, an air parcel starting from a condensation level at 860 mb and 10·5° C would take 4, 9, 15, and 24 minutes to reach the liquid water mixing ratios shown.

Though continued condensation undoubtedly takes place, these curves show that by itself it cannot account for the observed change in spectrum.

Condensation and coalescence combined—In an encounter between a drop, radius s, and a smaller droplet, radius r, the Langmuir collision efficiency depends critically on a parameter K which is proportional to r^2 and to U/s, where U is the relative

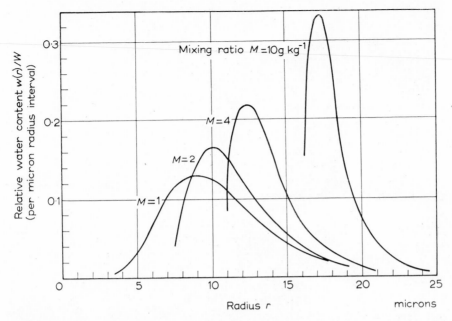

FIG. 3—Modification of distribution with time by condensation in the absence of coalescence;
the liquid-water mixing ratio increases but the curves are normalised to a constant area

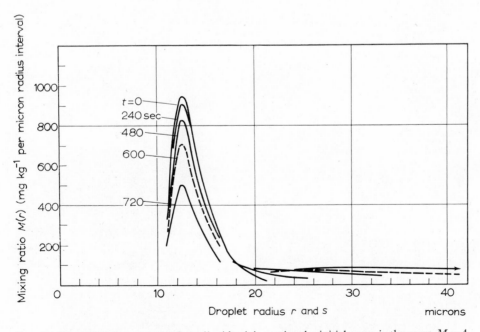

FIG. 4—Effect of coalescence at a large liquid mixing ratio; the initial curve is the curve $M = 4$
in Fig. 3; the final curve (ten minutes later) extends to 50 microns radius

velocity (approximately the terminal speed of s). Since U is proportional to s to a power between 1 and 2, K is proportional to a power of s less than unity, but to the square of r. Thus condensation, by increasing the radius of the smaller droplets particularly, greatly improves the chance of collisions.

Starting from curves such as those in Fig. 3, the effect of coalescence on each was calculated. Fig. 4 shows the calculated development of the curve for 4 g/kg. After 12

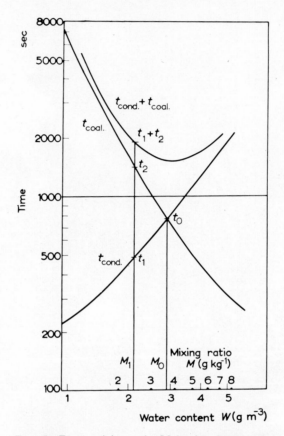

Fig. 5—For a mixing ratio M in the abscissa, the ordinates show t_{cond}, the time taken from cloud base to the value M ascending at 3 m/sec, t_{coal}, the time taken subsequently for coalescence acting alone at the value M to produce droples of 50 microns radius, and t_{cond} and t_{coal}. Cloud base is at 860 mb and 10.5°C

minutes a precipitating type of spectrum has resulted. The final curve in Fig. 4 represents a fairly advanced stage. The largest drops have a radius of 50 microns which is increasing at the rate of six microns per minute. The radar reflectively, as computed from ΣD^6, is such that it would give a discernable echo on an AN/CPS–9 working a full efficiency at 30 miles range, so from there on its progress could be followed by radar. The reflectivity is increasing at the rate of three decibels per minute, so that detection on a less powerful radar would only be delayed by a few minutes. Collisions among the larger drops have become nearly as important as those between larger and smaller droplets, so a raindrop distribution could be expected to develop shortly.

The condensation process and the gravity-induced coalescence have been calculated separately, as if they acted consecutively. Some insight into their combined action can be gained by comparing the times required for each process. In Fig. 5, t_{cond} is the time taken for an air-parcel to rise to a level at which the liquid mixing ratio is M g/kg, assuming a saturated adiabatic ascent at 3 m/sec. To summarize the development of a drop size distribution under gravity, we plot t_{coal}, the time taken for the largest drops to reach 50 microns radius through the coalescence process at a liquid mixing ratio M, no further condensation taking place. An important question is: When, and at what height, will drops of 50 microns radius first appear?

Consider a parcel rising through the cloud until it reaches height H at which the liquid mixing ratio is M. Condensation and coalescence both occur simultaneously, but at first as the parcel rises from the cloud base only condensation has an appreciable effect; later on, coalescence may predominate. Suppose that up to height H_1 (mixing ratio M_1), only condensation occurred; it took time t_1 (see Fig. 5). After that, suppose the mixing ratio stayed at M_1 and only coalescence occurred, taking time t_2 to produce 50-micron drops. The entire process would take t_1+t_2, a total which depends on the value of M_1 (or H_1) selected arbitrarily (see uppermost curve). In reality, some coalescence occurs during t_1, and the mixing ratio increases above M_1 during t_2, so the total time must be less than t_1+t_2, whatever value was chosen for M_1. Thus the minimum of the t_1+t_2 curve sets an upper bound to the time (and M and height H) at which 50-micron drops first appear.

The point M_0, height H_0, at which $t_{cond} = t_{coal} = t_0$ sets a lower limit. In order to produce 50-micron drops in time t_0, concurrently with condensation increasing the mixing ratio from zero at the cloud base to M_0 at height H_0, coalescence would have had to act as if the mixing ratio had been M_0 the whole time. Clearly the actual time must be longer.

The liquid mixing ratio at which 50-micron drops appear can be determined in this way within a range of 2 to 1 or less (between 3·7 and 6·6 g/kg in the example shown). The time of ascent from cloud base to this level is between 13 and 25 minutes. The curves, and therefore the values arrived at, will depend to some extent on the assumed environment and the rate of updraft. Doubling or halving the updraft velocity increases or decreases this mixing ratio by about 30 per cent.

This suggests a restricted range of liquid mixing ratios at which the first radar echo appears; further, it appears to offer a criterion for precipitation. Any cloud in which rising air does not reach a mixing ratio of about 4 g/kg is unlikely to produce rain (unless some other process happens to be available earlier), while one in which a mixing ratio of 7 g/kg can be reached will almost certainly produce rain, though evaporation in extremely dry air may prevent the rain reaching the ground.

BATTAN, BYERS and BRAHAM [1955] studied properties of cumulus clouds in relation to the presence or absence of a radar echo. Fig. 6 reproduces part of their experimental results; it shows, for each of three localities, the size of cloud which has a 20 per cent chance of showing a radar echo (larger clouds had, of course, a greater chance). For each such cloud, there are also shown the liquid-water content that an undiluted parcel would have acquired in ascending to the top of the cloud. The values (4·1 g/m³ for Puerto

Rico, 4·8 g/m³ for the central United States, and 5·0 g/m³ for New Mexico) are very similar despite wide variations in altitude, temperature, and the proximity of the ocean.

WORKMAN and REYNOLDS [1949] made measurements of the average height of the initial radar echo in thunderstorms in New Mexico. They give sufficient data to show that at the initial radar echo the liquid mixing ratio was 6·0 g/kg (on the average), and that the ascent to that height must have taken at least 15 minutes.

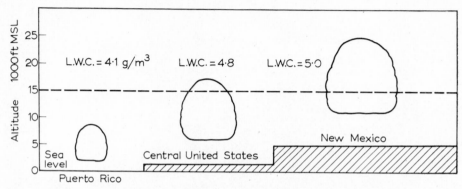

FIG. 6—Critical sizes of clouds for appearance of precipitation echo in three localities, with ground level and the 0 °C isotherm (after BATTAN, BYERS and BRAHAM 1955)

BOWEN [1951] reported two radar observations in cumulus near Sydney, Australia. From the accompanying data, the liquid mixing ratios at the first radar echoes can be calculated to be 4·6 and 3·1 g/kg. The use of airborne radar at very close range (leading to earlier detection of the droplets) could perhaps account for these somewhat smaller values. BATTAN [1953] found that the average height of the top of the first radar echo above the cloud base in Ohio thunderstorms was 10,500 ft. Taking the mean sounding for the atmosphere in Ohio at the time of the radar observations [BRAHAM, 1952], it can be shown that the liquid mixing ratio at this level would be 6·5 g/kg. In all these calculations, ascent of a parcel on the saturated adiabat without dilution has been assumed.

Conclusions—Within the limitations of the method, the agreement between the predicted appearance of 50-micron drops and the observed appearance of a radar echo is satisfactory. It appears, then, that the critical parameter which determines the presence or absence of precipitation in Cumulus is liquid-water mixing ratio.

In suitable circumstances giant nuclei or glaciation may play a part in initiating precipitation, but in their absence precipitation will still occur once a critical value of liquid water mixing ratio, which lies between 4 and 7 g/kg, is reached in the upper part of the cloud.

Acknowledgments—The writer wishes to thank J. S. Marshall for his advice and encouragement, and L. J. Battan and colleagues for permission to reproduce the material in Fig. 6. This work was performed under Contract AF 19(122)–217 of the Geophysics Research Directorate of the Air Force Cambridge Research Center.

REFERENCES

ADDERLEY, E. E., The growth of raindrops in cloud, *Q.J.R. Met. Soc.*, v.79, pp.380–388, 1953.

BATTAN, L. J., Observations on the formation and spread of precipitation in convective clouds, *J. Met.*, v.10, pp.311–324, 1953.

BATTAN, L. J., H. R. BYERS, and R. R. BRAHAM, JR., The formation of precipitation in convective clouds, Proc. Fifth Radar Weather Conference, Asbury Park, New Jersey, 1955; publication pending under title Precipitation processes in convective clouds, *J. Met.*

BATTAN, L. J. and C. H. REITAN, Droplet size measurements in convective clouds, paper in this publication, pp.184–191, 1957.

BOWEN, E. G., Radar observations of rain and their relation to mechanisms of rain formation, *J. Atmos. and Terr. Physics*, v.1, pp.125–140, 1951.

BRAHAM, R. R., The water and energy budgets of the thunderstorm and their relation to thunderstorm development, *J. Met.*, v.9, pp.227–242, 1952.

DIEM, M., Messungen der Groesse von Wolkenelementen, I, *Ann. Hydrographie und Maritimen Met.*, May 1942.

DIEM, M., Messungen der Groesse von Wolkenelementen, II, *Met. Rundschau*, v.1, p.262, 1948.

EAST, T. W. R. and J. S. MARSHALL, Turbulence in clouds as a factor in precipitation, *Q.J.R. Met. Soc.*, v.80, pp.26–47, 1954.

GUNN, K. L. S. and W. KITSCHFELD, A laboratory investigation of the coalescence between large and small water-drops, *J. Met.*, v.8, pp.7–16, 1951.

HOWELL, W. E., The growth of cloud drops in uniformly cooled air, *J. Met.*, v.6, pp.134–139, 1949.

KINZER, G. D. and W. E. COBB, Laboratory measurements of growth and of the collection efficiency of raindrops, paper in this publication, pp.167–169, 1957.

LANGMUIR, I., The production of rain by a chain reaction in cumulus clouds at temperatures above freezing, *J. Met.*, v.5, pp.175–192, 1948.

LUDLAM, F. H., The production of showers by the coalescence of cloud droplets, *Q.J.R. Met. Soc.*, v.77, p.402, 1951.

MALKUS, J. S., Some results of a trade-cumulus investigation, *J. Met.*, v.11, pp.220–237, 1954.

MASON, B. J., Production of rain and drizzle by coalescence in stratiform clouds, *Q.J.R. Met. Soc.*, v.78, pp.377–386, 1952.

SARTOR, D. S., A laboratory investigation of collision efficiencies, coalescence and electrical charging of simulated cloud droplets, *J. Met.*, v.11, pp.91–103, 1954.

SCHOTLAND, R., The collision efficiency of cloud droplets, paper in this publication, pp.170–176, 1957.

TELFORD, J. W., N. S. THORNDIKE, and E. G. BOWEN, The coalescence between small water drops, *Q.J.R. Met. Soc.*, v.81, pp.241–250, 1955.

WOODCOCK, A. H., Atmospheric salt particles and raindrops, *J. Met.*, v.9, pp.200–212, 1952.

WORKMAN, E. J. and S. E. REYNOLDS, Electrical activity as related to thunderstorm cell growth, *Bul. Amer. Met. Soc.*, v.30, pp.142–144, 1949.

ZAITSEV, V. A., Liquid-water content and distribution of drops in cumulus clouds, *Trudy Glavnoi Geofis. Observ.*, v.19, pp.122–132, 1950.

DISCUSSION

Mr. Vernon G. Plank—My question is in reference to the role of turbulence in the growth and droplets by coalescence. Could there be local turbulence motion of enough magnitude to produce a few big drops, but of such a small scale that it could not be detected with the usual airborne methods?

Dr. T. W. R. East—All I did was to take the very large scale motions and go through some of the most recent turbulence theory and work out an acceleration. The theory is supposed to take care of all motions, large or small scale, automatically. It is also possible to take some other scale and velocity of turbulence and put them into the formula and come out with another answer. I am fairly convinced myself, that turbulence is not an important factor in the growth process but admit that this conclusion may be open to doubt.

Mr. Charles E. Anderson—I am a little worried about your conclusion that by sharpening the droplet distribution, one can increase the coalescence, while the cloud physicists have been trying for years to find mechanisms for broadening the distribution so they can explain the coalescence.

Dr. J. S. Marshall—I think it might be fair to say that the improvement is in spite of the narrowing of the distribution. It is so important to get a large r that it is worth narrowing the distribution to get it, but this does not mean that r can be equal to s. You must maintain some width with the distribution.

Dr. East (after the meeting)—There is another point, not mentioned at the meeting. Narrowing the distribution at constant median radius would decrease all relative velocities. But condensation increases the median radius as it narrows the distribution, and because of the square-law dependence of velocity on radius, the relative velocities remain unaltered.

Dr. Raymond Wexler—I would like to suggest that since the collection efficiencies are not too well established it might have been better to make calculations on an upper limit and possibly a lower limit of the efficiency.

I would also like to point out the possibility of obtaining precipitation even from much smaller liquid-water contents, say two grams or less. Dr. Battan reported drops of 60 or 70 microns diameter with liquid-water contents of $0 \cdot 7$ to $0 \cdot 8$ grams per cubic meter, which indicates that your values of efficiency are a bit too small.

Mr. Vernon G. Plank—You assumed an initial distribution and then allowed the larger drops to grow at the expense of the smaller ones. Actually, however, the small particles will rise with the air currents while the larger droplets will be somewhat retarded. Then these larger drops will fall through some newly formed small cloud particles.

Dr. East—The fall velocity of 50-micron droplets is about 25 cm/sec. So that in the course of 1000 sec, one has fallen about 250 m. Hence if we start off with a fairly large parcel and lift it up, the fact that the large droplets tend to slip down is not important.

Dr. James P. Lodge, Jr.—One thing that has not been considered, as far as I know, is the fact that the original nuclei, irrespective of size, are randomly distributed in the cloud.

I think you can get initially quite a broad spectrum of particle sizes simply by the fact that there are very minute localized areas where the supersaturation must become extremely large simply because there are no suitable nuclei in them; and hence, where one nucleus wanders in, you get a very large droplet, whereas nearby you have some rather starved nuclei which are competing avidly for the small amount of water available to them.

Dr. East—I avoided consideration of the nuclei and by assuming that if I took the measured distribution for fair weather clouds, I'd be getting a good approximation to the situation which exists after the nuclei have sorted themselves out.

Mr. Alfred H. Woodcock—I am wondering to what extent you really do have the complete distribution for fair-weather cumulus. There are so many of the very small droplets and so few of the large ones that a compromise has to be made in the sampling technique. In most of the cases the samples are so small that when the numbers in the samples are related to the numbers per unit volume of air the distribution stops short of a concentration of one per cubic meter. Yet we believe that the nuclei which ultimately become raindrops are present in numbers much lower than this.

Dr. East—I have thought about that a little. In fact, probably the total volume of cloud samplings in the last ten years has been less than one liter. But, I would like to call your attention to the large numbers of droplets in the 20- to 100-micron region actually found in heavy cumulus. There aren't enough giant nuclei to account for these, although there may be enough giant nuclei to account for the number of rain drops.

Dr. L. J. Battan—My definition of a fair-weather cumulus is a cumulus which occurs in fair weather and never causes rain. If such is the case, then you are going from a cloud which never rains and extending the distribution to one that does rain. This may not be quite proper.

I also wish to ask to what extent do the new efficiency curves affect the data?

Dr. East—The eventual fate of a rising air-parcel in heavy cumulus differs greatly from that in fair weather, but in the first few hundred meters its development must surely be very similar. The calculations take over from this early stage. At the time I started this work, Langmuir's efficiency values were the only ones which were available. Since then experimental values from Dr. Schotland and others have become available. For the smaller droplets some of the experimental values are greater than Langmuir's and some are smaller.

Growth rates would be affected, but the steepness of the curve t_{coal} in Fig. 5 indicates that the condition for precipitation would not be greatly influenced. Calculations have been made with a revised efficiency curve which has values up to $0\cdot20$ where Langmuir gives zero, and $0\cdot15$ to $0\cdot20$ above Langmuir's elsewhere. At one g/kg t_{coal} was reduced to 65 minutes, still far out of line with cloud development times.

Dr. Roscoe R. Braham, Jr.—There is one point pertaining to the growth of drops by coalescence of droplets which should be mentioned. In most of the computations which have been made it is implied that the droplets are uniformly spaced. This condition doesn't necessarily exist in natural clouds. In discussions, about a year ago, I learned that Australian scientists are considering the consequence of a random array of the droplets. Local regions of high droplet density are more favored for coalescence than are the average condition. This might be a regenerative type of phenomenon because as soon as a drop becomes a little bigger than the average, it is going to grow at a faster rate and according to the reports, this effectively cuts to about one third the expected time required for the growth of a very small drop to some other much larger size.

Dr. East (after the meeting)—The work Dr. Braham apparently refers to has since become available (TELFORD, 1955, *J. Met.*, v. 12, p. 436). It seems that this effect is most potent in the early stages, and might considerably shorten the time taken to grow from 18 to 25 microns, but would not greatly reduce the 58 minutes required to grow from 25 to 50 microns, at one g/kg.

ATMOSPHERIC SALT IN NUCLEI AND IN RAINDROPS

A. H. WOODCOCK

Woods Hole Oceanographic Institution, Woods Hole, Mass.

Abstract—The observed salinities of rain waters, the weights and salinities of raindrops, and the weights of sea-salt nuclei in the atmosphere in Hawaii are quantitatively related. It is shown that the weight of salt in the nuclei is adequate to supply the total salt observed in the rains. Brief suggestions are made concerning the meaning of the above result in terms of raindrop formation on the large salt nuclei.

THE purpose of this note is to give an account of observations of salt nuclei and rain made in Hawaii during 1952. These observations lend support to the idea that raindrops, in trade-wind orographic showers, form on sea-salt particles in a manner which makes it possible to trace the salt in the nuclei to the salt in solution in the rain waters.

The methods used to sample the nuclei and the raindrops have been described [WOODCOCK, 1949, 1952; BLANCHARD, 1953]. It seems that the purposes of this communication will be briefly and, I hope, adequately met by immediately presenting and discussing some of the results which led to the 'idea' expressed in paragraph one above.

Fig. 1 shows relationships observed between the average number and salt content of the nuclei in the air and the average number and salt content of the raindrops. It also includes some data obtained in Hawaii by TURNER [1955] on the salinity of drops of various size ranges.

The curve at the lower right shows the distribution of salt nuclei near cloud base over the sea during force 4 winds. The three curves at the lower left represent the average drop size distributions observed in rains of several intensities. These rains were sampled within and near the base of orographic clouds and during a period of several days when force 4 winds were observed over the sea in the Hawaiian area.

Note that the numbers and the sizes of the salt nuclei and of the raindrops represented by curves A, B, C and D are given in common units of 10^{-12} grams. On the basis of an assumption of a one-to-one correspondence of nuclei and raindrops, the salinities of the individual raindrop size ranges may be computed. These computed salinities are shown in curves 1, 2, and 3 at the top of Fig. 1. These curves represent the salinities of the raindrops of rain curves A, B and C, respectively. Note for instance that point E on curve 3 represents a drop sea-salt concentration which is simply the ratio of the weight of salt represented by point F on nuclei curve D, to the weight of water in the drop represented by point G on curve C. All of the other points on curves 1, 2, and 3 were similarly computed from the salt-nuclei curve D, and the rain drop curves A, B, and C.

The first indication that these computed values for raindrop salinity represented those which naturally existed in these rains is shown on Fig. 2. The observed rain chlorinities given on this figure are averages of values determined by titration of salts in bulk-water samples. These bulk-water samples were taken at various rain intensities and at the same time that the raindrop size samples were taken.

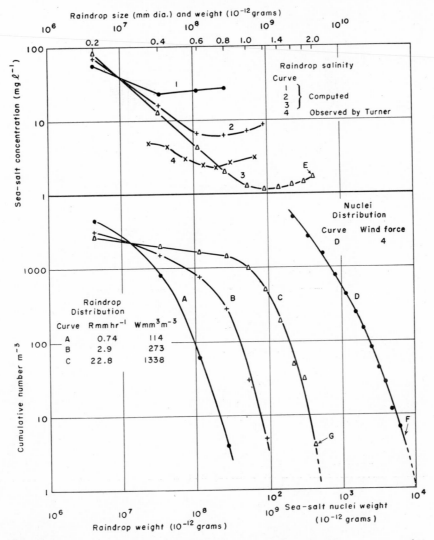

F<small>IG</small>. 1—The lower curves of this graph represent observed cumulative average number distributions for salt nuclei and for the drops in rains of various intensities; these curves are used to compute the average chlorinity of the rain waters (Fig. 2) and the raindrop salinities shown above

The computed average chlorinities on Fig. 2 were derived from a comparison of raindrop and nuclei size distribution curves *A*, *B*, *C*, and *D*, shown on Fig. 1. Table 1 gives the steps in this averaging process for the highest rain intensity shown on Fig. 1 (that is, 22·8 mm/hr). Column 8 gives the weight of the sea salt in nuclei which are present in the air (salt curve *D*) in numbers corresponding to the numbers of raindrops of the indicated diameters. On this basis of a one-to-one correspondence of nuclei and raindrops, the average salinity of the rain will be the ratio of the total salt falling (column 9) to the total water falling (column 6). This ratio, with the units adjusted, gives a rain

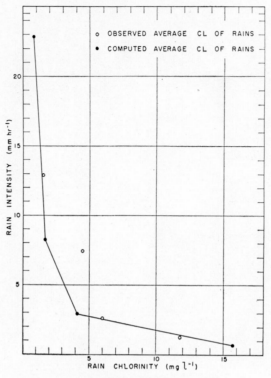

Fig. 2—Observed and computed chlorinities of rains
related to rain intensity

Table 1. *Average rain data derived from filter paper samples*

Drop diameter 1	Drop no. 2	Drop volume 3	Drop fall rate 4	No. of drops falling 5	Rain rate mm³ 6	Rain water in air 7	Wt. sea salt in each drop unit 8	Total sea salt falling in drops 9
mm	m⁻³	mm³	m/sec	m⁻²sec⁻¹	m⁻²sec⁻¹	mm³m⁻³	10^{-12}g	10^{-6} gm⁻²sec⁻¹
0·3	786	·0141	1·17	920	13	11·1	420	0·386
0·5	282	·065	2·06	581	38	18·3	485	0·282
0·7	163	·180	2·90	473	85	29·4	530	0·251
0·9	458	·375	3·65	1670	628	172	600	1·000
1·1	507	·700	4·30	2180	1523	354	830	1·810
1·3	304	1·14	4·90	1490	1700	347	1,350	2·010
1·5	143	1·73	5·45	780	1348	248	2,270	1·770
1·7	17	2·56	5·95	100	256	43	3,500	0·350
1·9	28	3·59	6·35	175	628	99	5,100	0·892
2·1	3	4·85	6·75	22	108	16	10,000	0·220
					6328	1338		8·971

The table uses the following column headers which also appear with units:
- m⁻²sec⁻¹ for columns 5 and 6
- mm³m⁻³ for column 7

salinity of 1·4 mg per liter, or a chlorinity of 0·8 mg per liter, as given on Fig. 2. The other computed chloride values given on Fig. 2 were derived from similar tables and computations. (Note on Fig. 1 that there is no raindrop size distribution curve for the 0·2 mm/hr rains. These data were excluded to avoid a confusion of lines.) For brevity these tables and computations are omitted here.

The similarity of the observed and computed average salinities of the rains revealed in Fig. 2 encourages the thought that the assumed relationship of nuclei to raindrops may naturally occur. Some recent measurements of the salinity of raindrops in Hawaii also lend support to the idea of a one-to-one correspondence of salt nuclei and raindrops. These raindrop salinity measurements were made, utilizing samples obtained, with a raindrop spectrograph, very near the location on the mountain side where our rain samples were taken.

The raindrop spectrograph, which was developed by BOWEN [1951] was later modified by TURNER [1955] so as to separate the waters coming from several drop size range categories. The salinity of the waters from each size range was separately determined. An account of the experimental procedure and some of the results was recently published [TURNER, 1955]. In the present note it seems satisfactory to compare our computed average raindrop salinities to the observed average salinities derived from the spectrograph samples.

Curve 4, near the top of Fig. 1, represents an average of 37 series of samples taken by Turner (see Turner's curve b, Fig. 4b). Each series involved many hours of continuous operation of the spectrograph in rains of various intensities. It is remarkable that the shape of Turner's raindrop-salinity curve and his actual salinity values are so similar to our computed curves and values. If Turner had been able to obtain his spectrograph samples in rains of nearly constant intensity, it is supposed that the shape of his drop salinity curve would more closely correspond to the curves computed from the raindrop and salt-nuclei size spectra of Fig. 1. It is unfortunate that no salt-nuclei data are available for the times when Turner sampled rains. His lower average salinities are thought to indicate a lower average salt content of the air during his sampling period.

Viewed conservatively, one can say that the above computations of rain-water salinities (Fig. 2) and raindrop salinities (Fig. 1) yield results which, when compared to observed salinities, do not exclude the possibility of a one-to-one correspondence of nuclei and raindrops. Viewed more optimistically, these computations and observations suggest the existence of a natural drop-forming process which (a) produces growth of raindrops on most of the larger nuclei in a manner which does not markedly alter their distribution, and (b) adds water to these nuclei without altering their salt content.

REFERENCES

BLANCHARD, D. C., Raindrop size distribution in Hawaiian rains, *J. Met.*, v.10, pp.457–473, 1953.
BOWEN, E. C. and K. A. DAVIDSON, A raindrop spectrograph, *Q.J.R. Met. Soc.*, v.77, pp.445–449, 1951.
TURNER, J. S., The salinity of rainfall as a function of drop size, *Q.J. Met. Soc.*, v.81, pp.418–429, 1955.
WOODCOCK, A. H., Atmospheric salt particles and raindrops, *J. Met.*, v.9, pp.200–212, 1952.
WOODCOCK, A. H. and M. M. GIFFORD, Sampling atmospheric sea-salt nuclei over the ocean, *J. Marine Res.*, v.8, pp.177–197, 1949.

DISCUSSION

Dr. Raymond Wexler—Mr. Woodcock suggests that if you have a cubic meter of air containing a certain number of particles of sea salt the same number of particles become raindrops. That seems a little difficult to believe, because the salt particles have a fall velocity of approximately one centimeter per second; but as they become water droplets, and grow, they attain fall velocities of say four hundred centimeters per second. They then spread out into a volume four hundred times as large as the original volume. So you should not expect a one-to-one correspondence between salt particles and raindrops.

I would like to suggest a different mechanism. Consider the classical model of a cloud. There is an updraft and a distribution of salt particles in the cloud both large ones and small ones.

Now the large nuclei are going to grow to particle size quite fast and will be lifted up into the cloud but will not be able to reach the top of the cloud because they acquire fall velocities equal to the updraft velocity in a relatively short time. Each large particle then becomes a small raindrop.

The next smaller size of particles will go up a little higher in the cloud and become a larger raindrop, because it falls through a much bigger mass of cloud. Now you can't carry this to infinitum because the smallest ones might never reach raindrop size. You might say there is an optimum nuclear size which will give you the maximum raindrop size. Those larger will give smaller drops and those smaller won't grow to raindrop size at all.

Now, let's try to explain this in terms of the salinity. The large particles which become small raindrops will have relatively high salinity, which fits essentially with what he observes. The bigger ones will have a smaller salt particle and a bigger water supply and would have a lower salinity.

Dr. Alfred H. Woodcock—I am familiar with this concept, however, things are very irregular in a cloud and one wonders to what extent such a picture approaches reality, especially if one thinks of precipitation occurring in turbulent buoyant elements, which perhaps have the shape of a bubble or ring vortex, and the precipitation is occurring rapidly.

Dr. Roscoe R. Braham, Jr.—I would like to add that the total lifetimes of cumulus clouds in this country are not long enough to allow this type of mechanism to proceed to the end point. It may go through the first few steps but certainly not through whole process as envisaged by Bowen.

CLOUD-SEEDING TRIALS USING COMMON SALT

E. M. FOURNIER D'ALBE

Instituto de Ciencias Aplicadas, Universidad Nacional de Mexico,
Mexico, D.F., Mexico

I WOULD like to say a few words about the cloud-seeding trials which were carried out in the Punjab last year by the Pakistan Meteorological Service. The scientific report on these trials has been published [FOURNIER D'ALBE and others, 1955], but as some rather inaccurate reports also appeared in the press I feel that this would be a good occasion to give you some first-hand information about them.

They were, I think, the first large-scale experiments in which salt has been used as a cloud-seeding agent. It had already been used on a small scale from aircraft (in Tunisia) or from balloons (in East Africa), but in the experiments in Pakistan our object was to try out a method of dispersal from the ground which we hoped would allow us to seed the atmosphere over a large area at a minimum cost.

The conditions during the monsoon season in the Punjab, where cloud-base temperatures often exceed 20°C, are such that seeding with hygroscopic particles has a much greater chance of success than seeding with a freezing agent such as silver iodide or dry ice. Furthermore, measurements made regularly during the previous two years had shown that the natural salt-particle content of the atmosphere in this area is of the order of ten particles greater than 10^{-9} gram per cubic meter of mass. We therefore had hopes of being able to increase significantly the salt-particle concentration over large areas with relatively simple equipment.

The salt was first ground to a fine powder (median particle mass approximately 10^{-9} gram) in a flour mill. This was done in Quetta where the low relative humidity allowed us to keep the salt dry during grinding. It was then packed in four-gallon (imperial) kerosene cans and sealed for shipment to the Punjab. The seals were only removed immediately before use, so as to reduce the chances of coagulation. To disperse the salt, air was blown through the can by means of a hand blower of the type used by silversmiths in Pakistan. Before entering the can the air passed through a tube from which was slung a wire gauze basket containing burning charcoal. This raised the temperature of air about 5°C and thus reduced its relative humidity to below 60 per cent. Apart from reducing the danger of particle coagulation, this also gave some lift to the air and helped to carry the particles clear of the ground.

We found that the salt could be blown into the air by this method at the rate of ten grams per second. Some fell to the ground in the immediate vicinity of the blower, but even allowing a 50-per-cent loss in this way, we estimated the rate of dispersal to be 5×10^9 particles per second.

We know very little about diffusion in the atmosphere under the conditions of active thermal convection under which we operated. However, basing our calculations on Sutton's theory, we estimated that the concentration of the particles we dispersed would

E. M. Fournier d'Albe

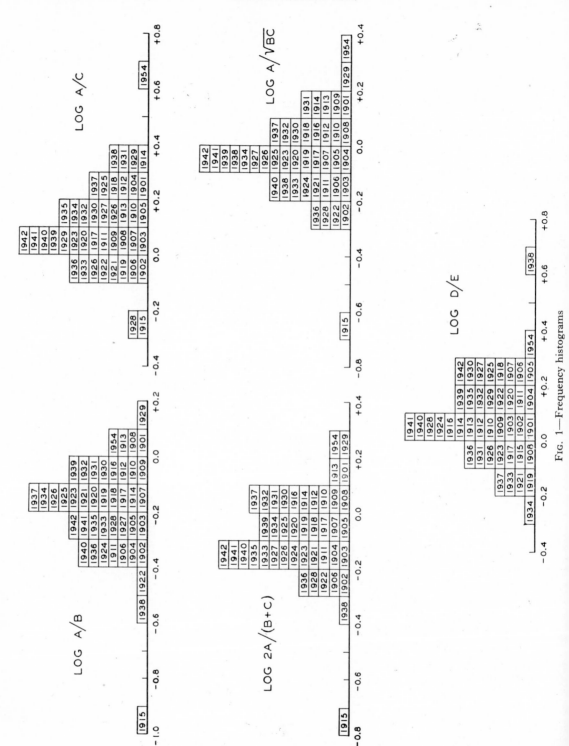

Fig. 1—Frequency histograms

fall to the level of ten per cubic meter at a distance of approximately 100 km downwind of the point of dispersal.

Eight long tons of finely powdered salt were prepared and distributed between two stations in the Punjab, one at Lahore, and one at Jauharabad in the Thal district, about 210 km WNW of Lahore. These were ready on July 16, 1954 and continued in operation up to September 15. The seeding program was determined by the weather conditions in the Punjab. During the monsoon season there is normally an easterly current of moist air which may vary in depth up to 20,000 or 25,000 ft. This is overlain by westerlies which may occasionally descend to the surface bringing drier air and cloudless skies. Rain is usually of the convective type, gradually increasing in frequency and amount from the southwest of the area towards the Himalaya foothills to the northeast.

These conditions allowed us to delimit the zone of influence of each seeding station, by limiting seeding to those days on which the surface wind blew from an easterly direction. During the first month we seeded only when low cloud was visible from the stations, but in the second month we seeded on all days of easterly winds regardless of the state of the sky.

Seeding was actually done on 39 days at each station during the 61-day period of the trials. Of these 39 days, the surface wind at Lahore blew from directions between ESE and SSE on 28 days. For the purpose of evaluation, we therefore drew an arc of radius 100 km with center at Lahore, and divided it into three segments. Segment A, limited by radii drawn in the directions 290° and 340° from Lahore, was taken to be the 'seeded area', while segments B and C, limited by radii drawn from Lahore in the directions 030° and 240° respectively were taken as 'control areas'. In the case of the second seeding station, the distribution of raingage stations did not allow us to use similar segments. We therefore simply drew two contiguous rectangles, D and E, each 75×55 km, one of which lay downwind and the other mainly upwind of Jauharabad.

The evaluation of the results was based on a comparison of the rainfall recorded during the seeding period at the raingage stations in each area with the rainfall recorded at the same stations during July and August each year from 1901 to 1942. Although we received reports from over 200 raingage stations in the Punjab, the evaluation was based only on the observations of those stations operated by the Punjab Government which had complete records for the period 1901–1942, that is to say of three or four stations in each segment.

The procedure was as follows. For each year we calculated values of the quantities A, B, C, D, E; A being the arithmetic mean of the actual rainfalls recorded by the stations in segment A during the two-month period each year; similarly, the quantities B, C, D, E. We then obtained values for each year of the quantities $\log A/B$, $\log A/C$, $\log A/[1/2(B+C)]$, $\log A/\sqrt{(BC)}$ and $\log D/E$. The years 1901 to 1942 and 1954 were then grouped in intervals of 0·10 in each of these quantities. The results are shown in Fig. 1.

The values of each of these quantities in 1954 are generally well above the normal, and in the case $\log A/C$ and $\log A/\sqrt{(BC)}$ the 1954 value is higher than any recorded in the 42-year period 1901–42. Similarly, $\log D/E$ for 1954 had been exceeded only once previously, in 1938.

This is brought out more clearly in Fig. 2, where the values for each year of $\log A/\sqrt{(BC)}$ are plotted against the corresponding values of $\log D/E$. There is obviously no correlation between the two quantities. Three years, 1915, 1938, and 1954, lie outside the main population, but 1954, apart from having the largest value of the product of the two quantities, also lies close to the line $\log A/\sqrt{(BC)} = \log D/E$, which is perhaps an indication of some factor operating to increase rainfall simultaneously in areas A and D. The values of $\log A/\sqrt{(BC)}$ and $\log D/E$ for 1954 do, in fact, both exceed the mean values of these quantities by more than twice their standard deviations.

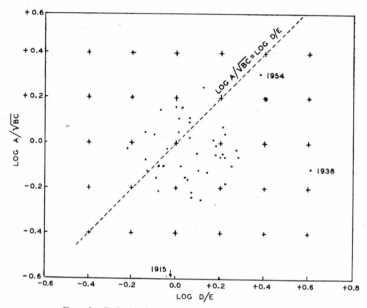

Fig. 2—Relation between $\log A/\sqrt{BC}$ and $\log D/E$

Those are the results. We would be glad if some statistician could tell us exactly what they mean. The only conclusion that we have drawn from them so far is that they justify a repetition of the experiment in 1955. I understand from Karachi that the Pakistan Meteorological Service is in fact repeating the experiment this year, with the same technique and the same seeding program. No results are yet available.

REFERENCE

Fornier d'Albe, E. M., A. M. A. Lateef, S. I. Rasool and I. H. Zaidi, The cloud-seeding trials in the central Punjab, July–September, 1954, *Q. J. R. Met. Soc.*, v.81, no.350, pp.574–581, 1955.

DISCUSSION

Dr. Roscoe R. Braham, Jr.—I would like to know more about the design of the experiment. Under what conditions, or during what period was salt dispersed into the atmosphere? Was it continually or during short periods of certain days?

Dr. Fournier d'Albe—The conditions for seeding were that the surface wind should be easterly and that there should be some low cloud visible. These two conditions are normally satisfied simultaneously in the Punjab, but towards the end of the trials we did in fact seed on some days of easterly wind without waiting for the appearance of suitable cloud. Seeding normally started at 08h 00m and continued up to 17h 00m or 18h 00m, except during rain.

Dr. Braham—Do these conditions mean that there are relatively uniform or equally likely conditions present then in all three sectors, *A, B,* and *C?*

Dr. Fournier d'Albe—The country is mainly flat plain, but rainfall increases towards the north, area *B* having a higher normal rainfall than *C,* due to the influence of the hills to the north. There are frequent days of convective showers over the whole area, though the showers tend to be heavier and more numerous in the north.

Dr. Helmut Weickmann—Was it warm showers? I mean, there are no thunderstorms.

Dr. Fournier d'Albe—The showers often, though not always, develop into thunderstorms, with signs of ice formation at the tops. But, as cloud-base temperatures were around 20°C we assumed that it was the coalescence process which produced the rain first, though the ice-process may have contributed later on.

Dr. E. J. Workman—Were the rainfall measurements for all days or just seeding days?

Dr. Fournier d'Albe—All days.

Dr. Workman—One conceivably could introduce bias into this by emphasizing this wind trajectory if indeed there is any difference in the moisture content of the wind which blows in this angle and some other angle. I suppose the humidity measurements here were approximately normal during this time, at least as they passed the seeding point.

Dr. Fournier d'Albe—Yes, as far as I know they were normal. We had the usual alternation of easterly with westerly surface winds. With westerly winds the sky is clear and although the humidity does not change much at the surface due to evapotranspiration it does decrease considerably aloft.

Dr. Hans J. aufm Kampe—Did you seed every day during the two months?

Dr. Fournier d'Albe—Not every day. Of the 61 days between July 16 and September 15, we seeded at both stations on 39 days.

Dr. aufm Kampe—What is the mean precipitation?

Dr. Fournier d'Albe—Speaking from memory, I would say the mean precipitation for the two-month period varies from about six inches in the southwestern part of the area up to as much as 20 inches in the hills to the northeast. At Lahore it is about ten inches.

Dr. aufm Kampe—I once analyzed the rainfall, not in Pakistan, but in a very similar country, and there I found that the clouds usually go up to about 26,000 ft and maybe higher, and most of the rain comes in the thunderstorm. Is that true there, too?

Dr. Fournier d'Albe—I think I remember what you mean. The monsoon air stream is much deeper in the Punjab than it is further west. Although thunderstorms are quite frequent, they are by no means an invariable accompaniment of rain.

Dr. aufm Kampe—Did you talk to statisticians for this evaluation?

Dr. Fournier d'Albe—Yes, I have tried to find somebody who could tell me what these results mean.

Dr. L. J. Battan—You seeded on 39 days. On how many days did rain actually fall?

Dr. Fournier d'Albe—I think there were less than ten days on which no rain was reported anywhere, even in the hills. Of these, perhaps one or two were days on which we seeded.

Dr. Battan—The second question I have is: I note that in area *B* the rain was greater than in area *C.* Did you calculate a distribution of log *B/C.*

Dr. Fournier d'Albe—No, that is something we haven't done. We ought to do it, perhaps, to see how this year's value compares with previous years.

Mr. Charles E. Anderson—Did you mention what the results of this statistical evaluation were for the days when you did not seed when it rained?

Dr. Fournier d'Albe—In the evaluation we just took the total rainfall for the whole period, seeded and non-seeded days together. This was because we could not assume that the particles dispersed on one day were all removed from the atmosphere by the following day. With light winds and strong convection they could certainly remain in the area for 24 hours. We did in fact prepare daily maps of rainfall over the whole area, and some of them showed interesting rainfall patterns, but we could not draw any conclusions from them.

Dr. Braham—I wonder about the last statement you made that these daily maps were not capable of analysis. Would it not be interesting to separate the data into the days you did seed and the days you didn't seed and go through the same analysis you made here?

Dr. Fournier d'Albe—Yes, it might be.

Dr. Braham—That would be one other way of checking sector *B*.

Dr. Fournier d'Albe—There is almost certainly more to be got out of an examination of the daily rainfall maps, particularly as they also show the times of commencement and end of rainfall. There were days, for instance, on which there appeared to be a maximum of rainfall on a line downward of a seeding station. These look nice, but it is extremely difficult to evaluate the observations of individual days, since we had no means of tracing the movement of our salt particles once they had left the generator, nor did we have a sufficiently detailed knowledge of the wind field. This is admittedly the weakest point of the whole experiment. Radioactive sodium chloride has been suggested as a tracer, but eight tons of that would have been rather expensive.

Dr. Battan—You mentioned the background was about ten particles per cubic meter. Where were they taken; at the ground or aloft?

Dr. Fournier d'Albe—At the ground, at a height of about two meters. They were taken at meteorological observatories where the exposure is good, and during the hottest part of the day when we hoped to get a fairly representative sample from the exchange layer.

Dr. Battan—I think Dr. Byers found that the measurements we took at the ground were not representative of the air aloft.

Dr. Fournier d'Albe—Yes indeed, we are very much concerned about that. But I do not like the idea of a sharp gradient of particle concentration near the ground.

Dr. Horace R. Byers—We don't like it either.

Dr. James E. McDonald—I wonder, since you did mention that these results encouraged the group to go on, whether this year they had planned to do any of the more obvious statistical refinements like seeding on only a part of the favorable days?

Dr. Fournier d'Albe—We did give a lot of thought to the question of whether we should seed on all favorable days or adopt some other scheme. For instance, we considered the possibility of having two stations functioning alternatively for five or ten-day periods, so that the same areas became alternately 'seeded' and 'control' areas. However, in looking into the past records, we found that this would have been even less sensitive than the straightforward comparison of a seeded and a control area. For instance the ratio of rainfall between odd and even five-day periods varies much more from year to year than does the total rainfall.

Dr. McDonald—I was thinking of just taking the days when the wind and moisture were normally favorable, and then not seeding on every one of those days, but randomizing that.

Dr. Fournier d'Albe—We had only a short period for the experiments, and we wanted to seed on as many days as possible, as we were relying on comparison between areas.

Dr. McDonald—I was wondering if this was going on.

Dr. Fournier d'Albe—As far as I know, the program in Pakistan this year is the same as last year. However, there is certainly a need for more trials. Why not try here in the United States? You have cloud-base temperatures of 15°C in the Middle West during the summer, quite a long way from the sea. There should be places where conditions are favorable.

Dr. Byers—Randomization certainly increases the power of any statistical analysis greatly, and where you have a small amount of data, you can accomplish a shortcut very quickly by randomization.

Dr. Fournier d'Albe—Our trouble lay in the nature of the rainfall in the Punjab. Convective shower-type rain is itself extremely variable both in space and time, much more so than frontal type rain.

Dr. Byers—Yes, that makes it even more complicated.

DISCUSSION OF RAINDROP DISTRIBUTIONS MADE DURING PROJECT SHOWER, HAWAII, 1954

D. C. BLANCHARD

Woods Hole Oceanographic Institution, Woods Hole, Mass.

Abstract—Concurrent with other Project Shower measurements in Hawaii, raindrop size distribution samples were obtained within the clouds with a portable mechanical device. At two-minute intervals these devices, called drop recorders, automatically collected a sample of rain on a section of a water-soluble dye-impregnated paper. The time rate of change of the drop size distribution was obtained from the exposed paper tapes. At the end of a shower the time rate of decrease of drop size has been found to be from $0\cdot07-0\cdot01$ mm min^{-1}. It is felt that this fact is in some way a reflection of the basic mechanism of the rain formation, but as yet no explanation has been forthcoming.

Introduction—During the fall months of 1954, Project Shower [SQUIRES, 1955], a cooperative cloud-physics study, was carried out on the Island of Hawaii. This project was an attempt to make simultaneous measurements of the wind field, cloud liquid-water

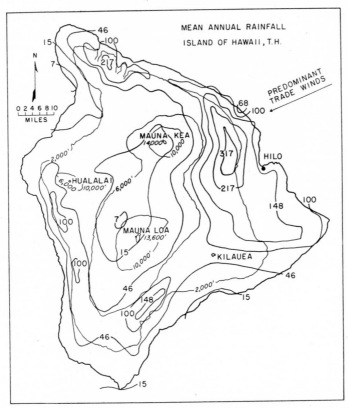

FIG. 1—The island of Hawaii, T. H.; the heavy lines represent the mean annual rainfall in inches; the light lines are elevation contours

213

content and drop size distribution, chemical constitution of the rainwater, salt-nuclei distribution in the free air in and below the cloud layer and the raindrop size distribution. Mr. Woodcock, Mr. Spencer, and the writer, all from the Woods Hole Oceanographic Institution, were concerned with the latter two measurements, the last of which will be discussed in this paper.

These measurements were made on the east slopes of the volcanoes of Mauna Kea and Mauna Loa on the Island of Hawaii, the largest and southernmost of the Hawaiian Island chain. This Island is located entirely within the Pacific northeast trades. These

FIG. 2—A drop recorder with the front cover removed and the sliding door open in the exposure position; a sample record is shown at the top

trades are characterized by a temperature inversion with a modal elevation of 6000 ft. Below the inversion the air is moist and turbulent with an average lapse rate of $8.3°C/$ 1000 m. The usual orographic clouds that form on the volcano slopes are affected by this inversion and do not penetrate it to any great extent. Nevertheless a high annual rainfall prevails on the east slopes and is illustrated on the map of Fig. 1. Further information on Hawaiian weather can be found in a paper by LEOPOLD [1949].

Although some of the drop size distributions were obtained with the filter-paper method, as used in an earlier field trip to Hawaii [BLANCHARD, 1953a], a majority of the measurements were obtained with the aid of portable mechanical devices called drop recorders (see Fig. 2). These drop recorders, powered by a 12-volt automobile battery, had the following sequence of operation. At approximately two-minute intervals a sliding door at the top opened for a 2·7-sec period. The raindrops that fell through the 33 cm² opening impinged on a methylene blue dye-treated paper tape. A fine mesh wire screen around the opening prevented splash from the drops that struck in the immediate vicinity. During the 2-minute interval between exposures a resistance-wire heater dried the paper tape and the tape was advanced to a new exposure position. In this manner a drop recorder was run continuously for 15 hours collecting some 450 drop distribution samples.

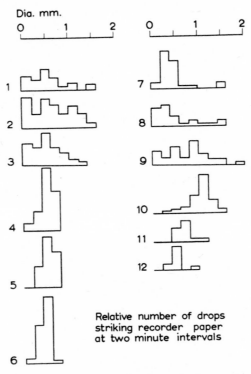

FIG. 3—Twelve consecutive drop recorder samples obtained at the 2000-ft level

Although the area exposed in each sample was only 33 cm², the raindrops are sufficiently small and numerous (usually less than two mm diameter and many thousands m⁻³) such that 60–200 can usually be collected. The laborious work involved in reducing the more than 4000 raindrops samples makes such a task somewhat unfeasible and thus, to date at least, only a few selected samples have been evaluated in respect to the rain intensity R and liquid water W. The results merely confirm the conclusion reached in an earlier paper [BLANCHARD, 1953a] in which relationships between R, W, and the radar reflectivity Z were given.

The three drop recorders were usually run simultaneously at three different elevations on the slopes of the saddle region between the Volcanoes Mauna Kea and Mauna Loa. They were positioned beside the saddle road which runs nearly due west from Hilo. The first recorder was placed at the 2000-ft elevation near the cloud base. The other recorders were placed at higher levels with the last recorder never above the 5500-ft level (about 14 km from the lowest recorder).

Raindrop distributions—The raindrop size distribution has been determined from a number of the drop recorder samples. It has become increasingly evident from examination of these records that any conclusions based on a single drop size sample can be very misleading. The rains are of a showery type and show great variations in drop size and number. Comparison of adjacent samples on the recorder records will often bring out the transient nature of any single sample. This is illustrated by Fig. 3 which shows the relative number of drops, in 0·2 mm size ranges, that were obtained with twelve consecutive drop recorder samples. The transient nature of the rain over a period of 22 minutes is clearly evident. In samples 1–6 a diminishing of the drops above one mm is occurring concurrent with an increase in the drops in the range 0·4–0·6 mm. In sample 7 the appearance of a relatively small number of drops of about 1·5 mm is followed by an increase in the number of larger drops in samples 8–10 and, finally, in samples 11 and 12 a decrease in drop size followed by the end of the rain. In studying the 12 samples as a whole one might conclude that sample 7 illustrates the beginning of the superposition of a second rain shower upon the end of the first shower of samples 1–6. It is probable that the drops smaller than 0·5 mm associated with samples 7 and 8 are the remains of the first shower while the larger drops are the initial drops of the second shower. Had only one or two samples been obtained at the time of samples 7 and 8 an interpretation of the drop distribution would have been difficult to make.

It should be kept in mind that the samples of Fig. 3 have been especially selected to illustrate the changes in drop size that may occur. On other occasions the rain has been steady over a sufficiently long period of time such that adjacent samples showed no significant change. In agreement with earlier work [BLANCHARD, 1953a] samples obtained high up on the mountain slope showed very small drops present in numbers of tens of thousands m^{-3}. It is probable that these small drops are the winnowed remains of the heavier rain that fell further down the mountainside. Table 1 gives, in tabular form, the results of five consecutive samples taken at an altitude of 5500 ft and about 14 km downwind from the 2000-ft elevation, the site where the samples of Fig. 3 were obtained. It is to be noted that these five samples, each obtained two minutes apart, indicates from about 250,000 to 430,000 drops m^{-3} less than 300 microns diameter. The diameters of the spots on the rain recorder tapes were measured with the aid of a low power microscope. Although the methylene blue dye had been thoroughly buffed into the paper, the dye particles often approached 20 microns diameter. This fact, plus the 'grain' of the paper, made it difficult to detect the spots left by drops smaller than 20 microns diameter. It is the writer's opinion that they were present in very low numbers, if at all, and this seems to be borne out by the fact that the 20–40 microns drops were, in general, less plentiful than those in the 40–60-micron size range. The sum total of the drops represents less than 0·5 drop cm^{-3}. With the usual methods of sampling cloud drops, which sample about one cm^3, these drops would be missed entirely.

Although only the five samples of Table 1 have been evaluated to date, there is no reason to believe that these are unique. Visual examination of other sections of the rain recorder record indicated a similar distribution. With filter paper techniques in the same

Table 1. Drop recorder samples, Hawaii, 1954

Sample	Date	Time (Hawaiian Standard)	Position	R	W	Number of drops m^{-3} within 20-micron size interval centered about indicated size (microns)				
		h m	ft	mm/hr	mg/m³	30	50	70	90	110
1	1954 Oct. 26	17 07	5500	0·129	99	38,800	77,000	34,000	33,000	27,500
2	Oct. 26	17 09	5500	0·374	197	101,360	120,000	78,000	44,000	26,000
3	Oct. 26	17 11	5500	0·171	118	91,650	95,000	76,000	40,000	26,500
4	Oct. 26	17 13	5500	0·361	177	71,640	60,000	62,000	37,000	22,500
5	Oct. 26	17 15	5500	0·177	118	52,220	56,000	34,000	39,000	30,000

Sample	Number of drops m^{-3} within 20-micron size interval centered about indicated size (microns)										
	130	150	170	190	210	230	250	270	290	310	330
1	25,200	9,400	2550	985	365	...	...	...	...	...	...
2	21,500	16,000	8100	4400	2300	1850	1940	380	195	100	235
3	16,500	8,800	3250	1600	870	880	473	127	...	...	...
4	17,000	13,000	8000	5500	2740	1620	1570	400	320	350	...
5	19,500	11,500	6400	2350	875	145	230	...	...	...	...

region [BLANCHARD, 1953a] drop concentrations approaching 100,000 m⁻³ were often
found. Due to limitations of the filter-paper technique in the detection of drops less than
100 microns diameter, it is felt that these earlier measurements gave an underestimate of
the actual number of drops.

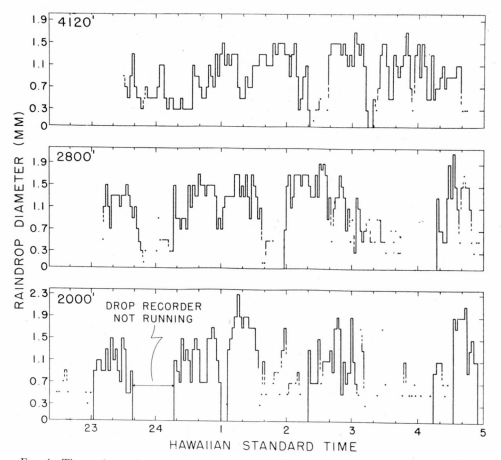

FIG. 4—The maximum drop size versus time for successive rain recorder samples, Dec. 1–2, 1954

Relation of maximum drop size to time—Although a determination of the raindrop distribution for each of the several thousand drop recorder samples has not been
made, it was felt that much may be learned of the rain mechanism from the rate of change
of the maximum drop size with time. Figures 4 and 5 illustrate this rate of change for an
eleven hour period during 1–2 December 1954.

These block diagrams were made by drawing lines through points that were obtained
at two minute intervals for the maximum drop size versus time. The points on Figures
4 and 5 through which lines have not been drawn represent samples on which ten or less
drops were counted. All three recorders were started prior to 22h 00m but no rain fell
until about 22h 28m when a few drops were picked up by the recorder at the 2000-ft

level. Note how the rain progressed up the mountain slope as indicated by successively later times of arrival at 2800- and 4120-ft elevations. The downward directed arrows indicate the times that the recorders were stopped.

The three recorders, placed along the volcano road at altitudes of 2000, 2800, and 4120 ft were not in a straight line. If the winds from the Hilo radiosonde can be taken as

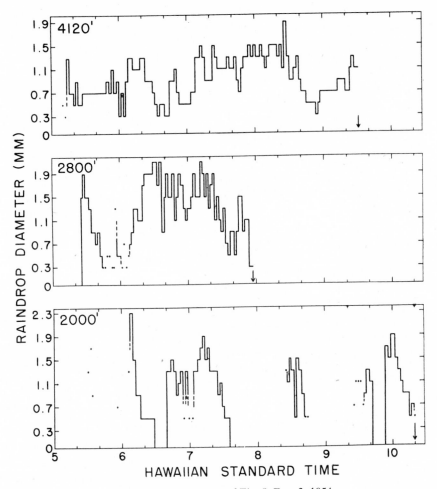

Fig. 5—A continuation of Fig. 5, Dec. 2, 1954

representative of the winds over the drop recorder area, and this is doubtful, then the rain showers can be considered as coming in from a bearing of N 70° E. Rain showers passing over the 2000-ft station would miss the upper stations by from three to four km, while the rain drifting over the 2800-ft station should pass within a km of the 4120-ft station. Hence one would not necessarily expect to find any correlation between the occurrence of rain showers at the lower two stations but might find it between the upper two. There is a suggestion on Fig. 4 that the showers at the 2800-ft station that began at about 00h 17m, 01h 00m and 02h 00m also passed over the 4120-ft station. If these are in fact the same showers, a decrease of maximum drop size of about 0·2 mm diameter occurred between stations. With the distance between the stations of 6·5 km and the time of passage of the showers, as obtained from Fig. 4, one computes transit speeds for the three showers mentioned above as 13, 10·5, and 5·2 knots, respectively. The Hilo radiosonde winds between 2000 and 10,000 ft at 23h 00m on December 1 and 05h 00m on December 2 were from seven to 21 knots.

One of the useful facts to come out of the drop recorder study is that the rain is far from a steady, uniform nature. A glance at Figures 4 and 5 shows that showers of one-half to one hour's duration closely follow one another and appear to be superimposed on a background of light, nearly continuous rain. Some of the fluctuations in the rain are extremely light and probably would not be picked up by a standard recording rain gauge [BLANCHARD, 1953b].

A characteristic common to many of the showers, and one that may be useful in the study of the mechanism of raindrop formation, is the rate of decrease of maximum drop size at the end of the shower. Examples of this may be found on Figures 4 and 5 at the 2000-ft station at 07h 20m and 10h 00m and at the 2800-ft station at 23h 40m and 05h 40m. The maximum drop size undergoes a steady decrease at a rate of 0·07—0·1 mm min^{-1} for a period of about 20 minutes. Two explanations for this have already been considered, and neither of them is, in all respects, satisfactory. When all of the data from the other investigators on Project Shower are available, including information on cloud tops and structure, an explanation may be forthcoming.

The simplest model that was considered was that of a stationary steady-state rain source producing a complete spectrum of raindrops at a height h above the observing station. At time t_0 the rain source stops, leaving only the rain in a column of height h to provide the end of the shower. The largest drops D_1, will continue to be observed at the ground for a time t_1, measured from t_0, which is merely h/V_1 where V_1 is the terminal velocity of the drops D_1. From time t_1 onward a steady decrease of maximum drop size will be observed. Drops of diameter D_2 ($D_2 < D_1$) will be the largest observed at a time $t_2 = h/V_2$. In this manner the rate of decrease of maximum drop size can be obtained. In Fig. 6 the results of calculations with $h = 1000$, 2000 and 4000 m are shown with the observed rates of decrease of drop size as found on the drop recorders. Only the calculation for $h = 4000$ m can compare with the observations and this cannot be accepted, as the rain source region does not extend 4000 m above the drop recorder stations and probably seldom reaches 2000 m.

A second model, a bit more involved than the first but perhaps more realistic, assumes that a wind exists that increases linearly with altitude. It can be shown that the rain, in falling from a steady-state source moving with the wind, will fall in parabolic trajectories with the smaller drops striking the ground at great distances from the cloud. The side view (neglect the top view and assume one-dimensional shear for the present) of the schematic sketch of Fig. 7 shows trajectories, with respect to the moving cloud, of the large and small drops. It is evident that any drop recorder placed in the path of such a rain system will record the end of the shower as a steady decrease in the maximum drop size. Calculations made with this model, assuming a rain source height of 1500 m and a wind of 10 m sec^{-1} at 1500 m uniformly decreasing to 2 m sec^{-1} at the ground, gave the result shown in the lowest curve on Fig. 6. It is apparent that this second model gives results that are even more widely at variance with the observations.

It thus appears that the above two models cannot account for the observed rate of decrease of maximum drop size. It is hardly worthwhile to consider more complicated models in the absence of the other observations that were made on these rain systems. When all the data has been tabulated it is hoped that the present picture will become clearer.

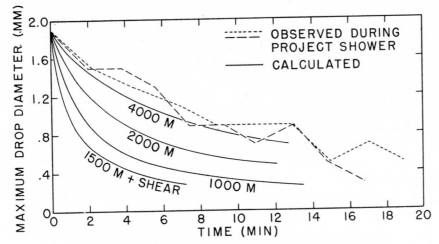

FIG. 6—The decrease of the maximum raindrop diameter with time

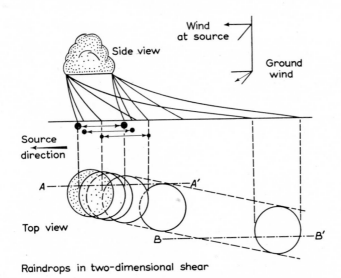

FIG. 7—The trajectories of raindrops subjected to wind shear

Two-dimensional shear—It is possible that the wind not only varies in speed with height but with direction as well. When this occurs the various drops in the spectrum will not only be spread out in the direction of motion of the source but also at right angles to it. The smallest drops, subjected to the wind shear for the longest period of time, would be deflected to the greatest degree. The schematic drawing of Fig. 7 illustrates how the drop size distribution on the ground is spread out at an angle to the direction of motion of the source. This angle will depend on the nature of the wind shear. A complete discussion of the effects of wind shear on rain has been given by Gunn and Marshall [1955].

It is evident that any observer on the ground in the path of an oncoming shower will receive only a certain range of the total raindrop distribution, this range varying with the orientation of the observer and the wind shear. For example, an observer at A in Fig. 7 would see the shower pass over him along the line AA' and an observer at B along the line BB'. The first observer would observe large drops only and the second observer only small drops. At intermediate points one may find only the middle of the raindrop spectrum with the largest and smallest drops missing entirely.

Although nothing can be said at the present as to whether any significant two dimensional shear existed in the region where Project Shower was carried out, some of the drop recorder samples suggest that this may have occurred. When the wind data are available the samples will be analyzed with this in mind.

Acknowledgments—I should like to thank sincerely my colleague, A. T. Spencer, who not only designed and built the drop recorders but assisted in obtaining the observations in Hawaii. This study was supported by the Office of Naval Research, Contract Nonr 798(00) (NR–082–124). Contribution No. 812 from the Woods Hole Oceanographic Institution.

REFERENCES

Blanchard, D. C., Raindrop size distribution in Hawaiian rains, *J. Met.*, v.10, pp.457–473, 1953a.
Blanchard, D. C., A simple recording technique for determining raindrop size and time of occurrence of rain showers, *Trans. Amer. Geophys. Union*, v.34, pp.534–538, 1953b.
Gunn, K. L. S. and J. S. Marshall, The effect of wind shear on falling precipitation, *J. Met.*, v.12, pp.339–349, 1955.
Leopold, L., The interaction of trade wind and sea breeze, Hawaii, *J. Met.*, v.6, pp.312–320, 1949.
Squires, P., Project Shower. An investigation on warm rain in the Hawaiian islands, *Nature*, v.175, pp.748–750, 1955.

DISCUSSION

Dr. Horace R. Byers—I think that in considering the effect of wind shear on drop size distribution in the shower, you must take into account the possibility of the existence of an outflow or first-gust type of flow, such as occurs in a well-developed thunderstorm and often in other types of showers. In this case the shear would be negative, with strongest winds at about two or three hundred feet and a sharp dropping off around two thousand or so.

Dr. David Atlas—As I remember a description of some of your work, trade-wind cumulus clouds move inland and seem to create pulsations on the orographic cloud. The pulsations in rain intensity that occur are in general attributed to this effect. The interaction between the cumulus impulse and the orographic cloud would vary with distance inland and that perhaps is why you always get your broadest distributions toward the shore.

Mr. Duncan C. Blanchard—These high-level distributions we find fit in rather well with the idea that they are nothing more than the remains of showers which have fallen further down. In the distributions at low levels, we find few small drops; at high levels we find the missing drops.

Dr. Helmut Weickmann—I would like to suggest the possibility of these differences in drop size occurring simply because the water gets swept from the cloud.

I will describe a model which I have considered. Underneath the melting level, there is a cloud, maybe several thousand feet thick, with one gram per cubic meter water content. We have a snow crystal falling from above, which seeds the cloud. If you want to have steady precipitation you need a continuous updraft in order to supply the water. If you don't have an updraft and you just let the particles fall through and sweep it out, then in the beginning you have large particles, but as the time goes on, in ten or twenty minutes, the size decreases. Simultaneously the water content of the lower layers decreases more rapidly than the water content of the upper layers.

One way to check up on this would be to observe the cloud base. If the cloud base lifts it would indicate that such a process takes place. But, it doesn't necessarily have to lift, because the water content may be appreciably reduced without visible lifting of the cloud base.

Dr. Roscoe R. Braham, Jr.—If the precipitation is of such nature that it is showery, having periodical bursts of rainfall to the ground, that is characteristic of what we get from cumulus clouds, and we usually ascribe it to a non-steady state condition with vertical motions but presumably the cloud under discussion is an orographic cloud, the trade wind being rather steady in its character; this means that the nature of the precipitation itself, not the motion, must have to provide some non-continuing or periodic showery aspect of the precipitation.

Mr. Alfred H. Woodcock—Although the usual picture of an orographic cloud is one which is exclusively over the mountain, actually the trade winds are continually flowing inland and, in many areas, individual cumulus clouds can be seen drifting in on the trades from the open sea and merging with the orographic cloud. Therefore, built into the orographic cloud are parcels with quite different cloud histories. This is a possible explanation of the irregular nature of the rain.

Dr. Braham—This then is an interesting example of nature's way of seeding with water drops. There must be rather large drops in the cumulus cloud to start with.

Q

SIZE DISTRIBUTION GENERATED BY A
RANDOM PROCESS

WALTER HITSCHFELD

McGill University, Montreal, Canada

(Presented by J. S. Marshall)

Abstract—Machine calculation on an idealized model of particles in motion relative to each other yield size distributions not in close agreement with those measured for rain. When the effects of some of the simplifications in the original model are considered qualitatively, agreement becomes close enough to demonstrate that a random collision process may play a major part in the early stages of the development of rain distributions.

IF a large number of particles is in random motion relative to each other, with coalescence resulting on at least some occasions, the size distribution changes in time. With almost any reasonable coalescence law the number of big particles will increase at the expense of the smaller ones. This process can be described mathematically by the integro-differential equation [MELZAK, 1953]

$$\frac{\partial f(x,t)}{\partial t} = \tfrac{1}{2} \int_0^x f(y,t) f(x-y,t) \phi(y,x-y)\, \mathrm{d}y - f(x,t) \int_0^\infty f(y,t) \phi(x,y)\, \mathrm{d}y$$

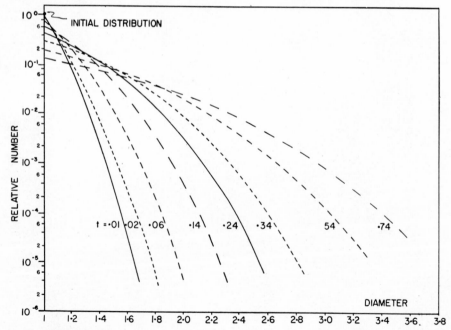

FIG. 1—Some of the curves calculated from the basic equation; units of time and diameter are arbitrary, initial 'distribution' is represented by the point with co-ordinates $(10^0, 1)$

224

Here, $f(x,t)\,\mathrm{d}x$ is the number of particles in unit volume at time t of mass x to $x+\mathrm{d}x$; $\phi(x,y)=\phi(y,x)$ is the 'coalescence function,' defined by

$$\left.\begin{array}{l}\text{Average number of coalescences per}\\ \text{unit volume of particles of mass}\\ x \text{ to } x+\mathrm{d}x \text{ and particles of mass}\\ y \text{ to } y+\mathrm{d}y \text{ in time interval}\\ t \text{ ro } t+\mathrm{d}t\end{array}\right\}=f(x,t)\,f(y,t)\,\phi(x,y)\,\mathrm{d}x\,\mathrm{d}y\,\mathrm{d}t$$

Some simple solutions of this equation deduced by the use of a desk computer have been described in an earlier report by MELZAK and HITSCHFELD [1953], but for general

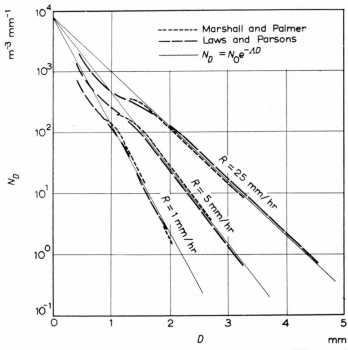

FIG. 2—Distributions of raindrops with diameter for three different rain intensities, obtained by LAWS and PARSONS [1943], and MARSHALL and PALMER [1948]

applications non-automatic methods do not suffice. More recently, the Computation Laboratory of the University of Toronto (with Mr. Ikashimo doing the programming) has worked out for us the development of the distribution as a function of time, for the case that the initial distribution is homogeneous [$f(x,0)=1$] and that the coalescence function ϕ for any two particles is proportional to the square of the sum of the particle diameter. Representative curves of this solution are shown in Fig. 1 in terms of particle diameters. The unit of time here is related to the assumed law of coalescence, and cannot be further specified, unless a precise physical description of the coalescence process is given. Similarly, diameters are measured in relative units, so adjusted that unity refers to the initial particle. The above model is, of course, too simple to serve as a complete description of the precipitation-forming process. This is apparent at once when the results obtained are compared with measured distributions (Fig. 2) which can be des- cribed as exponentials with a common point of departure. The computed curves on the other hand are convex, with continually decreasing frequency of the small particles.

Physically, the model is incomplete in several ways: (1) It does not provide for a size spread in the particles present initially. This is probably not too serious a defect as the initial particles may be assumed to be small in comparison with those fully grown. (2) In the calculations reported here, the spread in the mobilities was not taken into account.

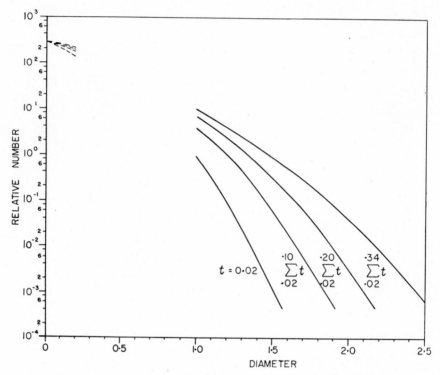

Fig. 3—These curves are summations of graphs of the type shown in Fig. 1, and so represent the kind of distribution to be expected when distributions of different ages are mixed

There is no basic difficulty about this however, and new calculations on the basic equation with this point in mind would probably be feasible. If the larger particles are assigned the greatest fall speeds, they would grow more quickly, and hence the right-hand portion of the resulting curves would be moved further to the right. The loci could thus be expected to straighten out somewhat. (3) More fundamental still is the objection that our simplified model does not allow for the fact that precipitation reaching the ground is a mixture of particles with very different histories. It is worth speculating on the effect of mixing distributions of different ages. In Fig. 3 we have simply added the ordinates of several members of the family shown in Fig. 1. Thus, the ordinates of the curve labelled $\sum_{0.32}^{0.34} t$ are the sums of the original curves at times $0 \cdot 02, 0 \cdot 04 \ldots 0 \cdot 34$. This very crude procedure seems to work in the proper direction. The curves shown correspond to different stages of growth and so to different water contents, just as the curves of Fig. 2 with which they should be compared correspond to different intensities of rainfall. The new curves are much straighter and they show some signs of emerging from a common point on the $D=0$ axis. It may, of course, be objected that an 'old' distribution in our calculated family has not aged in the same way distributions do in nature where during long periods of growth there may be a continuing supply of small particles. If the presence of such small particles were taken into account, the curves could be expected to straighten out even further, as their left ends would be raised, while their right ends would be moved towards the right, since the big particles would grow most rapidly (without becoming much more numerous) as they are the most efficient collectors.

These considerations lend some weight to the supposition that the particle size distributions in rain and snow are achieved initially by a random collision process which need be nothing more than sedimentation among randomly-spaced particles. These distributions then suffer modification by mixing, by accretion of clouds and by separation due to wind shear. Once the exponential type of distribution is attained, however, further modification by any process other than wind shear tends to be slow [RIGBY, MARSHALL, and HITSCHFELD, 1954]. The effect of wind shear is more pronounced and has been studied separately by GUNN and MARSHALL [1955].

REFERENCES

GUNN, K. L. S. and J. S. MARSHALL, The effect of wind shear on falling precipitation, *J. Met.*, v.12, pp.339–349, 1955.

MARSHALL, J. S. and W. McK. PALMER, The distribution of raindrops with size, *J. Met.*, v.5, pp.165–166, 1948.

MELZAK, A. Z., The effect of coalescence in certain collision processes, *Q. App. Maths.*, v.11, pp.231–234, 1953.

MELZAK, A. Z. and WALTER HITSCHFELD, A mathematical treatment of random coalescence, Scientific Report MW-11, submitted to Geophysics Research Directorate, Air Force Cambridge Research Center under Contract AF 19(122)–217, March 1953.

LAWS, J. O. and D. A. PARSONS, The relation of rain-drop size to intensity, *Trans. Amer. Geophys. Union*, v.24, pt.2, pp.452–460, 1943.

RIGBY, E. C., J. S. MARSHALL, and WALTER HITSCHFELD, The development of the size distribution of raindrops during their fall, *J. Meteor.*, v.11, pp.362–372, 1954.

DISCUSSION

Mr. Alfred H. Woodcock—Do you assume that you are sampling far beneath the cloud base and that the coalescence of drops occurs from cloud base to ground, or does coalescence occur in the cloud as well.

Dr. J. S. Marshall—Neither was assumed explicitly. Take a bunch of particles, it doesn't matter what, and shake them up. You start off with the same size and find out what sort of a size distribution you end up with. That sort of a size distribution does resemble the size distribution observed for rain at the ground, and there seems to be no reason to anticipate a change as you come from the cloud to the ground.

Mr. Woodcock—If this sort of thing is going on in such clouds as those we studied in Hawaii, then our relationships of the nuclei to the number of raindrops clearly could not occur. Also I wonder what ideas you might have as to whether or not raindrops actually do coalesce upon contact. This assumes that each time there is a collision there is coalescence. My results suggest that they must not coalesce in the process, otherwise one could not have any relationship between any initial nuclei population and the raindrops as they exist at cloud base.

Dr. Roscoe R. Braham, Jr.—We have other rather strong evidence to indicate that we should not expect every collision to result in coalescence.

Dr. Marshall—These aren't cloud droplets. They are already drizzle size. The assumption is that collisions between drizzle drops become significant in helping to create big drops.

Dr. Braham—If you take large particles, you get rid of the problems of viscosity of the air and so forth.

Dr. Hans J. aufm Kampe—In their equation Hitschfeld and Melzak assumed a very simple coalescence function, which I think it is not applicable to cloud droplets.

Dr. David Atlas—Melzak has been in touch with us recently, and he said he had succeeded in solving that equation analytically using a more realistic coalescence function.

Mr. Waldo E. Smith—Might there not be as much fragmentation as coalescence of the raindrops? If so, things might have a tendency to cancel out. Surface tension causes internal pressures in tiny droplets many times that in large drops (pressure varies inversely as the diameter). The effects of surface tension should not be disregarded.

Dr. Marshall—Some experiments that were done by Magarvey, now at Acadia University, indicated that when one droplet overtook another, they got together. They didn't necessarily stay together. They oscillated around, and the collision might end up with one, two, three, or four droplets.

Dr. J. P. Kuettner—Isn't the main difference between this consideration and the usual one the fact that gravity is completely neglected here?

Dr. Marshall—It comes in indirectly. You can get random collisions by turbulent motion of the air. That's not the only way. You can also get random collisions through gravity, because you have random arrays of big drops and little drops, and gravity can bring one down through the other. Then it's effectively a random process.

DISCUSSION OF THE QUESTION OF DRAG BY THE CLOUD OR RAIN PARTICLES IN INITIATING THE DOWNDRAFT

HORACE R. BYERS, Presiding

Dr. J. S. Marshall—There is a point about the initiation of downdrafts that I have misunderstood. In reading *The Thunderstorm* I got the idea that when cloud droplets change to much larger raindrops, they start drawing the air down. My erroneous notion was that the faster-falling rain would exert a greater drag force on the air, whereas in fact the effect of liquid water is to add its density to that of the air. The effect is independent of drop size, provided that all drops are falling through the air at their terminal speed. I wonder if someone who understands the process by which downdrafts are initiated, and its relation to the formation of raindrops, would explain these points to us.

Dr. Byers—In writing *The Thunderstorm* we tried to avoid an implication that it was something peculiar to the raindrops that caused this sudden downdraft. The idea was based on a belief that the total amount of water in the cloud volume was increasing very rapidly at this point, and that the great mass of water perhaps more than the fact that the water was in the form of large drops had something to do with it.

However, we were unable to specify just what form the aerodynamic drag took so just avoided the problem. As I recall, we had a number of discussions on it at that time and since there was a deadline in publication, we just let it go, that the water somehow draws the air down. Of course, it should also be pointed out that we didn't require this action to persist for very long. In the average sounding all we wanted was some mechanism that would bring the air down a few hundred feet. After that the cloud-air negative buoyancy would take care of it. So I don't want to say that we are depending too much on this drag.

Dr. Roscoe R. Braham, Jr.—As we understand it, it doesn't matter whether you have one gram of water dispersed in a million droplets or whether it is in one drop, with one minor exception: that is, if it is dispersed in tiny cloud droplets effectively acting on a large volume it affects a lot of little volumes of air a little bit; whereas if you put it together in a few large drops, the effect is more violent on a few larger volumes of air.

I used to think that the downdraft initiation could be likened to an infiltration of the updraft by many small bits of air in the wakes behind individual rain drops. Just a little infiltration from each of many drops.

There is one other point which must be remembered in considering the downdraft initiation, that is the matter of water storage. We must have water storage in an updraft. Whenever you have an updraft in which precipitation particles are formed, somewhere in that updraft you must store water and subsequently at some stage in the life of the updraft there is some region within which there will be not one gram or two grams of water such as was in the cubic meter of air to start with, but where you have added the water out of many other cubic meters of air. This idea has its difficulties, however.

The fact that the downdraft in thunderstorms was observed to form at very great heights is hard to reconcile with water storage because you wouldn't offhand guess the storage level to be at 30,000 ft. You'd think it would be at the middle of the storm somewhere. This is a little bit rough.

Still another consideration is the matter of the updraft beyond the level of density equilibrium. The subsequent return to the equilibrium level might serve to move the air downward the few hundred feet that appear to be necessary.

Dr. Marshall—You have to get it started.

Dr. Braham—Yes, and you have to move it only a few hundred feet after which it takes care of itself.

Dr. Byers—Also, I think it has been observed that for some unknown reason there are downdrafts in certain portions of the upper parts of the clouds which seem to exist even without precipitation. They are not strong downdrafts, but they are there. It is possible to get things started downward in such a way that an unstable downward descent of the air can be accomplished.

Dr. Braham—May I amplify your last statement? Turbulence may provide the means for forcing small air parcels down into the negative buoyancy region. It is conceivable that the effect of entrainment in modifying the thermodynamic properties of the updraft is such that a turbulence eddy of given size can't push the air down far enough to initiate a downdraft until the updraft has proceeded to a rather high level.

In other words, it is possible that big eddies, just such as you see on the sides of the clouds, coupled with an updraft which has undergone entrainment, may trigger the downdraft. But, you may have to have the updraft last for twenty minutes or reach to 30,000 ft before the thermodynamic conditions inside the updraft are such that an eddy can serve to start the air down.

Dr. East—On the question of drag, if the acceleration of the raindrops is neglected, then the total drag simply equals the weight of the liquid particles.

MELTING AND FREEZING; STUDIES OF SNOW AND ICE IN THE GENERATION ON PRECIPITATION

THE SUPERCOOLING, FREEZING AND MELTING OF GIANT WATERDROPS AT TERMINAL VELOCITY IN AIR

DUNCAN C. BLANCHARD

Woods Hole Oceanographic Institution, Woods Hole, Mass.

Abstract—Giant water drops have been freely suspended in a vertical wind tunnel at temperatures below 0°C. The manner of freezing of these supercooled waterdrops is a function of the wet bulb temperature. At temperatures above T_w −4 or −5°C, a shell of ice, first forming on the bottom of the drop, will envelope the drop and then freeze inward. This is thought to be analagous to the formation of sleet since many of the phenomena associated with sleet have been observed in this study. At wet bulb temperatures below −4 or −5°C the freezing appears to occur nearly simultaneously over the entire surface of the drop causing the drop to turn to an opaque white. An explanation for the clear and the opaque freezing is partially attributed to the scattering of light by minute air bubbles that form as air comes out of solution as the water freezes.

At temperatures above T_w −5°C drops will often remain supercooled for ten minutes or longer while at about T_w −8°C supercooling does not generally extend beyond a minute. The initiation of freezing in drops in this temperature range is explained by freezing nuclei that might be expected to be active at these temperatures.

The melting of a frozen drop of less than about 10 mm diameter will proceed with no shedding of liquid water. However, if the frozen drop exceeds this diameter water will be shed from a liquid ring that forms around the horizontal midsection of the ice pellet. Melting is such that a spherical ice pellet will transform into a disc.

Introduction—The literature on the supercooling of water presents a complex and confusing picture [BIGG, 1953a]. Recent investigations have stressed the importance of using doubly distilled water and scrupulously clean containers, and WYLIE [1953] has shown that the very nature of the glass containers that hold a water sample precludes the maximum degree of supercooling. By suspending water drops at the interface between two liquids and thus out of contact with glass or contaminated air, MOSSOP [1955] obtained the inverse relationship between freezing point and drop diameter that had been previously found by others with the exception that his freezing points were considerably lower. For example, he found that giant water drops (about eight mm diameter) would supercool to −32°C and smaller drops even lower. Measurements such as these, while possibly approaching the extremes in supercooling, cannot be interpreted as representing the freezing temperatures of raindrops at terminal velocity, at least not in the case of the giant drops. Raindrops are contaminated by collisions with particles within their fall path which, in turn, can bring about freezing at temperatures far higher than −32°C. It seems certain that the freezing of large raindrops is brought about by these collisions and the temperature at which freezing occurs can be best determined by observing the freezing during free fall through the air. The very manner in which the freezing occurs should shed light on the mechanism of the formation of sleet and hail.

The experiments to be discussed were started at the Pennsylvania State University in 1950 and continued during succeeding winters at Woods Hole, Massachusetts. The giant waterdrops were freely suspended at the top of a vertical wind tunnel [BLANCHARD,

DUNCAN C. BLANCHARD

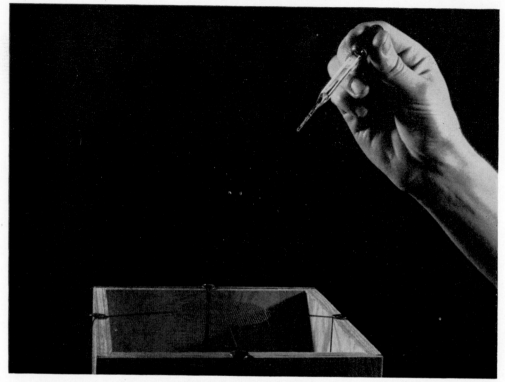

FIG. 1—The manner in which a giant water drop is freely suspended in the air stream at the exit of the vertical wind tunnel

1950] that was housed in an unheated shelter with free access to the outside air (see Fig. 1). This insured that the air temperature and nuclei content of the air through which the drop was falling was similar to that of the outside air. The wet- and dry-bulb temperatures were obtained in the air stream at the point where the drop was freely suspended. Readings were usually made before and after an observation of the freezing of a drop. Inasmuch as the waterdrop will closely attain the wet-bulb temperature of the ambient air [KINZER and GUNN, 1951] it is this temperature that governs the maximum amount of supercooling. The waterdrops, all about eight mm diameter, were injected into the air stream with an eye dropper. Water of various temperatures ($+60$ to $-1°C$) and from several sources (distilled, tap and water contaminated with dirt and dust) was used. As no obvious differences in the freezing of distilled and contaminated water were noted very little mention will be made of it in this paper. BIGG [1953a] found that water grey with room dust froze at almost exactly the same average temperature as distilled water. In order to eliminate one of the variables (the temperature of the waterdrop at the time of injection into the tunnel) the only experiments discussed here will be those in which the initial drop temperature was between 0 and $+5°C$.

Types of freezing—It soon became evident in the course of the experiments that two basic types of freezing occurred. In Fig. 2 an attempt has been made to summarize the results of over a hundred observations. These two types of freezing depend, in general on the degree of supercooling attained by the waterdrop at the moment at which freezing begins. The first type is characterized by the formation of a clear ice shell around the drop. This ice shell, which originates at the bottom of the drop, is remarkably clear in the initial stages of formation and often the only evidence of its existence is the cessation

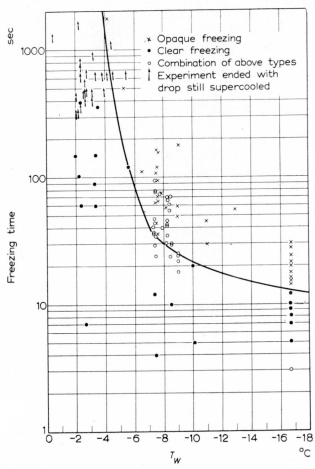

FIG. 2—The type of freezing of a giant drop as a function of time
and the wet bulb temperature

of the drop oscillation that occurs when the ice proceeds to grow up around the edges of the drop. It will be noted from Fig. 2 that clear freezing (represented by dots) will always occur if the T_w is higher than —4 or —5°C. If the T_w is below this temperature clear freezing may still occur if freezing commences within about 20 sec from the time the drop is injected into the air stream. Within this time, presumably, the drop has not had time to cool below a T_w of —4 or —5°C.

If, on the other hand, the drop remains for more than about 20 sec in an air stream below a T_w of —4 or —5°C an opaque form of freezing will occur. This freezing is characterized by what appears to be a near instantaneous formation of opaque or 'milky-colored' ice over the entire surface of the drop. The ice forms with such rapidity that it is impossible to visually determine at what point freezing began. Similar observations on water freezing in containers have been reported by DORSEY [1948] and JOHANNSEN [1948]. Close examination of these partially frozen drops reveals that the periphery is a mixture of ice, water and minute air bubbles. It is undoubtedly the scattering of light from the numerous air bubbles and ice planes that gives the characteristic opaque appearance. The curve on Fig. 2 is a rough boundary, above which only opaque or near opaque freezing usually occurs.

Discussion of two types of freezing—The formation of clear or opaque ice is probably familiar to all who have examined sleet pellets and hailstones. It has been observed by many investigators who have studied the riming of rods exposed to supercooled clouds. CLARK [1948], who carried out such studies on Mount Washington, New Hampshire, found that the temperature of about $-5°C$ could be considered a rough dividing point such that above this temperature the ice formation was mainly clear with virtually no entrapped air. At temperatures below $-5°C$ the ice was predominantly opaque or milky with considerable numbers of entrapped bubbles. Similar results have been obtained by WEICKMANN [1953]. It is interesting that these riming studies indicate a transition in ice type at about $-5°C$ but the results must be interpreted with caution. It is not clear as to what proportion of the numerous air bubbles found in the opaque ice are formed by air being forced out of solution when the water freezes or formed by trapping of the air in small 'pockets' in the spaces between the presumably frozen cloud droplets which form the rime.

The explanation of the clear and opaque ice in the present study is based on the fact that the solubility of air in water is an inverse function of temperature and that the solubility of air in ice is less than a thousandth that in water [SCHOLANDER and others, 1953]. The writer has found no data on air solubility in water at temperatures below $0°C$ but an extrapolation has been made from data obtained for temperatures above $0°C$ [DORSEY, 1940]. This indicates that a drop of eight mm diameter at air saturation at $-8°C$ might well contain 10.5 mm^3 dissolved air as compared to only 7.9 mm^3 at $0°C$. When freezing is initiated in an eight mm drop at $-8°C$ the release of the latent heat of fusion (80 calories g^{-1} of water) will rapidly raise the drop temperature to $0°C$ and allow only 0.1 of the available water to freeze. Subsequent freezing will occur at a rate dependent upon the latent heat transfer away from the drop. In the very short time that the first 0.1 of the drop changes into ice the same relative amount of air (0.1×10.5) or 1.05 mm^3 must come out of solution. This has to occur for, as pointed out above, the air solubility in ice is relatively insignificant. Inasmuch as the opaque structure is not observed on drops freezing at temperatures at $-4°C$ where about 0.5 mm^3 of air must initially come out of solution it appears that a trapping or retaining of the air must occur at freezing at $T_w -8°C$ while not at $T_w -4°C$. It was mentioned earlier that opaque freezing was characterized by an apparently instantaneous formation of ice over the entire surface of the drop. At $T_w -8°C$ the initial ice undoubtedly must start from a single point but rapidly envelopes the entire drop with the interior still liquid. It is probable that an intertwining maze of ice crystals exists with liquid water and the minute air bubbles that form from the air forced out of solution. At temperatures above $T_w -4°C$, on the other hand, the freezing can be seen to start in one region and progress slowly around the drop. The freezing is sufficiently slow to allow most of the air to escape and consequently produce clear ice.

Forms of clear ice—The manner in which the clear ice grows on a freely falling drop is indeed interesting to observe. With the proper lighting and background and by positioning himself at the edge of the tunnel an observer is able to be within four inches of the drop and observe the various phenomena that accompany the freezing. One of the most interesting of these is the formation of spicules [BLANCHARD, 1951]. Spicules have been observed when clear ice forms around the drop and then, due to expansion of

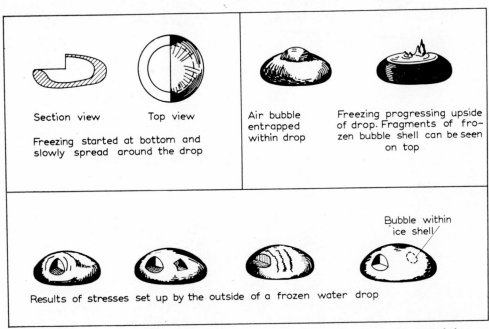

Fig. 3—Sketches of phenomena observed with the clear type of freezing of freely suspended water drops

the ice as it freezes inward, builds up a pressure on the interior water. This, in turn, will cause a fracture in the ice shell through which the remaining water will emerge. This water will form a spicule that freezes from the outside in. As the remaining water freezes along the central core of the spicule numerous air bubbles can be seen. This undoubtedly represents the air that is forced out of solution as the ice progresses inward. The writer has observed similar spicules on natural sleet pellets.

The slow clear freezing of an ice shell around a falling waterdrop results in high internal pressures with concomitant stresses within the ice shell. As ice is most easily fractured along its main crystallographic axis (which in the case of freezing waterdrops is usually radially inward) these stresses undoubtedly aid in producing radial fracture. The writer has never observed this fracture on freezing drops suspended in the air stream. However, the fracture was often noted on semi-frozen drops which had been removed from the air stream. This was definitely the case for the drop shown in the upper left of Fig. 3. The drop, injected into an air strem, of T_d —9·5°C, began to freeze from the bottom in a clear manner. Within a minute the ice had advanced upward and completely enveloped the drop. At that time the semi-frozen drop was removed from the air stream and examined. Nearly an exact quarter of the ice shell was missing revealing the liquid interior. It seems quite apparent that the stresses in the ice shell caused the fracture to occur when the drop was disturbed upon 'capture'.

The lower section of Fig. 3 illustrates smaller triangular-shaped sectors which were missing when the frozen drops were examined outside of the air stream. Here again it appears that this separation occurred as the drop was disturbed on removal from the air stream. On several occasions in natural sleet storms the writer has noticed sleet pellets with similar missing portions. In the light of the present work it appears that much of this separation occurs as the sleet pellet strikes the ground.

In an earlier study [BLANCHARD, 1950] the writer has described how the usual oscillations of the large waterdrops at terminal velocity are effectively eliminated when the drop contains an air bubble constituting upwards of about ten per cent of the drop volume. Not only is drop breakup in turbulent air eliminated but breakup by drop collision is diminished. One of these 'air-bubble' drops was observed to freeze in an air stream of about T_w —0·5°C. After three minutes, a surface layer of ice had advanced from the bottom to about half way up the drop. At this time the water film of the bubble, that had been protruding at the top of the drop, froze, broke, and left only a few jagged ice fragments. A sketch showing the drop before and after freezing is included in Fig. 3. It is not at all improbable that under some conditions raindrops would contain large air bubbles. Air bubbles have been observed by the writer both in natural sleet and in sleet artificially produced in the wind tunnel (see Fig. 3). If, in the case of natural sleet, the pellets were to fall through a layer of warm air and melt to raindrops the air bubble might stay intact. If so, the very presence of the bubbles would insure extreme stability of the large drops.

The initial freezing of a falling drop is occasionally accompanied by the growth of thin planes of ice up through the interior of the drop. An interesting observation of this was obtained with a drop in an air stream of T_w —3·3°C. When the drop oscillations ceased, close observation showed that a thin film of ice had formed on the comparatively flat bottom of the drop, and two extremely thin planes of ice had risen from the bottom ice layer. One appeared to rise perpendicular to the bottom plane, the other at an angle of about 45°. At this time neither the top surface nor the main bulk of the drop was frozen. The slow rotation of these ice planes about the drops vertical axis indicated a rotation of the entire drop. These rotary motions of about one quarter revolution per second would often stop and proceed in the other direction.

Photographs of partially frozen drops—Figures 4–6 are photographs of partially frozen drops and illustrate some of the types of freezing discussed in the last section. As it was somewhat difficult to focus the camera on the drops in the air stream or to insure proper lighting the partially frozen drops were removed and photographed outside the tunnel. The scale shown to the right of each photograph is one mm per square. The air temperature was T_a +0·3°C T_w —3°C.

The frozen drop shown in Fig. 4 was allowed to freeze for about two minutes before

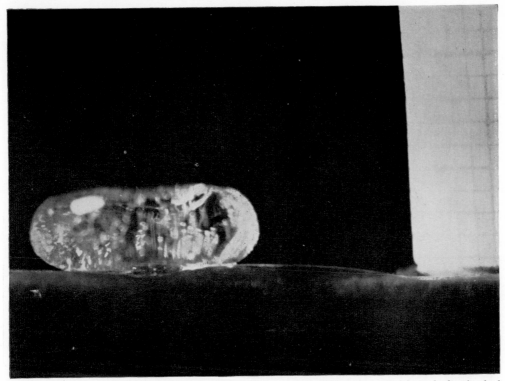

Fig. 4—Photograph of the side view of a drop that was removed from the wind tunnel after ice had formed completely around the drop; the concave appearance at the bottom is due to water melted by the flood light

removal from the tunnel. At this time the entire surface was frozen but the inside was still liquid. The stresses in the ice shell resulted in ridges that may be seen on the photograph extending from the upper left to the lower right section of the drop. Fig. 5 illustrates a drop that was removed from the tunnel when most of the upper part was still liquid. It is interesting to note that a three mm wide band of ice extended over the top of the drop at the mid section. This band was not observed when the drop was in the air stream. It was revealed only when the drop was removed and the water on either side allowed to drain away. Presumably this upward ice growth started with thin planes of ice growing up from the bottom.

Fig. 6 illustrates a drop that had been removed from the air stream with the top part entirely liquid. Much of the interior was still liquid giving the frozen part a bowl-like appearance. Over a hundred bubbles of approximately 200μ diameter were observed within the ice. Some of these can be seen in the photograph.

Stability of frozen drops—In a very thorough study of the equilibrium shape of a large water drop falling at terminal velocity McDonald [1954] has found that the aerodynamic plus the surface tension pressures combine to produce internal drop pressures that satisfy the hydrostatic equation. He has pointed out to the writer that the center of gravity of the drop is above the upward acting center of pressure for these aerodynamic

R

FIG. 5—Photograph of side view of a drop that was removed from the wind tunnel when a portion of the upper part was still liquid. The concave section is caused by liquid water

forces. This would, at first appear to be a case of unstable equilibrium but as the drop is liquid it can always adjust its shape to prevent the above couple force from acting. When the equilibrium shape is not subject to adjustment, as is the case when a shell of clear ice forms around the drop, it might be expected that the afore-mentioned couple would cause the frozen drop to turn upside down where it would fall in stable equilibrium Observation shows, however, that frozen drops will often remain stable for many minutes. On occasions their stability has been interrupted by rapid oscillations about a horizontal axis which sometimes are damped out but often end in the frozen drop falling out of the air stream. Could these oscillations be a result of the couple force in which the aerodynamic center of pressure is continually changing in a direction to bring the drop back to the equilibrium position?

If the drops freeze opaque the stability is noticeably changed. Almost immediately upon freezing oscillations will begin and only rarely will the drop remain in the wind tunnel for more than a few seconds. The drop has often been observed to be carried up and out of the air stream at the instant of freezing. This suggests that a slight increase in cross section has occurred or that the drag has been increased.

An explanation for the freezing of the giant drops—In literature on the supercooling of water [BIGG, 1953a] there is general agreement that freezing temperatures of

FIG. 6—Photograph of the side view of a drop that was removed from the wind tunnel when the top was
still liquid; only the ice portion is shown here

the order reported here are considerably higher than those that would be obtained in
the absence of freezing nuclei. As was mentioned earlier in this paper MOSSOP [1955]
found that drops of the size used here supercooled to about −32°C. With the present
results indicating freezing of drops as high as −3°C it appears that freezing nuclei carried
by the air stream and impinging on the supercooled drop could be responsible for the
freezing.

Investigations by FINDEISEN and SCHULZ [1944] on ice crystal formation as a function of temperature have been studied by BIGG [1953b] who has explained the results,
at temperatures below about −20°C, on the basis of homogeneous nucleation which
does not necessitate the existance of any external freezing or sublimation nuclei. However,
he cannot explain observations of ice at higher temperatures, an example of which are
those reported by BOWEN [1952] where, on three separate water-seeding flights through
clouds whose tops were −6, −6, and −7°C, both rain and hail was found. With the
cloud tops at these temperatures the freezing of the drops probably occurred at even
higher temperatures and suggests the existence of freezing nuclei that are active at these
temperatures.

If, then, we assume that freezing nuclei, and not homogeneous nucleation, are
responsible for freezing at temperatures above about −10°C, then it must be shown that
such freezing nuclei do exist in the atmosphere and that they might be expected to impinge on falling supercooled raindrops. There is little doubt that great numbers of

minute fragmentation crystals exist during and shortly after a fall of snow. What is believed to be an example of the effect of fragmentation crystals in seeding supercooled drops is illustrated in Fig. 7. The symbols have the same interpretation as those in Fig. 2. The numbers beside the points represent the initial temperature of the water. The observations on the five drops which froze in a clear manner in a minute or less were made at a time when a moderate snowfall was going on outside the small wooden structure that housed the wind tunnel. Although fragmentation crystals were not evident to the eye they presumably were entering the shelter through the many cracks and open louvers

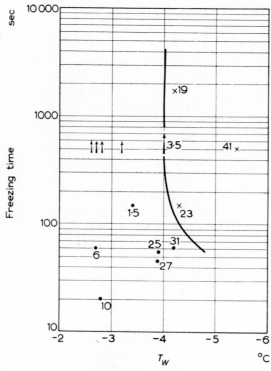

FIG. 7—The effects of seeding supercooled drops with natural ice crystals

and were being carried by the air stream to the drops. With such a continual supply of ice crystals long periods of supercooling were impossible. Several hours later and sometime after the snow fall had stopped the observations were repeated with the result that out of nine drops all but two remained unfrozen for at least seven minutes. One drop remained supercooled for 29 minutes, at which time opaque freezing occurred. It appears that the fragmentation crystals associated with the earlier snow fall had diminished in number and thus increased the probability of prolonged supercooling.

Freezing has been successfully initiated in supercooled drops by burning strips of AgI impregnated paper at the intake of the wind tunnel. It was found that at temperatures near 0°C the AgI nuclei were inactive but became active as ice crystal nuclei somewhere between −3 and −5°C. VONNEGUT [1947] and HEVERLY [1949] found that large grains of AgI placed in bulk water or suspended in drops, respectively, made it difficult to supercool the water below about —4°C. In this case the AgI was acting, not as a sublimation nucleus but as a freezing nucleus and, as SCHAEFER [1952] has shown, AgI is quite effective in either role.

The main bulk of the observations of Fig. 2 cannot be accounted for on the basis of fragmentation nuclei as much of the data were obtained at times when the ground and atmosphere were free from snow. The only recourse in these cases is to look for other natural aerosols that may be acting as freezing nuclei. Our knowledge of freezing nuclei active at temperatures above —10°C is very incomplete. The small volumes of air which have been used by most investigators are quite sufficient for the determination of natural

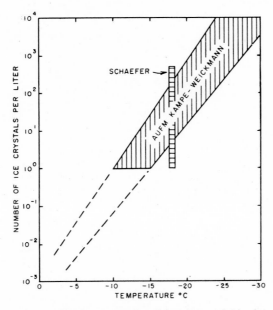

FIG. 8—The concentration of freezing nuclei in the northeastern U.S. as a function of temperature; see text for the interpretation of the data, especially those of Schaefer

freezing nuclei at temperatures below —10°C, but are much too small to determine the concentrations of nuclei of the order of one every 10 or 100 liters. It is just this range which may be of importance to the supercooling of the large drops. AUFM KAMPE and WEICKMANN [1951] have carried out investigations on the occurrence of freezing nuclei in natural aersols as a function of temperature. Although their results indicate higher concentrations of nuclei for a given temperature than other investigators [PALMER, 1949, FINDEISEN and SCHULTZ, 1944], only their results will be considered. In the first place the aerosols they tested were from a variety of air masses all of which were probably simultaneously common to the present experiments. (Asbury Park, N. J., the place where their work was carried out is only about 200 miles WSW of Woods Hole, Mass., the site of most of the present work.) Secondly, SCHAEFER [1954] has reported on more than 15,000 observations of natural ice nuclei made atop Mt. Washington, New Hampshire (about 200 miles NNW of Woods Hole) over the past few years. Though he finds seasonal fluctuations, and fluctuations from day to day, the great majority of observations which were made during the winter months and concurrent with the work reported here, indicated from one to 500 ice nuclei per liter at a cold box temperature of −18°C. It can be seen that Schaefer's values are centered very well (see Fig. 8) around those found by aufm Kampe and Weickmann at the same temperature. The good agreement between these investigators, whose work was carried out in locations that are reasonably near the site of the present work, leads the writer to believe that the relation of freezing nuclei to temperature at Woods Hole might be most nearly approximated by the aufm Kampe and Weickmann data. One must realize that great fluctuations probably occur around the values which they have found. Schaefer reports that over the years the count has varied from none to a maximum of 10^4 per liter.

Considerable disagreement with the aufm Kampe-Weickmann and Schaefers freezing nuclei values have been found in recent measurements of freezing nuclei over Arizona, Australia, and Hawaii [KASSANDER and others, 1956]. It was found that, in general, the number of freezing nuclei activated at about −29°C was of the order of one per liter, far less than would be expected from the data of aufm Kampe-Weickmann and Schaefer. It must be realized however that the above locations are probably not subjected to such a high degree of contamination from industrial smokes as is the northeastern United States where the aufm Kampe-Weickmann and Schaefer work was done. These industrial smokes may well be responsible for the higher level of freezing nuclei.

An estimate of the order of magnitude of the freezing nuclei that might be expected at temperatures above −10°C has been arrived at by extrapolating aufm Kampe and Weickmann's data. From Fig. 8 it can be seen that one might expect about one freezing nucleus per 100 liters at −4°C and one every ten liters at −8°C. (As the freezing nuclei are determined by examination of a water cloud the T_d is assumed to equal T_w.) Now a simple calculation shows that a drop of eight mm diameter (flattening during fall gives a cross section of about nine mm diameter) falling at a terminal velocity of nine m sec^{-1} would have to fall for five minutes to sweep out 100 liters and, at a temperature of −4°C to overtake one freezing nucleus. At a temperature of −8°C where one freezing nucleus every ten liters is expected, the drop would have to fall only 0·1 as long or 30 seconds. Reference to Fig. 2 indicates that at T_w −4°C the freezing times were centered at about five minutes or 300 sec. Wide deviations occur but this is to be expected and may only reflect the great variation that can exist in freezing nuclei. At T_w −8°C it is seen that the freezing times are indeed of the order of 0·1 those at −4°C or 30 sec.

It is realized that the explanation for the observed freezing of drops as advanced above is far from being conclusive. We know almost nothing about the collection efficiency of freezing nuclei for large water drops. The value of unity as assumed here is probably too high. Secondly, there is doubt about the validity of the extrapolation of aufm Kampe and Weickmann's data. SCHAEFER [1949] has examined a considerable number of naturally occurring dusts to determine their temperature range of activity for producing sublimation nuclei. He reports that none of these has shown any activity at temperatures above −12°C. However, it is believed that Schaefer was not too much concerned with low nuclei concentrations such as one per 100 liters that might exist at −4°C. The volume of air that was illuminated in his cold chamber and examined for ice crystals was probably not more than one liter and, even allowing for air motion through the illuminated volume, it is probable that nuclei of concentrations of less than 0·1 per liter would be undetected. A conclusive answer to the whole problem will not be obtained until freezing nucleus counts are made concurrent with observations of the freezing of large drops. The writer is hopeful that he will be able to carry out such experiments in the near future.

The melting of a frozen drop—The manner in which a frozen drop melts and sheds water has always been an interesting one to the cloud physicist. Besides the changes in raindrop size distribution that may be brought about, the radar meteorologists must be concerned with any basic change in the shape of the particles which produce the radar return.

In order to find out the nature of the melting process, experiments were carried out with giant drops in the following way. A water drop in an air stream of $T_d+0.5°C$, $T_w-2.7°C$ was allowed to freeze for about 2·5 minutes. At this time the outside of the drop was covered with clear ice and stresses were beginning to cause surface irregularities to appear. A 2000 watt heater was then placed near the tunnel intake. Within 40 sec, the ice shell on the drop, which had appeared greyish-white, became covered with a film of liquid water that reflected the light of a flood light as if it were a mirror. As the ice shell melted, a few entrapped air bubbles were released and rose to the top of the drop. Finally the characteristic rigidity of the ice pellet was gone and the drop was entirely liquid. During this freezing and melting process, the drop was stable and showed no tendency to change in shape or to shed water. This behavior is just what would be expected, since the equilibrium shape of the drop does not change as freezing occurs and, consequently, no change should occur upon melting. At the completion of the melting process the air temperature at the tunnel exit was T_d 11·4°C, T_w 3°C.

Water drops at terminal velocity are not stable at sizes much above 10 mm diameter [BLANCHARD, 1950], so it would appear that shedding of water must occur with the melting of ice spheres above this size. As the literature appears to have no information on this subject it may be of interest to briefly describe some simple experiments carried out at about 25°C. Crude ice spheres of about 20 mm diameter were fashioned from ice cubes obtained from a refrigerator. These spheres were mounted at the exit of the wind tunnel in several ways. One procedure was to drill a small hole through the sphere and thread it upon a thin string mounted along the vertical axis of the tunnel. Proper adjustment of the air speed will allow the sphere to 'fall' at terminal velocity and remain suspended on the string. With this same air velocity the sphere was sometimes supported from a horizontal string. Another technique of holding the ice sphere was to mount it at the end of a stiff thin rod and support it in the air stream from above. Regardless of the manner in which it was held, the following melting phenomena were noted. As shown in the sketch of Fig. 9 the water from the melting sphere would collect in a ring around the horizontal midsection, a region where the air pressure is probably lowest [McDONALD, 1954]. As the melt water builds up in this water ring instability sets in and drops up to perhaps five mm will break away. With rapid motions they often will be carried over the top of the sphere and coalesce with the ring on the opposite side from whence they came. (This recapturing effect has been observed in earlier studies [BLANCHARD, 1949] and is believed to be important in raindrop growth.) Sometimes these drops do not coalesce with the liquid ring, but travel out beyond the edge of it, receive the full impact of the air flow there, and break into many fragments. On other occasions the drops will break away from the ring and continue upwards being but little influenced by the large ice sphere. In any event all shedding of water is confined to the liquid ring around the mid-section.

The ring of water tends to insulate part of the ice sphere, causing most of the melting to occur on the top and bottom. This differential melting results in the sphere of ice becoming a horizontally oriented disc of ice. As the transition is going on, the ice pellet often begins to spin about the vertical axis with such rapidity that the water is centrifuged off in small drops. The spin appears to be upwards of five revolutions sec^{-1} and not always in the same direction thus it does not appear to be due to a rotary nature of the air stream.

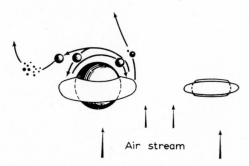

Air stream

FIG. 9—A proposed melting process for large freely falling ice pellets; the sketch at left shows the shedding of drops from the ring of water that develops around the mid-section of the pellet; the insulating effect of this water causes the pellet to transform into a disc, as seen edgewise in the sketch at the right

The observations described above were made on spheres suspended with threads. Some preliminary attempts to freely suspend the large spheres have been successful for only a few seconds, but it appears from this that the behavior is still as described. It is possible that a large ice pellet in nature will rotate and tumble as it falls but as melting occurs the water will tend to remain oriented around the horizontal mid-section and thus provide a drag force that will tend to oppose the tumbling motion of the pellet. If any rotation about the vertical axis sets in, the resultant centrifugal forces should further stabilize the ice pellet. Further experiments on this interesting and potentially important phenomenon are badly needed before one can fully understand the melting process of these large ice pellets in nature.

Conclusions—It seems likely that the time a supercooled drop in free fall can exist before freezing is a function of the freezing nuclei content of the atmosphere. Certainly the occurrence of clear or opaque freezing is a function of temperature. Further work must be done to determine the behavior of the drops as the opaque freezing process proceeds to completion. This work to date has been difficult as the drops become unstable very shortly after freezing. It may be necessary to remove the drops from the air stream after the initial freezing has occurred and observe the final freezing process while they are artificially supported.

The melting of an ice pellet less than ten mm diameter can occur with no shedding of water. On the other hand, the fascinating behavior of an ice sphere greater than ten mm diameter, as it undergoes melting, indicates that water is shed from the liquid ring that forms around the horizontal periphery of the drop. It is probable that this ring, and the spinning motion of the ice pellet around the vertical axis, are responsible not only for the stability of the drop but for its final evolution into a circular disc.

Acknowledgments—The writer would like to thank Hans Neuberger, head of the Division of Meteorology at the Pennsylvania State University for his guidance in the initial phases of the work. Thanks are also due to A. H. Woodcock of the Woods Hole Oceanographic Institution for critical discussions as the experimental work evolved.

This is Contribution No. 809 from the Woods Hole Oceanographic Institution. A part of this work was drawn from a thesis submitted to the Pennsylvania State University in June 1951 for the partial fulfillment of the degree of Master of Science. The rest of the work was done under the Office of Naval Research, Contract Nonr 798(00) (NR–082–124).

REFERENCES

AUFM KAMPE, H. J. and H. K. WEICKMANN, The effectiveness of natural and artificial aerosols as freezing nuclei, *J. Met.*, v.8, pp.283–288, 1951.

BIGG, E. K., The 'freezing point' of water, *Scientific J. R. College Science*, v.23, pp.107–114, 1953a.

BIGG, E. K., The formation of atmospheric ice crystals by the freezing of droplets, *Q.J.R. Met. Soc.*, v.79, pp.510–519, 1953b.

BLANCHARD, D. C., Experiments with water drops and the interaction between them at terminal velocity in air, *Occ. Rep.* 17, Proj. Cirrus, Gen. Elec. Co., 1949.

BLANCHARD, D. C., The behavior of water drops at terminal velocity in air, *Trans., Amer. Geophys. Union*, v.31, pp.836–842, 1950.

BLANCHARD, D. C., A verification of the Bally-Dorsey theory of spicule formation on sleet pellets, *J. Met.*, v.8, pp.268–269, 1951.

BOWEN, E. G., A new method of stimulating convective clouds to produce rain and hail, *Q.J.R. Met. Soc.*, v.78, pp.37–45, 1952.

CLARK, V., Icing nomenclature, in Harvard-Mt. Washington Res. Report 1946–1947, Air Force Tech. Rep. 5676, pp.415–481, 1948.

DORSEY, N. E., *Properties of Ordinary Water-Substance*, Amer. Chem. Soc., Monograph ser., Reinhold Pub. Corp., New York, 673 pp., 1940.

DORSEY, N. E., The freezing of supercooled water, *Trans. Amer. Philosoph. Soc.*, v.38(3), pp.247–328, 1948.

FINDEISEN, W. and G. SCHULZ, Experimentelle Untersuchungen über atmosphärische Eisteilchenbildung, 1, *Forschungs-und Erfahrungsberichte Reichswetterd.*, A, no.27, 1944.

HEVERLY, J. R., Supercooling and crystallization, *Trans., Amer. Geophys. Union*, v.30, pp.205–210, 1949.

JOHANNSEN, R. S., Some experiments on the freezing of water, *Science*, v.108, pp.652–654, 1948.

KASSANDER, A. R., L. L. SIMS, and J. E. McDONALD, Observations of freezing nuclei over the southwestern U.S., paper in this publication, pp.392–401, 1956.

KINZER, G. D. and R. GUNN, The evaporation, temperature and thermal relaxation-time of freely falling water drops, *J. Met.*, v.8, pp.71–83, 1951.

McDONALD, J. E., The shape and aerodynamics of large raindrops, *J. Met.*, v.11, pp.478–494, 1954.

MOSSOP, S. C., The freezing of supercooled water, *Proc. Phys. Soc.*, v.68, pp.193–208, 1955.

PALMER, H. P., Natural ice particle nuclei, *Q.J.R. Met. Soc.*, v.75, pp.15–22, 1949.

SCHAEFER, V. J., The formation of ice crystals in the laboratory and the atmosphere, *Chem. Reviews*, v.44, pp.291–320, 1949.

SCHAEFER, V. J., Formation of ice crystals in ordinary and nuclei-free air, *Ind. and Engr. Chem.*, v.44, pp.1300–1304, 1952.

SCHAEFER, V. J., The concentration of ice nuclei in air passing the summit of Mt. Washington, *Bul. Amer. Met. Soc.*, v.35, pp.310–314, 1944.

SCHOLANDER, P. F., W. FLAGG, R. J. HOCK, and L. IRVING, Studies on the physiology of frozen plants and animals in the arctic, *J. Cellular and Comparative Physiology*, V.42, sup.1, pp.1–56, 1953.

VONNEGUT, B., The nucleation of ice formation by silver iodide, *J. App. Phys.*, v.18, pp.593–595, 1947.
WEICKMANN, H., Observational data on the formation of precipitation in cumulonimbus clouds, in *Thunderstorm Electricity*, Univ. Chicago Press, pp.66–138, 1953.
WYLIE, R. G., The freezing of supercooled water in glass, *Proc. Phys. Soc.*, v.66, pt.3, pp.241–254, 1953.

DISCUSSION

Dr. L. J. Battan—Have you tried any experiments where you permitted small drops to collide with the bigger drop in any of these stages of freezing or melting? When it occurred did it accelerate freezing or did it have no effect; or did it accelerate break up of the drop when it started melting? Furthermore, how often did bounceoff occur?

Mr. D. C. Blanchard—I'm afraid I can't answer either. I did not make that kind of experiment; my main concern has been trying to see at what temperature a drop would freeze.

Dr. Battan—It would be interesting to do some work with a one-mm drop bouncing off a six-mm drop, for example.

Mr. Blanchard—I haven't done that, either. I admit it's something that should be tried.

Dr. Battan—We took some photographs in Chicago taken with a Fastex camera where water was injected through a jet and one could follow the drops at this high speed and see the bounceoff. When the drops collided, the smaller one would sink into the larger one and come right out again. What effect would this have on the drop size distribution?

Mr. Blanchard—I couldn't say; however I have also observed what you just mentioned.

Dr. Richard M. Schotland—I have two comments. One concerns the appearance of the murky type of ice which you describe. I obtained similar results except when I changed the rate of freezing. By varying the cooling rate I could vary the line of separation between clear and murky ice. If the rate of cooling was high, I obtained this murky type of ice at a relatively high temperature and conversely, at a low rate of cooling the murky ice appeared at a lower temperature.

The second comment is on the case where a large water droplet is hit by a smaller droplet. I have used a Fastex camera, and the results indicate that with freshly formed water drops sometimes one can get coalescence and sometimes not. This apparently depends strongly upon the nature of the collision.

Dr. E. J. Workman—I should like to mention an idea of Reynolds in connection with the question raised about collisions and bouncing and the effect upon freezing. If one could form the union of two drops which are so structurally organized as to be unable to freeze by themselves, then the disorder which would be introduced by bringing these two drops into coalescence might account for or favor the freezing of supercooled droplets in thunderstorms, even when they are quite small.

Dr. James E. McDonald—There was one thing I want to ask. Did you say that after the drops froze they still stayed in the air stream?

Mr. Blanchard—If they freeze clear, they will. If they freeze in the opaque manner, they will fall out. They become unstable almost immediately.

Mr. McDonald—Well, the freezing does proceed from the bottom.

Mr. Blanchard—In the clear ice.

Dr. McDonald—The difficult thing to understand about the frozen raindrops falling in the way they do is that the center of pressure of an object of raindrop shape is below the center of mass, which is an aerodynamically unstable situation. Once, then, the drops lose their fluidity by virtue of freezing, it is not clear how they can avoid tumbling out of the airstream. Fluidity and the attendant ability for dynamic balance between shape and aerodynamic factors are essential to the stable (non-tumbling) movement of a raindrop shaped object through the air.

Dr. Horace R. Byers—Mr. Blanchard's method appears to have a very good application to the problem of hailstones. I wonder, if you would care to express any ideas on that subject in amplifying the paper that you have given.

Mr. Blanchard—Well, if you mean growing hailstones by suspending frozen pellets in the wind tunnel, I think a lot more work would have to be done actually to do that. I haven't been able to suspend an ice pellet for more than five or ten seconds. It is something that might be worth trying although I do not plan to try it, at least not this winter. I think I shall continue on the problem of the shedding of water from a melting ice pellet. This can be easily done by the methods outlined in my paper.

Dr. Vincent J. Schaefer—I wonder if this is not being done by Prof. R. Sänger and his group at the Polytechnic Institute at Zurich, Switzerland, because when I was there last year, they had a working vertical wind tunnel in which they were suspending large spheres of clay, much heavier than any of the hailstones we have to worry about. And, at that time, the plan was to install this at an observatory for research on this problem. So my guess is that this is already being done.

Dr. Byers—There is no published material however.

Dr. Schaefer—No.

OVERSEEDING OF CUMULUS CLOUDS

ROSCOE R. BRAHAM, JR. AND JOHN R. SIEVERS

Cloud Physics Project, Department of Meteorology,
The University of Chicago, Chicago, Ill.

Abstract—Data obtained from numerous aircraft flights through cumulus clouds in central United States are presented together with theoretical considerations of dry-ice seeding. It is shown that an expected concentration of sublimation nuclei of $10^8/m^3$ could convert an average cumulus cloud into ice crystals only within 100sec and the resulting ice crystals would not grow to a size sufficiently large to be detected by the methods of measurement indicated. Flight observations indicate that this 'drying-up' of a cumulus cloud is not generally observed in clouds treated with dry ice and that the formation of clear ice on aircraft surfaces in the majority of treated clouds suggests that the resulting concentration of ice crystals from dry-ice seeding is much less than a theoretical yield would indicate.

EVER since Schaefer introduced the techniques for initiating the sublimation-coalescence precipitation process in clouds, through the introduction of suitable sublimation (or freezing) nuclei, the problem of the consequences of too many such nuclei has plagued the cloud physicist. The release of too many such nuclei is known as 'overseeding' and a cloud is said to be overseeded whenever the number of nuclei is so large as to inhibit the effective formation of precipitation. The physical and chemical principles through which this condition might occur are reasonably well established, theoretically. However, the frequency with which this condition occurs naturally, and the extent to which one can produce it artificially (either intentionally or accidentally) has never been satisfactorily determined.

Meteorological literature contains conflicting evidence concerning the amount of treatment material required for overseeding, particularly in the case of cumulus clouds. There are cases of supposed overseeding with a treatment rate of a few pounds of dry ice per mile of traverse. Also one can find alleged successes resulting from treating a single cumulus turret with several hundred pounds of dry ice.

The in-cloud measurements of the University of Chicago cumulus flight program contain considerable data bearing on the problem of overseeding cumulus clouds. These data are currently being analyzed. It is the purpose of this paper to report on the current status of this research.

BASIC DATA

The University of Chicago, under the sponsorship of the U.S. Air Force, for the past several years has been engaged in a program of study of the precipitation-forming processes in cumulus clouds. These studies consist of making in-flight measurements of as many as possible of the physical and chemical parameters which affect the formation of precipitation. Repeated passes are made through individual cumuli to provide data concerning the number, size distribution and time rate of change of the cloud droplets and the size, number and physical state of the precipitation particles and the time and level of their first formation. Measurements of cloud air temperature, liquid-water content, internal cloud motions, electric-charge structure, etc., also constitute an important aspect of the measurement program.

During the period from August, 1953, through November, 1954, operations were conducted in central United States and in the vicinity of the island of Puerto Rico. During this period several hundred clouds were examined and approximately 350 individual clouds were selected for detailed study throughout the major part of their life-spans. Half of these 350 clouds were subjected to treatment, making use of a randomization scheme for deciding whether each individual cloud would or would not be treated. The purpose of treating one-half of the selected clouds was to determine, if possible, the extent to which such treatment would alter the subsequent behavior of the cloud.

The clouds were treated either with dry ice, in the case of subcooled clouds, or with water spray, in the case of clouds entirely warmer than freezing.

The details of the instrumentation, the methods used to free the data from bias due to experimenter, season, locality and day-to-day meteorological conditions, and a thorough discussion of the results of these experiments have been described in a special report to the Air Force. (R. R. Braham, Jr., L. J. Battan, and H. R. Byers, Artificial nucleation of cumulus clouds, Cloud Physics Project, Special Report 24, Univ. Chicago, 1955; general publication delayed.) It suffices here to state that it was possible to reach certain positive conclusions concerning the treatment of warm cumuli with water spray. The effects, if any, of treatment of subcooled clouds with dry ice, however, were too small to be detected in the sample of 27 valid pairs of dry-ice-treated clouds. (A pair of clouds consists of one treated and one untreated cloud. A pair was considered valid if both clouds individually met the initial eligibility requirements, did not contain precipitation on the 'treatment pass' and if there were no malfunctions of vital scientific equipment) [BATTAN, 1953; BROWN and WILLETT, 1955; BYERS and HALL, 1955; GOYER and and HANDLER, 1955; LODGE, 1955; LODGE and BAER, 1954].

Effect of dry-ice treatment—The results of dry-ice treatment of cumulus clouds over central United States are given in Table 1.

Table 1. *Results of dry-ice treatment on subcooled clouds in central United States; total number of pairs,* 27

Response	No.
Both with echo	1
Treated with echo, untreated without ...	7
Untreated with echo, treated without ...	5
Both without echo	14
	27

Note that in seven pairs the treated cloud developed an echo whereas the untreated cloud did not; in five pairs the reverse situation prevailed. The probability of obtaining the observed seven-five distribution (or a more unusual result) by pure chance is 0·39. Thus it cannot be concluded that the treatment increased the probability of precipitation initiation, neither can it be concluded that it does not have such an effect.

The fact that 19 of the 27 treated subcooled clouds did not develop a precipitation radar echo raised the question of overseeding. In the Special Report cited above it was concluded that this did not occur. In the present paper we will re-examine this point in the light of still further analyses and theoretical development.

Rate of dry-ice treatment—Dry-ice pellets were dispersed into the subcooled clouds directly from an ice crusher mounted in the waist sections of the B-17 aircraft used for the flights. During the first half of the measurement program (prior to Flight 116) a dispersal rate of dry ice of about 17 lb/mi of traverse was used. Beginning with Flight 116, the dispersal rate was increased to about 50 lb/mi. These rates are substantially higher than used by many investigators and should, therefore, provide valuable information concerning the problem of overseeding. The size distribution of the dry-ice pellets characterizing each of these rates is given in Table 2.

Table 2. Size distribution of dry-ice pellets used for cloud-treatment tests

Size	Prior to Flight 116	Flight 116 and later
inch	per cent	per cent
$> \frac{1}{2}$	4	2
$\frac{1}{2} - \frac{3}{8}$	39	$\left\{ \begin{array}{l} 6 \\ 28 \end{array} \right.$
$\frac{3}{8} - \frac{1}{4}$		
$\frac{1}{4} - \frac{1}{8}$	13	17
$< \frac{1}{8}$	44	...
$\frac{1}{8} - \frac{1}{16}$	...	7
$< \frac{1}{16}$	...	40
	100	100

A more meaningful value for the rate of treatment comes from a consideration of the amount of material in each of the size classes given in Table 2. Obviously the larger the pellet, the larger will be the vertical range through which the effects of the pellet will be distributed. Further, the larger the pellet the faster will be its rate of descent so that it is proportionately less effective at any given level. In order to study the relative effectiveness of these two rates, a simple computation was made of the evaporation of the pellets during their fall through the cloud. These computations, based upon the work of LANGMUIR and others [1947] and SQUIRES and SMITH [1950], have value inasmuch as it is the cooling

Table 3. Effective dry-ice treatment rate (assuming no updraft or downdraft in cloud)

Flights	Depth interval below treatment level (feet)			
	0–1000	1000–2000	2000–3000	3000–4000
	lb/mi	lb/mi	lb/mi	lb/mi
Prior to Flight 116 ...	9	3	1	1
Flight 116 and after ...	26	2	1	1

due to the evaporation of dry ice that lowers the ambient air temperature to the point where the large number of drops produced by condensation in the cooled air can undergo freezing nucleation. The results of this computation are presented in Table 3.

Change of phase of hydrometeors after treatment—Throughout all the experiments, an effort was made to determine the physical phase of the cloud particles and the precipitation elements as a function of the life of the cloud, both in treated and untreated clouds. This is one of the reasons for adopting the procedure of making repeated probes on a single cloud. In the analysis of the results of the dry-ice treatment experiments, the measurements of cloud droplets and precipitation particles have been given special study in order to determine, if possible, the degree to which the cloud was changed from water droplets to ice precipitation particles. In 24 dry-ice-treated clouds the data were sufficiently detailed to permit study. These data are tabulated in Table 4, which presents the data divided into three groups depending upon the phase of the water present (ice,

Table 4. *Distribution of dry-ice treated clouds in terms of subsequent phase of precipitation particles and temperature of the treatment pass*

Cloud		Treatment temperature	Echo formation	Time observed*
No.	Type			
		°C		sec
149D	Ice	−1·9	No	539
114D	Ice	−4·9	No	239
122E	Ice	−2·0	Yes	638
116E	Water	−0·6	No	412
161B	Water	−1·5	No	261
122G	Water	−1·6	No	384
128I	Water	−3·1	No	642
173C	Water	−3·6	No	257
126I	Water	−4·0	No	237
126M	Water	−4·0	No	222
114A	Water	−4·9	No	469
112G	Water	−3·1	Yes	1001
144F	Both	−1·4	No	211
161E	Both	−1·5	No	274
144C	Both	−1·8	No	432
142D	Both	−3·1	No	281
124F	Both	−3·8	No	534
128E	Both	−4·2	No	1487
100E	Both	−8·8	No	574
149E	Both	−1·9	Yes	539
136A	Both	−2·2	Yes	825
142G	Both	−2·8	Yes	871
124E	Both	−3·7	Yes	810
113C	Both	−4·6	Yes	224

* Pertains to the elapsed time between treatment and the last pass. Almost without exception, the termination of observations on a cloud was occasioned by cloud dissipation.

water, or both) on subsequent passes. Clouds, which on any pass subsequent to treatment were judged to be composed only of ice particles, were placed in that group even though on an earlier pass they may have contained both ice and water. Similarly 'mixed clouds' (both) are those which contained both ice and water particles on one of the passes but which, at no time, were judged to be all ice. Clouds in which only water particles were found are called 'water only' clouds.

Three of the 24 clouds completely turned to ice following treatment. An echo formed in one of the three. There is a distinct possibility that the other two were overseeded.

Of the 24 clouds, 12 were observed to be mixed ice and water, and five of these subsequently developed echoes. The other seven failed to develop echoes even though it appears that the mixed phase would be ideal for this. In clouds 100E and 124F the records are incomplete on the last run, and it is not positively known that ice was present on the last pass. All other no-echo, mixed-phase clouds were known to remain of mixed phase up until cloud dissipation. Each of the no-echo clouds were observed and studied until they dissipated so that there is no question of an echo developing after the termination of measurements.

The most surprising feature of these data is the fact that in nine of the 24 dry-ice-treated clouds, the ice crystals were either absent or were too sparse or too small to be detected. The passes through these 'all water' clouds were characterized by clear ice accumulating on the dome and other exposed airplane surfaces and by the collection of cloud droplets (as opposed to ice crystals) on the sampler.

Three of these nine clouds were treated at temperatures warmer than $-2°C$ which might account for their behavior, although in five other clouds treated at these temperatures ice particles were detected.

It is difficult to understand why these nine clouds failed to show ice particles after treatment. In the Special Report above cited, it was suggested that the 'rate of lateral mixing within a cumulus cloud is much slower than has been believed with the result that the plane . . .' in subsequent passes . . . 'missed the treated areas'. Another possibility suggested was that dry-ice pellets are vastly more effective in the laboratory than in the field. A third possibility is that the crystals, although present, grew too slowly to be detected and to use up the available water during the life of the cloud. This possibility is considered in the following paragraphs. First, however, it is well to consider the minimum size required for an ice particle to be detected in the measurement program.

List of symbols—The following symbols are used:

a = diameter of collector
a_d = diameter of collected droplets
C = electrostatic capacitance
C_p = specific heat at constant pressure
D = coefficient of diffusivity of water vapor in air
$e_{a, d, i}$ = vapor pressure over ambient air, droplet, ice crystal
Δe_d = vapor pressure gradient (air-droplet surface)
Δe_i = vapor pressure gradient (air-ice surface)
k = thermometric conductivity of air
$Kv_{d, i}$ = ventilation coefficient for droplet, ice crystal
$L_{d, i}$ = latent heat of evaporation, sublimation

Λ = non-dimensional parameter
m = molecular mass
$M_{d,i}$ = mass of water droplet, ice crystal
$M_{T_{d,i}}$ = total mass of water in droplet form, of ice in crystal form
μ = viscosity of air
n_d = number of droplets in any class interval
N_i = number of ice crystals
P = total atmospheric pressure
$r_{d,i}$ = radius of water droplet, ice crystal
$r_{0_{d,i}}$ = initial radius of water droplet, ice crystal
R = universal gas constant
ρ_a = density of air
ρ_w = density of water
t = time
$T_{a,d,i}$ = temperature of ambient air, water droplet, ice crystal
U_0 = relative speed of droplet and collector

Minimum-size ice particle for detection—There are three methods in which the presence of ice particles can be detected in these flight measurements. Two of these methods involve direct observation, the other involves inference from other observations.

The most useful observation of ice particles is that in which the particles impinge on the dome on the top of the airplane. As a part of the instrumentation a large hemispherical plastic dome, four feet in diameter, was installed in the top turret position in the B-17. The senior scientist, head and shoulders above the skin of the airplane, rides in this dome position. Ice particles impinging on this dome are easily seen and measured. It is of importance, however, to consider the minimum size of particles which will impinge on the dome.

From JOHNSON [1954] (after Langmuir and Blodgett) we know that the collection efficiency of the dome can be expressed in terms of a non-dimensional parameter given by

$$\Lambda = \frac{\rho_w U_0 a_d^2}{18\mu a} \tag{1}$$

The collection efficiency is a function of Λ only. LANGMUIR and BLODGETT [1946] suggest that the collection efficiency is given by

$$E = \frac{\Lambda^2}{(\Lambda + \frac{1}{2})^2} \tag{1a}$$

Substituting the relevant values for the dome on the B-17, we find the collection efficiency for cloud and precipitation particles as given in Table 5.

Although it is theoretically possible for the dome to collect cloud particles as small as a few tens of microns radius, it is obvious that ice particles of such size could not be detected. All things considered, it seems reasonable to accept about 250 microns radius as the lower limit of particles which could be reliably counted. The presence of sub-cooled cloud droplets mixed with the crystals is a favorable situation for the detection

s

Table 5. *Collection efficiency of the B-17 dome for cloud droplets and precipitation particles (assuming unit density spherical particles)*

Particle radius	Collection efficiency
micron	
10	0
20	0·13
40	0·45
60	0·62
80	0·73
100	0·80
150	0·90
200	0·94
250	0·97

of the crystals. In these circumstances the droplets freeze into a clear ice sheet into which the crystals are impacted and where they remain for easy identification and measurement.

The second means of identifying ice particles involves the droplet sampler. A multiple slide droplet collector is used for obtaining measurements of the sizes and numbers of cloud particles. Ice crystals, snow pellets, etc., can be recognized in the collections by their shapes. It is likely, however, that many such particles escape detection because of melting prior to being photographed immediately after collection. Furthermore, the crystal concentration must exceed about 0·05 particles per cm³ in order to be detected reliably in the volume sampled.

The third source of information concerning the number of ice crystals in a cloud comes indirectly from the icing of the dome. Obviously, for the dome to ice, the cloud must contain liquid water. This condition, if it persists for a sufficient time interval, permits one to infer the absence of a large number of ice crystals because it will be shown that, with a concentration of crystals of about $10^6/m^3$ or greater, the growth of an ice crystal is sufficiently rapid to evaporate the entire cloud within the average lifetime of the clouds studied. In the case of a mixed cloud, something concerning the relative mass of the liquid and ice phase may be inferred.

THEORETICAL ANALYSES

Number of nuclei expected—The starting point for any study of overseeding should be the number of nuclei expected from the treatment method employed. It has been seen that the amount of dry ice which evaporated after dispersal ranged from about 26 lb/mi for the 0–1000 ft interval to one pound per mile for the 2000–3000 ft interval.

It has been shown, both theoretically and experimentally, that one can expect between 10^{11} and 10^{16} crystals per gram of dry ice evaporated [Langmuir and others, 1947]. Accepting the more conservative value of 10^{11}, we compute the expected crystal concentrations per meter³ in the various 1000-ft intervals below the airplane. We assume an initial mechanical spread of ten meters which is just that which is measured for the spread of a water spray released from the bomb bay. (Experimentally it is a lot easier to measure the spread of the water spray than it is to measure the spread of the dry-ice plume.) The computed concentrations are given in Table 6.

Table 6. Computed ice crystal concentrations expected from dry-ice treatment, particles per cubic meter

Flights	Interval below treatment level (feet)		
	0–1000	1000–2000	2000–3000
Prior to Flight 116	$7 \cdot 7 \times 10^7$	$2 \cdot 6 \times 10^7$	$8 \cdot 6 \times 10^6$
Flight 116 and after	$2 \cdot 2 \times 10^8$	$1 \cdot 7 \times 10^7$	$8 \cdot 6 \times 10^6$

On the basis of these values, we can expect a concentration of approximately 10^8 particles per cubic meter in the region immediately below the treatment level.

Ice-crystal growth in a cloud with updraft—The first step in an analytical study of the overseeding problem is to determine the rate of growth of a single ice crystal, growing without restraint under conditions of abundant water supply. This condition is approached in a cloud containing an updraft which can supply new water as fast as it is used by the growing crystal. Such a computation has been made using the ambient conditions for cloud 114A (Table 4). This cloud represents the most extreme conditions found in the no-echo, all-water clouds.

It is assumed that the initial crystal is a hexagonal plate with an aspect ratio and bulk modulus as given by REYNOLDS [1952]. It is assumed that the crystal rimes in collision with cloud droplets. The mean of 21 non-echo producing cumulus congestus over the central United States is used as representing the relevant droplet spectrum. The liquid water content of this distribution is about $0 \cdot 75$ g/m³. The falling speeds used were values computed for a disk of initial density of $0 \cdot 6$ g/cm³. For sizes of ice crystals between 100–400 microns falling speeds were obtained from a smoothed curve joining the curve of velocities for graupel as given by NAKAYA [1954]. Collection efficiencies were assumed to be equal to spheres of equal radii. It is assumed that the ventilation coefficient is unity throughout the computations. For the purposes of this study, it was not considered worth the effort to try to refine the value used for the ventilation coefficient.

Table 7. Size and mass of growing ice crystals as a function of time, with a free air temperature of $-4 \cdot 9°C$ and ambient pressure of 500 mb. Critical number refers to the number required to have a total mass equal to that of the cloud liquid water content, viz., $0 \cdot 75$ g/m³

Time	Radius	Mass	Critical number for cloud of 0·75 liquid water content
sec	micron	gram	g/m³
0	$2 \cdot 5$	$1 \cdot 35 \times 10^{-11}$	$5 \cdot 6 \times 10^{10}$
100	36	$3 \cdot 6 \times 10^{-8}$	$2 \cdot 1 \times 10^7$
300	65	$16 \cdot 1 \times 10^{-8}$	$4 \cdot 7 \times 10^6$
500	97	$41 \cdot 0 \times 10^{-8}$	$1 \cdot 8 \times 10^6$
700	144	$101 \cdot 0 \times 10^{-8}$	$7 \cdot 5 \times 10^5$
900	245	$298 \cdot 0 \times 10^{-8}$	$2 \cdot 5 \times 10^5$

These computations show that an ice crystal, 2·5 microns radius at $t = 0$, would grow at the rate shown in Table 7. These values compare favorably with the computed values derived by Houghton [1950]. Furthermore, the values for the first 200 sec compare favorably with the experimental values given by Reynolds [1952].

There are two important points to be learned from these computations. Firstly, one learns that it is unlikely that an ice crystal will grow to a size large enough to be detected in the Chicago experiments within the lifetime of most of the clouds studied. Secondly, one learns that with a concentration of 10^8 per meter^3, the crystals will completely 'dry up' any average cloud in less than 100 sec. Thus, even though the individual particles would be too small to be detected, there could be no liquid water within the cloud and thus it would be possible to obtain the icing conditions which characterized the clouds in the 'water only' and 'mixed ice and water' categories.

Ice growth in a cloud without an updraft—Perhaps a more pertinent model upon which to base the considerations of ice-crystal growth following treatment of a cloud with dry ice, is that characterized by a cloud which does not contain an updraft. In this case, the water for the growth of the ice crystals must come from the cloud droplets. It is immediately obvious that the ice-crystal growth will be slower in this case than in the case of unrestrained growth in a cloud with updraft. In this case we consider a cloud to contain a certain distribution of cloud droplets with a certain number of admixed ice crystals. The droplets will evaporate because of a difference in vapor pressure at the surface of the droplet and in the free space surrounding them. Evaporation will cool the droplet and tend to reduce this difference. The ice crystals will grow because the vapor pressure in the surrounding space exceeds that over the ice-crystal surface. Sublimation on the crystal will cause an elevation in its surface temperature which in turn will retard the rate of growth of the crystal. In such a system it is also obvious that the time rate of change of mass of the droplet spectrum must equal the time rate of change of mass for the collection of ice crystals. In the initial stages when the crystals are very small, the ambient vapor density will be approximately that corresponding to saturation over a water surface at the initial temperature. As the process goes to completion, however, the vapor pressure of the surrounding space must approach that of saturation over ice at the final temperature. This problem has been solved by numerical integration for the cases of crystal counts of $10^8/m^3$ and $10^5/m^3$, growing in a cloud having a droplet spectrum equal to that measured by the Cloud Physics Project in non-echo-producing cumulus congestus (same droplet spectrum referred to under the paragraph on ice-crystal growth in a cloud with updraft). These computations go far toward indicating the reasons for the failure to obtain an 'overseeded' condition in these treated clouds. Not only is this problem of interest in the case of a treated cloud, but also it is exactly the problem occurring in a cloud-filled deep freeze when it is seeded with a few grains of dry ice or with silver iodide smoke.

The initial conditions for these computations are as follows:

Free air temperature	$-4\cdot9°C$ and $-1\cdot0°C$
Total atmospheric pressure	500 mb
Crystal concentration	$10^8/m^3$
Initial size of ice crystals	2·5 microns radius

The initial cloud-droplet spectrum, grouped into rather large class intervals in order to simplify the computations, is indicated in Table 8.

Table 8. *Cloud-droplet spectrum for ice crystal-growth computation*

Class interval	Mean radius	Droplet concentration	Water content
	micron	cm^{-3}	gm/m^3
1	5	95·0	0·05
2	10	67·0	0·28
3	15	20·0	0·28
4	20	3·0	0·10
5	25	0·5	0·03
6	30	0·08	0·01
Totals		185·58	0·75

The rate of growth of an ice crystal is given by

$$\frac{dM_i}{dt} = \frac{4\pi mD}{RTa} C K_{v_i} \Delta e_i \tag{2}$$

Similarly, the rate of evaporation of a water droplet is given by

$$\frac{dM_d}{dt} = \frac{4\pi mD}{RTa} r_d K_{v_d} \Delta e_d \tag{3}$$

Using the values of radius to thickness ratio for hexagonal plates given by REYNOLDS [1952], and expressing the mass in terms of the radius of a circumscribed circle (2) can be integrated to give

$$M_i^2 = M_{0_i}^2 + \frac{16}{2 \cdot 6} \frac{mD}{RTa} K_v \Delta e_i t \tag{4}$$

and substituting values for the ambient conditions at a free air temperature of $-4 \cdot 9°C$

$$r_i^2 = M_{0_i}^2 + 2 \cdot 17 \times 10^{-1} K_v \Delta e_i t \tag{5}$$

where r_i is in microns.

Similarly (3) becomes

$$r_d^2 = r_{0_d}^2 + \frac{2mD}{RTa} K_{v_d} \Delta e_d t \tag{6}$$

which can be reduced to

$$r_d^2 = r_{0_d}^2 + 7 \cdot 06 \times 10^{-2} K_{v_d} \Delta e_d t \tag{7}$$

Since all the water for the growth of the crystals must come from the evaporating droplets, the right side of (2), summed over all ice crystals, must be equal to the right side of (3) summed over all droplets. Since the droplets are of several sizes, the summation of equation over the droplets requires several terms, one for each class interval.

However, since it is assumed that all the ice crystals are of equal size at time zero, it is sufficient to multiply the right side of (2) by N_i, the total number of crystals per unit volume, to obtain the proper summation.

Thus, from (2) and (3) we obtain

$$\frac{\Delta e_i}{\Delta e_d} = \frac{\Sigma r_d K_{v_d} n_d}{C K_{v_i} N_i} \tag{8}$$

This expression means that the ratio of the two driving forces is determined by the relative number and size of crystals as opposed to the number and size of the water droplets. The value of this ratio changes continually as the crystals grow and the droplets evaporate to provide the water.

Two other conditions are needed for the solution of this problem. It is appreciated that the evaporation of the droplets and the growth of the crystals cause the temperature of the surfaces of the droplets and crystals to differ from the temperature of the ambient air. The magnitude of this difference is given by

$$\Delta T_{i,d} = \frac{DL_{i,d}}{k_{c_p} P} \Delta e_{i,d} \tag{9}$$

Under the conditions of this problem (9) reduces to

$$\Delta T_i = 6 \cdot 74 \Delta e_i \tag{10a}$$

$$\Delta T_d = 5 \cdot 97 \Delta e_d \tag{10b}$$

(The constants on the right side of (5), (7), (10a) and (10b) are only slightly larger for the case having a free air temperature of $-1 \cdot 0°C$.)

In addition, it is to be noted that the temperature of the air surrounding the particles will change with time because of the liberation of latent heat in the system. This effect is given by

$$\Delta T_a = \frac{(L_i - L_d) \Delta M_{T_i}}{\rho_a c_p} \tag{11}$$

The mechanics of solving this problem is to assume values for the vapor pressure gradients over the ice crystals and over the water droplets. At any step in the solution the ratio of these two quantities is known from (8). This assumed value of Δe_i is used in conjunction with (10b) and the known temperature of the ambient air, to compute the vapor pressure of the ambient air. Similarly the assumed value of Δe_d is used to make a second computation of the vapor pressure of the ambient air. Obviously these two estimates of the vapor pressure in the ambient air must be equal. Should this not be the case, new values for Δe_i and Δe_d are assumed and checked through the use of (10a) and (10b). In every case the ratio of the assumed values must be that specified by (8).

Having found a set of values for Δe_i and Δe_d which satisfy (8) and which are consistent with the implications of (10a) and (10b), one can proceed with the computation of the change in sizes of the crystals and water droplets. In practice, however, it is necessary to limit the computation to small increments of time, particularly when the ice crystals are small and growing at the most rapid rate. Under these conditions, the ratio of the two driving forces changes rapidly.

This computation has been completed making use of the initial conditions outlined above. For a crystal count of $10^8/m^3$ and at a free-air temperature of $-1\cdot0°C$, computations were made in five-second steps for the first 30 sec, for ten-second intervals for the period from 30 to 230 sec, and for 30-sec intervals for the period from 230 to 420 sec; and with a free-air temperature of $-4\cdot9°C$, computations were made at five-second

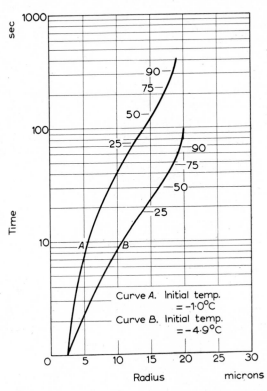

Fig. 1—Ice crystal growth; small figures indicate per cent of total liquid-water content of cloud evaporated

intervals throughout the growth period of the ice crystal. The results of these computations are summarized in Tables 9 and 10, and in Fig. 1. The essential features of Tables 9 and 10 and Fig. 1 are as follows:

(1) The ice crystals grow rapidly at first, reaching one-half of their final size within the first tenth of their entire growth period. The rate of growth decreases continually from the start until the time the cloud is composed only of ice particles. The final size of the ice particles is about 20 microns radius which is reached in about 100 and 420 sec for the case of a free-air temperature of $-4\cdot9°C$ and $-1\cdot0°C$, respectively. By way of contrast, a freely growing crystal at the same temperature and pressure would grow to a size of about 50 microns radius in 200 sec.

(2) The vapor pressure of the ambient air is initially equal to saturation over water, finally it is equal to saturation over ice at the final temperature. The change in ambient

air vapor pressure is rapid at first, while the crystals have the highest growth rates and decreases as larger and larger fractions of the droplets are evaporated.

(3) The temperature of the ambient air rises slowly from the beginning to the end of the process. This is in response to the release of latent heat of fusion.

(4) Even under these conditions of growth restraint, the crystals grow at a rate which would completely evaporate the water droplets within the periods of observation listed in Table 4.

The same computation was carried out using an ice crystal count of $10^5/m^3$. In this case, the value of $\Delta e_i/\Delta e_d$ is 10^4. This means that the crystals are too few in number to be affected materially by the requirement that the water comes from the droplets. In other words, with this concentration, initially the droplets outnumber the crystals 1800 : 1 and the initial growth of the crystal follows that computed for an unrestrained crystal. This condition will prevail for about 15 to 20 min by which time the crystals will have grown to several millimeters diameter, primarily due to riming.

It is important to note, however, that 10^5 crystals/m^3, growing unrestrained, would not use up the measured water content in the cloud within the periods of observation. Thus the observational data are not inconsistent with an assumed crystal count of 10^5. A concentration of 10^6 would exhaust the water in the cloud in approximately 500 sec.

CONCLUSIONS

The theoretical studies fail to establish a means of understanding the observed frequency with which dry-ice-treated clouds failed to develop ice particles, unless it is accepted that the crystal concentration is about 10^5 to 10^6.

It has been established that within the periods of lifetime of the clouds studied, the ice crystals are not likely to grow to a size where they can be detected by the methods of measurement. On the other hand, the crystals very quickly grow to a size where their total mass will equal that of the measured liquid water content of the original cloud. The fact that clear ice, resulting from freezing of cloud droplets on the dome, was characteristic of the majority of the treated clouds can only mean that the number of crystals present was very much less than the theoretical yield of the dry ice used for treatment.

These observations and computations suggest that the solution to the overseeding problem must come from continued observation and measurement in the *field* as well as in the laboratory.

Acknowledgments—The basic data upon which this paper is based represents the combined efforts of the entire staff of the Cloud Physics Project and of the Air Force Detachment supporting the Project. It can be appreciated that the very nature of flight program research requires a co-ordinated team of scientists working together for a common goal. In particular, the authors wish to acknowledge the help of H. R. Byers, Project Director, and L. J. Battan for helpful discussions of the overseeding problem. The research reported in this paper has been sponsored by the Geophysics Research Directorate of the Air Force Cambridge Research Center, Air Research and Development Command, under Contract AF 19(604)–618.

Table 9. *Values of computed parameters at various times after treating at rate of 10^8 crystals per meter^3 at initial free air temperature of $-4.9°C$*

Parameter	Elapsed time, seconds										
	0	10	20	30	40	50	60	70	80	90	100
$\Delta e_i/\Delta e_d$	10·0	2·04	1·08	0·67	0·40	0·20	0·14	0·08	0·04	0·035	0·029
Δe_i^a	0·055	0·041	0·031	0·025	0·018	0·011	0·008	0·005	0·003	0·002	0·002
$\Delta e_d^{a,b}$	0·005	0·020	0·029	0·037	0·045	0·053	0·056	0·059	0·062	0·062	0·062
T_i^b	4·53	4·57	4·55	4·55	4·54	4·56	4·55	4·55	4·55	4·55	4·55
T_a^b	4·90	4·85	4·76	4·72	4·67	4·63	4·60	4·58	4·57	4·56	4·56
T_d^b	4·93	4·97	4·93	4·94	4·93	4·94	4·93	4·94	4·94	4·94	4·94
e_i^a	4·18	4·16	4·17	4·17	4·17	4·17	4·17	4·17	4·17	4·17	4·17
e_d^a	4·24	4·21	4·20	4·20	4·19	4·18	4·18	4·18	4·17	4·17	4·17
e_d^a	4·24	4·22	4·23	4·23	4·24	4·23	4·24	4·23	4·23	4·23	4·24
r_i^c	2·5	10·8	14·2	16·3	17·6	18·5	19·1	19·5	19·7	19·9	20·0
MT_i^a	....	0·11	0·25	0·37	0·48	0·55	0·61	0·64	0·67	0·68	0·69
MT_d^a	0·756	0·68	0·53	0·38	0·25	0·17	0·11	0·07	0·05	0·03	0·02
RH	99·8	98·9	98·2	97·4	96·9	96·4	96·3	96·0	95·8	95·8	95·8

[a] Vapor pressure in millibars
[b] Negative values
[c] Radius in microns
[d] Mass in gm/m^3

Note—For computational stability, it was necessary to carry all values to four decimal places and round off as above.

Table 10. *Values of computed parameters at various times after treating at rate of 10^8 crystal per meter^3 at initial free-air temperature of $-1.0°C$*

Parameter	Elapsed time, seconds																
	0	20	40	60	90	120	150	180	210	240	270	300	330	360	390	420
$\Delta e_i/\Delta e_d$	10.0	3.15	2.13	1.58	1.04	0.80	0.62	0.44	0.30	0.22	0.18	0.14	0.11	0.071	0.033	0.030
Δe_i^a	0.012	0.010	0.009	0.008	0.006	0.005	0.005	0.004	0.003	0.002	0.002	0.001	0.001	0.0007	0.0004	0.0003
Δe_d^{ab}	0.001	0.003	0.004	0.005	0.006	0.007	0.007	0.008	0.009	0.010	0.010	0.010	0.010	0.011	0.011	0.011
T_i^b	0.92	0.91	0.90	0.88	0.85	0.82	0.79	0.77	0.75	0.74	0.72	0.71	0.70	0.70	0.70	0.70
T_a^b	1.00	0.98	0.96	0.93	0.89	0.86	0.82	0.79	0.77	0.75	0.74	0.72	0.71	0.70	0.70	0.70
T_d^b	1.01	1.00	0.98	0.96	0.93	0.90	0.87	0.84	0.82	0.81	0.80	0.78	0.77	0.77	0.77	0.76
e_i^a	5.66	5.66	5.67	5.68	5.70	5.71	5.72	5.73	5.74	5.75	5.75	5.76	5.76	5.76	5.76	5.76
e_a^a	5.67	5.67	5.68	5.69	5.70	5.71	5.73	5.74	5.74	5.75	5.75	5.76	5.76	5.76	5.76	5.77
e_d^a	5.68	5.68	5.68	5.69	5.71	5.72	5.73	5.74	5.75	5.76	5.76	5.77	5.77	5.77	5.78	5.78
r_i^c	2.5	7.4	9.9	11.6	12.9	14.8	15.8	16.7	17.3	17.7	18.1	18.4	18.6	18.8	18.9	19.0
$M\tau_i^a$	...	0.03	0.08	0.13	0.19	0.28	0.35	0.40	0.45	0.49	0.52	0.54	0.56	0.57	0.58	0.59
$M\tau_d^a$	0.756	0.73	0.66	0.61	0.55	0.42	0.34	0.27	0.22	0.17	0.13	0.10	0.07	0.05	0.04	0.03
RH	99.9	99.8	99.7	99.7	99.6	99.6	99.6	99.5	99.5	99.4	99.4	99.4	99.4	99.4	99.4	99.3

[a] Vapor pressure in millibars
[b] Negative values
[c] Radius in microns
[d] Mass in gm/m^3

REFERENCES

BATTAN, L. J., Observations on the formation and spread of precipitation in convective clouds, *J. Met.*, v.10, pp.311–324, 1953.

BROWN, E. N. and J. H. WILLETT, A three-slide cloud droplet sampler, *Bul. Amer. Met. Soc.*, v.36, pp.123–127, 1955.

BYERS, H. R. and R. K. HALL, A census of cumulus cloud height versus precipitation in the vicinity of Puerto Rico during the winter and spring of 1953–1954, *J. Met.*, v.12, pp.176–178, 1955.

GOYER, G. G. and G. S. HANDLER, Water vapor condensation as a cloud charging mechanism, *J. Met.*, v.12, no.6, pp.569–570, 1955.

HOUGHTON, H. G., A preliminary quantitative analysis of precipitation mechanisms, *J. Met.*, v.7, pp.363–369, 1950.

JOHNSON, J. C., *Physical Meteorology*, John Wiley and Sons, 393pp., 1954.

LANGMUIR, I. and K. B. BLODGETT, A mathematical investigation of water droplet trajectories, AAF Tech. Rep. no.5418, 1946.

LANGMUIR, I., V. J. SCHAEFER, B. VONNEGUT, R. E. FALCONER, K. MAYNAR and R. SMITH-JOHANNSEN, First Q. Proj. Rep., Project Cirrus, Gen. Electric Res. Lab., Schenectady, N.Y., 1947.

LODGE, J. P., A study of sea salt particles over Puerto Rico, *J. Met.*, v.12, no.5, pp.493–499, 1955.

LODGE, J. P. and F. BAER, An experimental investigation of the shatter of salt particles on crystallization, *J. Met.*, v.11, pp.420–421, 1954.

NAKAYA, U., Snow crystals, Harvard Univ. Press, 510 pp., 1954.

REYNOLDS, S. E., Ice-crystal growth, *J. Met.*, v.9, pp.36–40, 1952.

SQUIRES, P. and E. J. SMITH, The artificial stimulation of precipitation by means of dry ice, *Aust. J. Sci. Res.*, v.2, pp.232–245, 1950.

DISCUSSION

Dr. Helmut Weickmann—I believe that with the seeding experiments we did, we can offer two additional observations that may help our understanding of these results. (1) When we seeded supercooled clouds with temperatures warmer than −4°C, in many cases we didn't detect any modification. Since your cases are mostly around this temperature, they might be a little too warm. (2) You have to consider a cloud as a living organism in which the ice crystals might no longer be where you are looking for them. When seeding clouds which were not convective, the seeding track started to broaden on both sides into a large modified area. But, if the cloud deck was convective and we seeded one track, we got some smaller areas of modification irregularly lined up left and right of the seeding track. We happened to be lucky enough to find why this is so when we once seeded a cloud line.

5500 ft

4000 ft

FIG. 2—Cross section of circulation in cloud line as revealed after seeding with dry ice

The seeding was done by throwing dry ice pellets into the cloud tops along a path of about eight miles. Normally, with the temperatures existing, we would have expected the water clouds to turn to ice. About four to ten minutes after seeding, however, two ice clouds came out at the left and right sides along the line, but we did not modify the cloud line at all. This indicated the action of a circulation as indicated on Fig. 2. The circulation was strong enough to carry the ice crystals with it.

Something similar may have happened in your cumuli. It will have some circulation system and the ice crystals may be carried up to the outer edge.

Dr. Vincent J. Schaefer—In all the work we did with Project Cirrus, we considered a temperature of −8°C was about as warm as we should work with, unless there were no better clouds. The value of 10^{16} particles per gram of dry ice is based on a temperature of −12 to −15°C. I am sure that at −1 or −4°C, one is not going to get anything like that.

Dr. Roscoe R. Braham Jr.—I should have pointed out that the 10^8 concentration of ice nuclei is based upon an assumed actual yield of 10^{10} instead of 10^{16}.

Dr. Schaefer—I think we need to learn a lot more about how to treat clouds with seeding materials. This paper seems to show this beautifully.

Dr. Hans J. aufm Kampe—What was your seeding rate per mile?

Dr. Braham—The gross seeding rate, the rate at which the material was put out of the airplane, was initially 17 lb/mi and later raised to 50 lb/mi. The amount of dry ice that evaporated in the first thousand feet of fall in the 17 lb/mi treatment was actually only nine pounds; and in the 50 lb, was of the order of 26 lb.

Dr. aufm Kampe—Before we went into the field, we made some experiments in the chamber to see how many ice crystals would develop if we dropped certain sizes of dry ice. If we dropped a pellet of about bean size, then we obtained a certain amount of ice crystals per unit volume. Applied to flight conditions, we found that with one pound dry ice per mile seeding rate and a temperature of −10°C, we should get an ice-crystal concentration within the cloud of about one crystal per cubic meter in the wake of the plane.

According to our experiences in stratus clouds, I would say with 50 lb/mi of dry ice one would get of the order of fifty ice crystals per cubic meter.

Mr. Charles E. Anderson—When seeding from the B17, we always notice that the effluent is entrained in the wake of the airplane. If you are at −4°C, it might be possible that the heat from the engines is enough to raise that temperature momentarily above the freezing point and destroy the ice crystals, so you don't get the same results as when you drop a pellet in a static case, because of the dynamics around the aircraft.

Dr. Braham—I am sure you are right. However, the evaporation of the ice pellets must be considered separately for various unit distances below the airplane, that is, the important point is not what you put into the air, but rather what evaporates in various intervals below the ship. Most of the material is not dust. Most of the material is composed of small pellets and grains and they fall surprising distances.

It is true that some small material is carried away in the wake of the airplane. It is also true that some of the material may have evaporated. But allowing for these losses the expected number of crystals is reduced by less than a factor of ten, and we are still unable to reconcile theory and measurements.

Dr. Schaefer—Dr. Brooks requested a couple of minutes on an earlier paper.

Dr. Charles F. Brooks—The Bergeron-Findeisen theory has been very loosely mentioned I think it well to review what the theory consists of.

There are three points. (1) When there are ice particles in a liquid cloud at temperatures below freezing, the ice particles will grow and the liquid particles will tend to evaporate. I think this is fundamental.

(2) In view of the fact that ice nuclei are generally much less numerous, a thousand times or more less numerous than liquid droplets, the effect of the collection of the molecules of water on the ice particles and the reduction of the liquid particles at the same time is that you ultimately have particles at least a thousand times as heavy as the original droplets in the supercooled cloud. Therefore, they will have a fall velocity and volume sufficient to reach the Earth's surface as rain or snow.

(3) Bergeron and Findeisen claimed this is the only way by which rain of substantial amount can form. Findeisen lived in Germany and Bergeron in Scandinavia, and in order for a cloud to be thick enough vertically for precipitation to form, the top at all times of the year would have to be above the freezing level. Therefore, no rain ever fell from any cloud that did not have an icy top.

If they had traveled in the tropics, they would have seen the difference. We can't discard it as a theory, because the basic principles are correct; but we can say they made a mistake in saying this is the only way which rain can form.

A DISCUSSION OF GENERATING CELL OBSERVATIONS WITH RESPECT TO THE NATURAL EXISTENCE OF FREEZING OR SUBLIMATION NUCLEI

ROBERT M. CUNNINGHAM

Geophysics Research Directorate, Air Force Cambridge Research Center, Bedford, Mass.

Abstract—The question of whether the water phase is involved in all natural condensation processes is discussed with respect to aircraft soundings in storm areas over the past ten years. It is concluded that clouds appearing for the first time at temperatures warmer than about $-40°C$ always start out as a water cloud. A special case of infection of an updraft by a cirrus haze, preventing the water phase, is illustrated by photographs taken during a flight.

THIS short paper will serve to introduce a classical question in the field of cloud physics: Does evidence from observation in the free atmosphere indicate that ice crystals appear only after the freezing of a droplet, initiated by a freezing nucleus, or do ice crystals appear directly from the vapor, initiated by a sublimation nucleus?

I would conclude from aircraft observations carried out intermittently over the past ten years, usually in stormy weather, that all ice crystals (except perhaps from levels at temperatures below $-40°C$), originate from a generating cell initially composed of liquid water. The lifetime of the water in the generating cell may be very short, however.

The anvil from a thunderstorm obviously derives its moisture and crystals from the

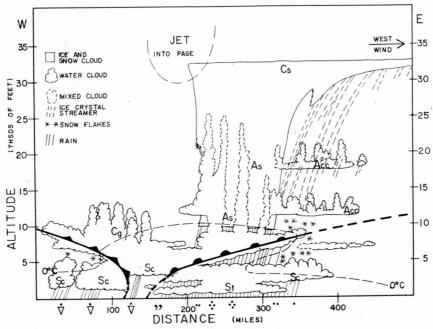

FIG. 1—Generalized sketch of a vigorous storm

267

lower level water clouds. The parent cumulonimbus usually disappears long before the anvil. The anvil is ordinarily in a region of high winds and cirrus streamers very often travel far to the lee of the parent cumulonimbus, often even up to hundreds of miles. The cumulonimbus is therefore a prolific source of ice crystals which later travel over the observer without any apparent water source.

I believe the cumulonimbus model can also be applied to a great number of cyclonic storms. Fig. 1 is a generalized sketch of such a storm. This sketch is based largely on material given by CUNNINGHAM [1952] and CUNNINGHAM and ATLAS [1953]. Just to the east of the trough axis there is an active water cloud mass composed of cumulonimbus

FIG. 2—Initial appearance at a new updraft through a cirrus haze

clouds which, in a later stage, are often surrounded by an ice crystal cloud. The jet-stream axis is generally located above this active area. Down stream, or in front of the advancing storm, you see many forms of ice-crystal clouds, all presumably derived from the active water-cloud area.

Very often the cyclonic storms are not as vigorous as illustrated above. In these weaker storms the lower atmosphere is not as unstable, cumulus clouds may not grow up into the higher levels (<20,000 ft). I do not remember a case, however, where, upon flying up through the cloud system and then flying to the trough line, a high-level water cloud was not found. I believe that these water clouds are the source of the down-wind ice-crystal clouds. Weakening cyclonic systems can be found where the original water clouds no longer exist.

The tops of a great many ice-crystal clouds in cyclonic storms, even at 25,000 ft, turn out to be a broken layer of altocumulus clouds extending for hundreds of miles which are the source of a cirro-stratus or altostratus cloud mass. Dr. Atlas showed a radar photograph just previously which is a good example of this type of system.

FIG. 3—Later stage, lighter crystal elements have blown off in different wind stream above haze layer

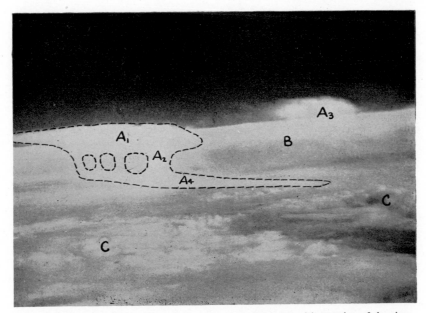

FIG. 4—Whole pattern of a cirrus convective cell visible in a thin portion of the cirrus haze (cell is outlined by dashed lines); $A1$ and $A3$, portion of cell similar to one shown on Fig. 3; $A2$, what is left of original condensation region (generating level in weather radar terminology); $A4$, streamer caused by fall of heavier crystal elements into a lower different wind stream; B, thin cirrus haze; C, altocumulus deck some 12,000 ft below

A variation of the above pattern was photographed at 27,000 ft last winter (temperature −35°C). A residual cirrus haze existed after the passage of a general storm area. Convective activity apparently resumed at the haze level, vertically developed clouds appeared, no connection with the much lower cloud system was apparent. I believe that these new ice-crystal clouds did not go through a water stage in their development, as the new updraft was thoroughly infected by the existing ice-crystal haze. Fig. 2 shows the beginning of this ice-crystal cloud bulging out from the top of the cirrus haze. Fig. 3 shows a similar development at a later stage after the strong wind shear at the cirrus haze top had affected the cloud shape. Fig. 4 shows a similar development at a much later stage, the haze had thinned out in this region and the trailing snow cloud, so evident on radar pictures of generating cells, is visible. Remains of the sheared off top can also be seen.

My answer, from visual aircraft observations alone, to the classical question mentioned above, is then (as long as an updraft is not infected by existing ice crystals), that the outdoor atmosphere requires the freezing of a pre-existing water drop, presumably by the action of a freezing nucleus, to start the growth of an ice crystal.

REFERENCES

CUNNINGHAM, R. M., Distribution and growth of hydrometeors around a deep cyclone, Mass. Inst. Tech., Dept. of Met., Tech. Rep. 18, 1952.

CUNNINGHAM, R. M. and D. ATLAS, Growth of hydrometeors as calculated from aircraft and radar observations, *Proc. Toronto Met. Conf., R. Met. Soc., London*, pp.276–289, 1953.

DISCUSSION

Dr. Charles F. Brooks—Frequently alto-cumulus cloud develops tall towers that go up to a limit and begin to spread out. They have inertia which will carry them beyond equilibrium. If the unstable lapse rate extends up indefinitely, a stronger mass from below will go higher up and perhaps will spread out at a greater height, even though weaker ones have spread out at a lower level. The alto-cumulus deck that you showed below did have protuberances on it. You said that there were no columns extending through the cirrus deck. I wonder if it could be that one formed, but that before the top appeared above the cirrus deck the lower parts had gone to pieces.

The International Cloud Committee recognizes such protuberances as cirrus castellatus or, if there are individual puffs as shown here, cirrus floccus.

In spite of the presence of ice, you may have liquid water forming; at a later stage the ice quickly removes the liquid. This is the type of cloud that gives you hail storms and tornadoes. Cloud masses that rise beyond their equilibrium height by inertia must of course fall back.

Dr. Cunningham—I am fairly sure there weren't any connecting clouds; none were seen when observation permitted. The lapse rates somewhat below the cirrus were fairly stable. I also meant to add the comment that the photographs illustrated a case of cirro-cumulus cloud or a generating cell forming without the aid of freezing nuclei, but with the aid of an already existing very thin cirrus haze.

Dr. Hans J. aufm Kampe—It is very possible that in this case sublimation was the only process involved. The residue of an old ice cloud may have provided sublimation nuclei, in line with Dr. Workman's comment several years ago.

Talking about freezing and sublimation nuclei, we must keep continually under review just what we mean by our definitions of freezing nuclei and sublimation nuclei. Recalling Dr. Weickmann's work in Germany, it would appear that at −20°C or −25°C or even somewhat lower, the appearance of ice crystals is subsequent to that of water droplets. At still lower temperatures, just how low depending on the abundance of freezing nuclei, it may be that no water drops are observed before the ice crystals, although water saturation is still prerequisite.

Dr. Cunningham—I presume in this case we had plenty of ice crystals to act as nuclei.

OBSERVATIONS OF SPACE AND TIME VARIATIONS IN THE RADAR ECHO INTENSITY OF SHOWERS

PAULINE M. AUSTIN AND RAYMOND WEXLER

Weather Radar Research, Department of Meteorology,
Massachusetts Institute of Technology, Cambridge 39, Mass.

Abstract—Since the intensity of the radar signal from precipitation is extremely sensitive to the size and composition of the particles and reasonably sensitive to the particle concentration, detailed measurements of the signal intensity from various regions within storm areas yield information concerning both the growth and development of the precipitation particles and the small-scale atmospheric motions.

A technique for making measurements of the time and space variations of the radar signal intensity from convective showers is described and examples of the data are presented.

Observations of eleven convective showers on nine days indicate the following general pattern of development. In the early stages the shower consists of a single cell with a narrow intense core. There is a tendency for several turrets to develop at the top of the cell which subsequently weakens in intensity and becomes broader and irregular in shape. Finally it often resolves itself into several small separate cells which may be only a few tenths of a mile in horizontal dimensions while the spaces between them are of the same order of magnitude.

THE observations which are described represent part of a program whose object is to study small-scale atmospheric circulation patterns and the development of precipitation particles by using measurements of radar signal intensity from various regions within storms. These two fields of study are grouped together for two reasons. In the first place they are interdependent since the atmospheric motions affect the development of the precipitation patterns while at the same time the heat exchanges and drag forces associated with the precipitation particles influence the small-scale circulation of the air. The second reason is the fact that while the radar signal intensity is extremely sensitive to the size and composition of the precipitation particles, it is also reasonably sensitive to the concentration. In situations where the vertical motion in the atmosphere may be assumed to be small as in the cases studied by WEXLER and AUSTIN [1954] and ATLAS [1955], the increase in radar signal intensity at different levels may be used as an indication of the growth of precipitation particles. In convective situations, however, the dependence of particle concentration on up- and down-drafts should not be neglected

Measurements of the intensity of the radar signal received from different levels in a convective shower are made by means of an instrument called the 'profile plotter', which is attached to an AN/CPS-9 radar. The profile plotter consists of a pulse integrator [WILLIAMS, 1949] whose sampling gate moves continuously through a range of seven miles in about one-half minute, recording the signal intensity at each point. The antenna elevation is varied so that profiles are obtained at height intervals of two to three thousand feet throughout the depth of the shower. For each setting of the elevation angle the azimuth is adjusted so that the profile is made through the most intense part of the shower. The intensity measurements are normalized to a range of one mile and points are plotted on a chart so that intensity contours may be drawn as shown in

T   271

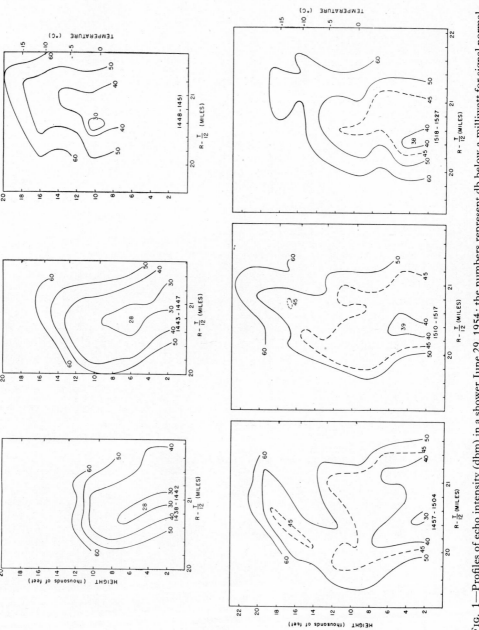

FIG. 1—Profiles of echo intensity (dbm) in a shower June 29, 1954; the numbers represent db below a milliwatt for signal normalized to a range of one mile

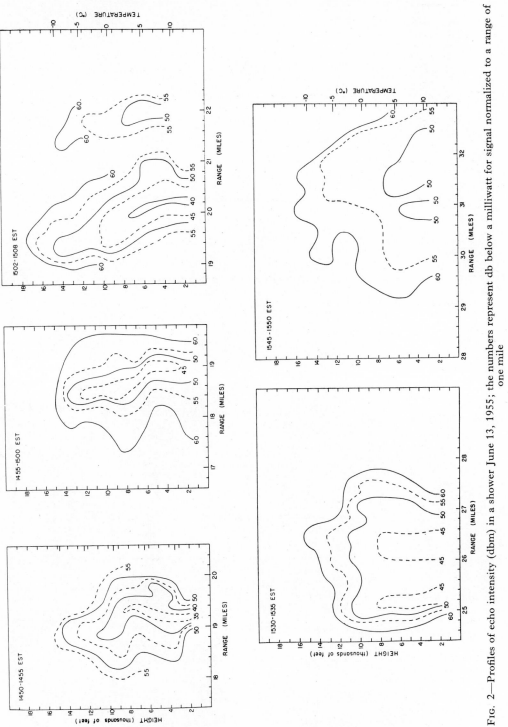

FIG. 2—Profiles of echo intensity (dbm) in a shower June 13, 1955; the numbers represent db below a milliwatt for signal normalized to a range of one mile

Figures 1 and 2. When the storm is moving either toward or away from the radar, range corrections are made to compensate for the motion of the shower during the time when the measurements are being made.

The type of measurement described is suitable for the study of relatively small isolated showers. Measurements cannot be made sufficiently rapidly to obtain a satisfactory time-space intensity record for a large complex shower or thunderstorm. Although attempts were made to begin observations on showers when they were developing rather than dissipating, these measurements are not expected to yield significant information concerning the growth of the first precipitation particles. It is believed that particles have reached precipitation size before a radar echo is detectable, and observations of the initial radar echo [REYNOLDS and BRAHAM, 1952; BATTAN, 1953] indicate that development is very rapid at that time.

Observations of 11 cells on nine different days have been analyzed. Four of these were relatively simple isolated shower cells during their entire existence. All of the others developed into several cells and a few became extremely complex. Examples of both these types of shower are given in the figures. The numbers on the contours represent decibels below a milliwatt. Hence the 40-db contour represents a signal intensity which is ten times as strong as that received from the regions marked by the 50-db contour. The storm of June 29, 1954 was moving away from the radar at a rate of 12 mph. For this reason an appropriate correction was applied to the range. The range correction was not made for the shower of June 13, 1955 because the motion away from the radar site was not uniform. The numbers below the contour lines for the first shower and in the upper left-hand corner of the figures for the second shower indicate the time of day (EST).

The normalized signal intensity of −28 dbm received from the core of the shower on June 29, 1954 is very strong for a precipitation echo. A signal of such intensity might be expected from a rainfall rate of about 100 mm/hr if the rain had an average drop-size distribution and the drops were falling with the terminal velocity which they would have in still air. Such an intense signal is quite unexpected in a shower of small dimensions and short duration such as this one. The shower observed on June 13, 1955 is a more typical example of the showers which were observed.

Since relatively few storms have been observed and they are rather dissimilar as to intensity and size, no conclusive results are available. However, the following general tendencies may be pointed out.

The most intense signal is usually obtained near the beginning of the observations. At this time the shower consists of a single cell with a narrow intense core. Probably the updraft is decreasing the effective fall velocity of the particles, thus causing a high concentration and enhanced signal intensity.

In practically every case there was a tendency for several turrets to develop at the top of the single original cell. These are not separate new cells since they are associated with a single cell at lower levels. This single cell tends to broaden somewhat and become irregular. Finally it does often resolve itself into several separate cells which extend all the way to the ground.

In only one case was there evidence of the existence of a bright band. This was in the longest storm which was observed, and the bright band occurred several hours after the beginning of the storm.

Acknowledgment—The research reported on has been carried out under the sponsorship of the Signal Corps Engineering Laboratories, Contract No. DA–36–039–SC–64472.

REFERENCES

ATLAS, DAVID, Radar measurements of precipitation growth, Paper in this publication, pp.288–304, 1956.
BATTAN, LOUIS J., Observations on the formation and spread of precipitation in convective clouds, *J. Met.*, v.10, pp.311–324, 1953.
REYNOLDS, S. E. and R. R. BRAHAM, Significance of the initial radar echo, *Bul. Amer. Met. Soc.*, v.33, p.123, 1952.
WEXLER, RAYMOND and PAULINE M. AUSTIN, Radar signal intensity from different levels in steady snow, M.I.T. Weather Radar Research, Research Rep. 23, 27pp., March 1, 1954.
WILLIAMS, E. L., JR., The pulse integrator, part A; Description of the instrument and its circuitry, M.I.T., Weather Radar Research, Tech. Rep.8, 35pp., August 1, 1949.

DISCUSSION

Dr. Braham—Were these echoes totally warmer than freezing?

Dr. Weickmann—Do you have data on the level of the cloud base?

Drs. Austin and Wexler—On the first and simpler shower, the cloud base was at about 6000 ft (from synoptic reports), the melting level at about 12,000 ft. The strongest part of the echo was definitely below the melting level, although at one stage echo of considerable intensity extended above that level. We do not know the height of the first detectable echo in any case. In most cases there was some echo above the freezing level when the cell was first sighted, but in general most of the intense part was 'warm'.

Dr. Battan—Have you studied any bigger clouds, and any echoes extending to 40,000 ft?

Dr. Austin—About 30,000 ft is the highest, but tall storms take longer to scan, so that there tends to be too much variation from one scan to the next to give a good sequence.

Dr. Battan—In the records from the Thunderstorm Project, cells maintained very high intensity for five or ten minutes, even when they went up to 40,000 ft. What is your experience with your more quantitative technique?

Dr. Austin—The maximum intensity tended to occur shortly after the first sighting, and tended to persist for quite a while. We cannot back up in time as with continuous-search records to determine how long before our first sighting the cell was first detectable.

Dr. Battan—With observations at shorter intervals, we noticed sometimes that as the cell grew older several bulges appeared on the top of it. One tower would build up quite high; the wind would carry it away and another would appear building up from a lower level at almost the same rate as the previous one, and then a third one. With your longer intervals, you might get the impression that the top was spreading out rather than that something was poking up from below.

Dr. Austin—We get the impression of something new poking up from below, but not from the bottom, and so not a completely new cell. The bearing of the new occurrence from the old does not seem to be related to the direction of the wind.

Dr. Battan (in answer to the Chairman)—We defined a cell as something whose shape was not altered materially during its life. On a PPI scope, a cell appears roughly elliptical or circular. Most often, a new development occurs right next to it, and after a while the shape of the echo becomes quite irregular. In about 60 cases there was no development of this sort, and the single cell persisted as such for the order of 20 minutes. Anything lasting longer became progressively more complicated.

Dr. Austin—I believe that complexities develop aloft first, above the beam of a PPI-scanning radar, and work down into irregularities in the lower levels. The single, solid cylinder of precipitation seems to maintain itself in the lower part of the storm considerably longer than in the higher regions.

Dr. Fournier d'Albe—The intense echo seems to start low in the cloud and spread out both radially and upward. To me this suggests large drops breaking up and the fragments rising in an updraft.

Dr. Austin—Usually, this spread outward and upward is the case, but there are exceptions. In one case an intense cell extending in one scan from 14,000 ft down to 8000 ft was found on the next scan (five minutes later) to reach all the way to the ground.

Dr. Fournier d'Albe—Do you get any idea at all of the drop sizes?

Dr. Austin—Not from the radar records, and since the shower under observation is from ten to 20 miles distant we cannot go out and sample the drops. Rate of descent of echo might be related to terminal speeds of drops, but in a convective situation we must be doubtful of such procedures.

SNOW GROWTH AND AGGREGATION IN GENERATING CELLS

R. H. DOUGLAS

Stormy Weather Group, Meteorological Service of Canada,
Toronto, Ont., Canada

Abstract—In moist stable air in which ice crystals grow, significant vertical development may occur as the result of the supply of latent heat of sublimation. The vertical development is comparable to the observed depth of snow generating cells as observed by radar; calculated updraft velocities are comparable to the terminal velocities of snow crystals or of aggregates. In air containing supercooled water cloud the sublimational updraft is very much lower than in cloud-free air; thus shear and turbulence could develop across a cloud boundary in the presence of growing ice crystals, and be a significant factor in the aggregation of crystals. It is suggested that cloud boundaries, along which aggregation is favored, serve as the bases for the snow-generating cells which are so frequently observed by radar.

Introduction—Radar observations of snow indicate its intensive development in compact cells aloft (Fig. 1) [MARSHALL, 1953]. These cells are about one mile in diameter and up to one mile high and have lifetimes of the order of two hours. They usually occur in stable air and the level of generation is on the average some 1200 ft above a frontal surface [GUNN and others, 1954].

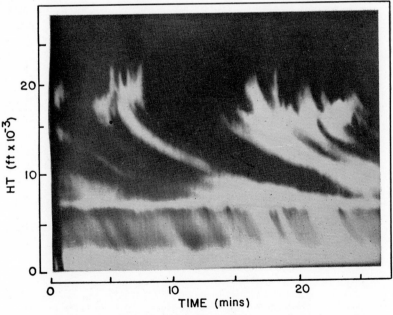

FIG. 1—Height-time record obtained with a vertically pointing radar

277

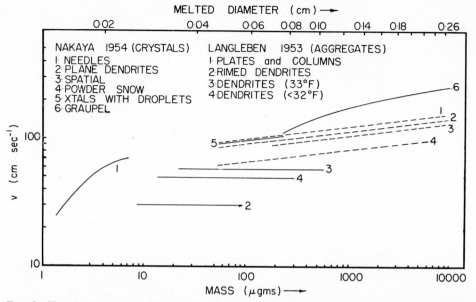

FIG. 2—Terminal velocities of snow crystals (solid curves, NAKAYA [1954], (1) needles, (2) plane dendrites, (3) spatial, (4) powder snow, (5) crystals with droplets, (6) graupel) and aggregates (dashed curves, LANGLEBEN [1954], (1) plates and columns, (2) rimed dendrites, (3) dendrites, 33°F, (4) dendrites, <32°F)

The fall speeds of the snow particles in the trails of streamers can be determined from the slopes of the trails provided that the upper wind data are available. Such analysis of RHI records for November 2, 1951, indicated a terminal velocity of four ft/sec just below the generating level [LANGLEBEN, 1954]; further analyses of zenith pointing

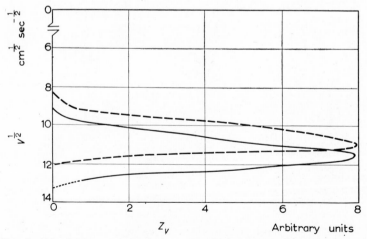

FIG. 3—Distribution of scattering intensity Z_v with square root of terminal velocity of snowflakes; depth below generating level is proportional to $v^{0.5}$; solid curve is for an observed snowflake size-distribution, dashed curve for an assumed exponential distribution

radar records have indicated values from 2·9 to 4 ft/sec. Considering the available fall velocity data for single crystals and for aggregates [NAKAYA, 1954, p.111–116; LANGLE-BEN, 1954] (Fig. 2), it would appear that the trail, at least in part, consists of aggregates and that some aggregation occurs within the generating cells themselves.

The radar measurements were made on the sharply defined leading edges of the snow trails, which consist of the larger particles. The variation of radar reflectivity with height, through a trail, is illustrated in Fig. 3, in which a size distribution of snowflakes collected at the ground has been combined with LANGLEBEN's [1954] velocity data (solid curve); the dashed curve is derived from an exponential distribution [MARSHALL and GUNN, 1952]. In either case, there is a 90 per cent chance that the high reflectivity of the leading (lower) edge corresponds to particles having fall velocities between about 115 and 165 cm/sec; certainly a rather narrow range of relatively high velocities, suggestive of aggregates, is involved.

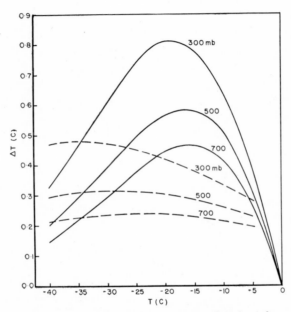

FIG. 4—Isobaric temperature increase as a function of temperature for various pressures due to sublimation in cloud-free air initially at water equilibrium (full curves) and in water cloud of density one g/m³ (dashed curves)

The individual cells appear to change in shape, suggestive of continuous vertical circulation or convection. Recently DENNIS [1955] has found radar evidence of turbulence in the cell structure, deducing root-mean-square turbulent winds of the order of one m/sec. Such turbulence would be expected to promote aggregation in the cells.

Such observations suggest a type of convective motion in stable air, in which turbulence may play a part in aggregation. The possibility of such convection is examined by considering the behavior of a parcel of air, in a stable environment, into which heat is injected or from which heat is withdrawn. In the former case the parcel rises buoyantly to a new level of equilibrium at which its temperature will, in general, be less than its initial value. In the latter case the extraction of heat and the subsequent subsidence of the parcel will result, in general, in a final parcel-temperature higher than its initial value. Given the rate of heat injection or withdrawal, the resulting vertical velocity of the parcel may be deduced. Hewson [1948] referred to Napier Shaw's use of the term 'heating through cooling' in describing the latter process, and made use of this concept in a study of the subsidence and dissipation of cumulus as the result of radiational cooling.

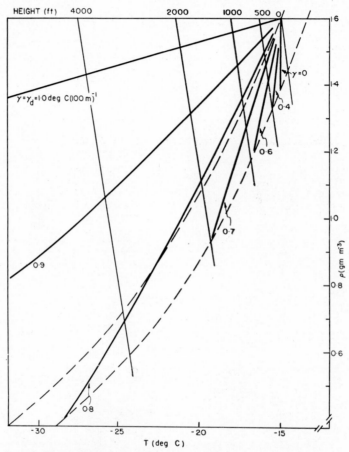

Fig. 5—Vapor density within a parcel as a function of temperature (or of height) for various ambient lapse-rates. Upper broken line — water saturation, lower broken line — ice saturation

Radar data suggest vertical motions, and one need not look far for a suitable source or sink of thermal energy. In moist air the provision of the latent heat of sublimation due to ice-crystal growth may be appreciable, as may also its removal in dry air, due to evaporation. The present paper examines some of the results of the sublimational heat release in moist air through which growing ice crystals are falling.

Vertical development—It is convenient to consider first the heat released into a parcel of air during the complete reduction of the vapor content to ice equilibrium, treating the process as an **isobaric one** in which the parcel, although receiving thermal energy, is retained at its **original pressure level.** At constant pressure, the reduction of the vapor content of a parcel by **sublimation** from water- to ice-equilibrium results in a temperature increase as indicated in Fig. 4 (full curves). The air, while initially at water equilibrium, is assumed to **contain no liquid-water cloud.** On the other hand, if a water cloud is initially present, the net heat release is reduced substantially due to the evaporation of the liquid phase. The isobaric temperature increase in cloudy air per gram sublimed is only about 1/13 of that in cloud-free air at 700 mb and −15°C. In Fig. 4 the

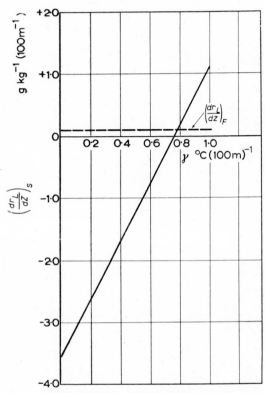

FIG. 6—Rate of change with height of liquid water content (r_L = grams of liquid water per kg dry air) as a function of lapse rate (at 700 mb, −15°C); dashed line indicates rate of increase of cloud content due to frontal lifting along a saturated adiabat (water)

dashed curves indicate the **net temperature** increase accompanying the evaporation of water cloud of density one g/m³; for the more usual densities of stratiform cloud (about 0·1 g/m³, according to the **data of** PETTIT [1954]) the net heating will be but about a tenth that indicated. Once the **water cloud is** consumed, sublimation of the vapor excess supplies the full latent heat to the parcel.

In examining the buoyant rise of the parcel (as opposed to the completely isobaric sublimation process of the **preceding paragraph**) it's convenient to consider the sublimational heat-release in small **increments** (isobaric), followed by ascent to equilibrium, these processes continuing in steps until the vapor content of the parcel is reduced to ice equilibrium. The vapor density within the parcel, as a function of temperature, is shown in Fig. 5 for a number of ambient lapse-rates; the parcel is assumed initially free of liquid water cloud but containing vapor at water equilibrium at 700 mb, $-15°C$. The intersection of the parcel 'path' (along the appropriate lapse-rate curve) with the ice-equilibrium curve indicates the final equilibrium temperature, or height; the vertical development may be found from the superimposed height-lines. It is clear that, even in an extremely stable environment, vertical development of the order of hundreds of feet may be realized; in a more normal environment, development of the order of several thousands of feet may occur, comparable to the vertical extent of cells as observed by radar.

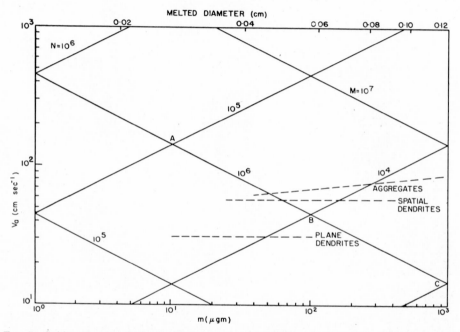

FIG. 7—Sublimational updraft velocity due to growth of N dendrites/m³, each of mass m micrograms; M = mass of ice, micrograms/m³ (for a monodisperse distribution); environment is assumed isothermal, free of water cloud, at water equilibrium, 700 mb, $-15°C$; dashed lines indicate terminal velocities of crystals and of aggregates

Consumption of cloud—Examination of Fig. 5 reveals the fact that for high-lapse rates, such as $0·9°C/100$ m, the vapor density within the parcel will exceed the water equilibrium value, and that water cloud may be expected to form, or that any cloud initially present will thicken. For lesser lapse rates, either no cloud will form or any cloud initially present will be consumed. The critical lapse rate separating these two conditions can be shown to be nearly equal to, though slightly less than, the saturated (water) adiabatic lapse rate.

The desiccation or thickening of water cloud as a consequence of sublimation is indicated in Fig. 6, from which it is seen that the complete desiccation of cloud containing about $0·1$ g/m³ can occur within an extremely small vertical distance. At this height, and with desiccation complete, the parcel reverts to the condition described in the previous section, that is, free of liquid water, but at water equilibrium, and the further 'clear-air' rise of Fig. 5 follows. Consideration of Figures 5 and 6 suggests that, of the total vertical development, the second or 'clear-air' portion is usually the major contributor.

Updraft velocities—The vertical velocity of the parcel has been computed by considering the rate of heat input due to crystal growth, using HOUGHTON's [1950] growth rates for plane dendrites at 700 mb, −15°C, at water saturation. The results in an isothermal environment, free of water cloud, are shown in Fig. 7. It is recognized that excessively high values of the computed updraft velocity are unrealistic, since drag forces will come into play. Nevertheless, it is evident that even in an isothermal environment appreciable updrafts may occur, even in excess of the fall velocities of the snow particles (as indicated by the terminal-velocity data of LANGLEBEN [1954] and NAKAYA [1954, pp.111–116] superimposed upon Fig. 7). In a more normal environment, with a steeper lapse rate, the updraft velocities of Fig. 7 must be increased by a substantial factor (about four for a lapse rate of 0·7°C/100 m).

The role of aggregation may be considered qualitatively in the following way. A monodisperse distribution of 10^5 crystals/m³, each of mass ten micrograms, is indicated by point A; if these be aggregated arbitrarily by tens, the new distribution of 10^4 aggregates is indicated by B. Further aggregation by tens leads to point C. As aggregation proceeds from A to B to C, the corresponding updraft velocity decreases; in this example, single crystals (at A) would be carried aloft in the updraft, whereas the aggregates (B and C) would precipitate earthward. Thus aggregation inhibits the updraft, increasing the net fall speed of the particles.

When water cloud is present, the net heat release is reduced by a substantial factor, as indicated above. The updraft is likewise modified. This is indicated in Fig. 8, in which updraft velocity is plotted against stability (γ/γ_w). Curves (a) and (b) indicate, the updraft velocities in cloud-free and in cloudy air, respectively, for an arbitrary concentration of 10^5 crystals/m³ of $10\,\mu g$ mass, at 700 mb, −15°C, and water equilibrium. It has been assumed here that the crystal growth-rate in water cloud is the same as in clear air. According to MARSHALL and LANGLEBEN [1954] the growth rate is slightly enhanced in cloud; however, the heat release in cloudy air is reduced far more than the growth rate is enhanced, and so the enhancement has been neglected in the present study.

If ice crystals are introduced into the region of the edge of a cloud sheet, updrafts of different magnitude will develop in the cloud and in the adjacent moist clear air, resulting in a shear across the boundary (as indicated by curve c, Fig. 8). The resulting turbulence may well be a factor in the aggregation of the crystals. Stability (γ/γ_w) of the air in which the cells were embedded was determined in 14 well-defined cases, and the mean stability was found to be 0·84 (the modal value was approximately the same), corresponding closely to that value for which the shear is a maximum. While 14 cases constitute a limited sample, the above observations do suggest that generating cells tend to occur under those stability conditions in which the maximum shear across a cloud-boundary may be expected.

Active environment—In the preceding sections, it has been assumed that the environment is inactive, that is, that there exists no large-scale, overall, vertical motion.

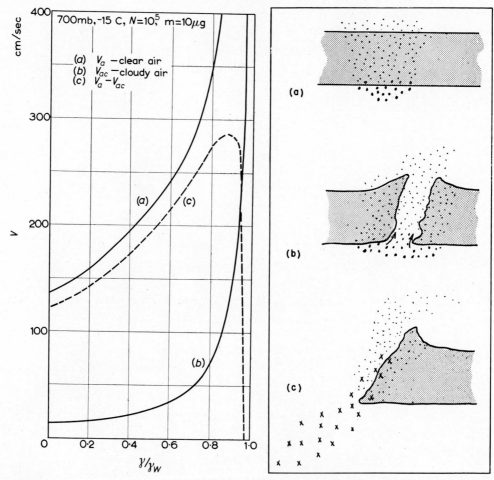

FIG. 8—Updraft velocity as a function of stability (a) in clear air, (b) in cloudy air; curve (c) is the difference, or shear

FIG. 9—Schematic diagram of the development of new cloud boundaries due to the introduction of ice crystals; (a) growing crystals fall through cloud; (b) near-vertical 'chimneys' are formed; and (c) turbulence, aggregation, and precipitation at a new cloud boundary

In an active environment there is a general upglide motion (such as occurs over a frontal surface) upon which is superimposed the sublimational updrafts previously discussed. There are two main features in which the active case differs from the inactive one. First, the total updraft is greater, the sublimational updraft being augmented by the frontal upglide; and second, the basic upglide motion provides a rich resupply for the parent water cloud, in opposition to the desiccation process of sublimation (Fig. 6). Whether the initial water content of the parcel increases or is depleted now depends not only upon the lapse rate (as is the case in the inactive environment) but also upon the concentration and size of the growing crystals, and hence upon the sublimation updraft (which is proportional to $\Sigma m^{0.5}$ for dendritic crystals). For any specified frontal upglide velocity and lapse rate, a critical value of $\Sigma m^{0.5}$ exists which, if exceeded, results in the desiccation of the cloud-parcel. Rough calculations, based upon snow data collected at the ground, suggest that $\Sigma m^{0.5}$ may often exceed the critical value, ensuring cloud desiccation aloft.

Cloud boundaries—Where ice crystals are growing in the region of a cloud boundary, differential updrafts and turbulence may be expected to promote aggregation. Local differences, within the cloud, of water content and of ice-crystal content will result in uneven desiccation and the appearance of new internal cloud boundaries. The most elementary picture of such a process is offered here as a tentative suggestion of how the foregoing considerations may be pertinent to the cell structure.

Suppose that ice crystals fall through a layer of water cloud into the liquid-free sub-cloud layer in which the vapor content is high (Fig. 9). In this moist layer there will be initiated much greater updrafts than are initiated in the cloud itself. These may be imagined as penetrating the cloud-sheet in 'chimneys', producing new internal cloud boundaries across which turbulence and aggregation may occur and from which the aggregates fall to form the observed snow-trail. On this basis the cloud boundary, along which aggregation appears likely, constitutes the region of the cell as observed by radar.

Conclusion—The latent heat of sublimation released by growing ice crystals in a moist, stable environment is a significant source of energy for vertical development and motion, of orders of magnitude comparable to the observed cell-heights and to the terminal velocities of the snow particles themselves (either single crystals or aggregates). Since the presence of supercooled water cloud inhibits the sublimational updraft, shear and turbulence (favorable to aggregation) may appear across a cloud boundary. The desiccation of water cloud by the growing crystals offers a means whereby new internal cloud boundaries may be formed, and the tentative suggestion is offered that such boundaries may constitute the basis of the snow-generating cell as observed by radar.

It must be emphasized that the updrafts, as considered here, are local, pertaining to a parcel only as it crosses a fixed level (specifically, at 700 mb, $-15°C$); the study of an individual parcel, throughout its history of snow growth, has not been attempted here. Clearly such a study, with close attention to microphysical detail within the parcel, is necessary before the detailed application of the above concepts to a cell-model can be attempted. Nevertheless, it is considered that the above study indicates the relevance, to the process of snow generation aloft, of the vertical development and motion resulting from the release of sublimational heat by growing ice crystals.

Acknowledgments—Radar data studied in this research were recorded by the McGill Stormy Weather Group under the sponsorship of the Defence Research Board of Canada (Project No. 9511–08). The author is indebted to J. S. Marshall of McGill University and to W. L. Godson of the Meteorological Service of Canada for their many suggestions. The author's participation in this research is by permission of the Controller, Meteorological Service of Canada.

REFERENCES

DENNIS, A. S., Measurement of fluctuations in radar echoes from snow, Ph.D. thesis, Dept. of Physics, McGill University, 1955.

GUNN, K. L. S., M. P. LANGLEBEN, A. S. DENNIS, and B. A. POWER, Radar evidence of a generating level for snow, *J. Met.*, v.11, pp.20–26, 1954.

HEWSON, E. W., Dissipation of scattered and broken cloud, *Q.J.R. Met. Soc.*, v.74, pp.243–265, 1948.

HOUGHTON, H. G., A preliminary quantitative analysis of precipitation mechanisms, *J. Met.*, v.7, pp.363–369, 1950.

LANGLEBEN, M. P., The terminal velocity of snowflakes, *Q.J.R. Met. Soc.*, v.80, pp.174–181, 1954.

MARSHALL, J. S., Precipitation trajectories and patterns, *J. Met.*, v.10, pp.25–29, 1953.

MARSHALL, J. S. and K. L. S. GUNN, Measurement of snow parameters by radar, *J. Met.*, v.9, pp.322–327, 1952.

MARSHALL, J. S. and M. P. LANGLEBEN, A theory of snow crystal habit and growth, *J. Met.*, v.11, pp.104–120, 1954.

NAKAYA, U., *Snow Crystals*, Harvard Univ. Press, pp.111ff., 1954.

PETTIT, K.G., The characteristics of supercooled clouds during Canadian icing experiments, 1905–53, *Proc. Toronto Met. Conf.*, R. Met. Soc., pp.269–275, 1954.

DISCUSSION

(This paper was preceded by a summary by Dr. M. L. Langleben regarding information about snow-generating cells provided by radar, which is incorporated in the paper above.)

Dr. Raymond Wexler—The fall velocity of the particles involved, estimated from the trail shape as from three to four feet per second, has been compared with fall velocities of ice crystals and snowflakes as measured at the ground. Now, fall velocities at 500 or 700 mb might be 50 per cent greater. The correction can be computed easily enough from known methods, and should be taken into consideration in your deduction of whether the particles are snowflakes or crystals.

Mr. R. H. Douglas—Fall velocities were measured all the way down the trail, and the values were fairly consistent.

Dr. Wexler—We are used to having updrafts first, then cloud, then precipitation. I find the sequence in the present paper rather confusing: first precipitation, then heat, then updraft, and then perhaps cloud.

Mr. Douglas—There are situations, almost always frontal so that sheets of water cloud are implied, in which we observe, by radar, localized centers of snow formation. We are simply looking for a process that would serve to develop these localized centers in such a situation, with enough turbulence to promote aggregation. We are not worrying too much about the initiation of such activity, nor do we suggest that the mechanics of our model cell is a final answer.

Dr. Wallace E. Howell—I gather that your 'upward velocity' is not necessarily, at least to begin with, the upward velocity of the air, but rather that of the level at which that air would be in equilibrium with its surroundings. That would have the quality of a force or an acceleration, and I doubt if it represents the actual velocity of the air.

Mr. Douglas—For our calculations we assume a series of steps, in each of which a brief interval of crystal growth and heating of the air parcel at constant pressure is followed by the adiabatic rise of the parcel to hydrostatic equilibrium. This amounts in the limit to having the parcel move up the ambient lapse rate. The rate of this ascent is the updraft that I mentioned.

Dr. Howell—Then you have neglected the inertia of the air. You have a measure of the force that accelerated the air upward, but not the actual upward velocity.

Dr. J. S. Marshall—For the more reasonable of the velocities shown, the kinetic energy is a small term relative to the energy required to lift the parcel 2000 ft.

Mr. Douglas—Agreed, and at high lapse rates the method implies infinite updraft velocities.

Dr. Hans J. aufm Kampe—You explained the growth of clouds by heat of sublimation or condensation, and sometimes seeded clouds build up on this account. There is another way to explain the formation of generating cells by evaporation. Sometimes on a day with cirrostratus cloud you can see, below this cloud sheet, wide puffs that are really altocumulus or cirrocumulus clouds. We have flown below this sort of cirrus many times, and noted considerable turbulence. This is due to the cirrostratus crystals falling out, evaporating, and thus forming a cooler layer, which increases the temperature gradient beneath it. The steeper the lapse rate is initially, of course, the easier it is to get this cumulus-type cloud.

Another fact to consider is the turbulence related to the jet stream which leads to dynamic formation of clouds.

Dr. Marshall—Suggestions such as these leave the latent heat release still to be taken into account.

Dr. Aufm Kampe—The upglide on the warm front is usually very small compared to the updraft that has been mentioned.

Dr. Charles F. Brooks—The fall velocity obtained by analyzing slopes of fall streaks will never be too small, and may be too large if you assume the line of motion of the fall streak to be parallel to the plane of the radar picture.

Dr. M. L. Langleben—This has been taken into account.

Prof. Charles L. Hosler—What was the lowest temperature for which you found evidence of aggregation?

Dr. Langleben—About $-16°C$. Observing at ground level, without radar, we have on occasion observed aggregates at about this temperature. One of Dr. Weickmann's slides showed some aggregates forming at extremely low temperatures.

Dr. Helmut Weickmann—Your 'generating level,' when seen with normal eyes from an aircraft, is not the sort of thing you would draw with a rule. It has ups and downs, in altitude and in temperature, and presumably crystals are generated at the lower temperatures. The water cloud is not a static, but a dynamic phenomenon, with parcels going up and down, say on the order of a half meter to one meter per second. The crystals that are formed do not fall out right away, but stay for a bit in the cell. Therefore, you do not get a fall streak right away, but first a vertical echo. We must rely not only on the eyes of radar, but also on our own.

Dr. J. Kuettner—One striking fact is that you do not seem to have shear at the generating level. I think that there are alternative mechanisms for these so-called generating cells. At the point of the strong curvature of the wind profile there is an inertial stability introduced which is quite akin to a thermal stability, and is sensitive for the formation of unstable waves which, after a short while, give the picture of a convective cell. The theory of it is a little involved, but it certainly is a more likely mechanism in a thermally stable atmosphere than any gravitational instability. A strong curvature in the wind profile, that is, the existence of a vorticity gradient, is one way in which the flow pattern can become dynamically unstable and break up into cells. (In reply to a query from Dr. Austin, Dr. Kuettner said that the theory was available in a number of reports from UCLA on the Mountain Wave Project and the contract on Stability of Parallel Flows. The question is also discussed in Dr. Kuettner's article in the *Aeronautical Engineering Review* [v. 11, no. 12, Dec. 1952].)

U

RADAR MEASUREMENTS OF PRECIPITATION GROWTH

DAVID ATLAS

Geophysics Research Directorate, Air Force Cambridge Research Center, Bedford, Mass.

Abstract—Quantitative radar measurements of the growth of precipitation and aircraft cloud observations are considered in the light of existing theories of growth and moisture supply. In two cases of stratiform precipitation, the number concentration of ice crystals released from the generating elements differed greatly; 470 m^{-3} were computed in the last streamer associated with a weak cyclone passing far to the south, while 15,000 m^{-3} were estimated in the active forward central region of an intense cyclone. In both cases the crystal growth proceeded at rates corresponding closely to a water-saturated environment, and in reasonably good accord with Houghton's theoretical values. However, the smaller crystal concentration in the weaker storm permitted the coexistence of a water cloud, while the higher concentration of the more intense one prevented cloud formation.

Although 1 cm radar measurements are subject to question in the melting layer, they suggest, nevertheless, that this region is one of major growth when active cloud masses are present. This indication is strongly supported in one instance by independent meteorological observations showing the rapid depletion of a dense cloud as it rises to the 0°C level. The estimated rates of growth are consistent with the growth of a large melting particle by accretion of cloud droplets. Growth of the raindrops below proceeds at a reduced rate both because of the lower cloud water contents and the smaller collection areas. Thus, while the rain may be inadequate to remove the excess cloud formed in the lower levels, the melting snow may do the job quite well.

Introduction—This paper concerns only the results of radar measurements of precipitation growth which are reported in great detail elsewhere [ATLAS, 1955]. In general, the method involved is the quantitative measurement of echo intensities from all precipitation passing through the vertically pointing beam of a 1·25-cm radar and the simultaneous sampling of drop size distribution in the rain at the ground. Detailed aircraft observations of the clouds, precipitation elements, and related meteorological variables have been furnished in two cases by Dr. Cunningham's group, which usually makes such co-ordinated flights in conjunction with the ground radar observations. The radar observations were made in Lexington, Mass.

The method of computing precipitation growth from the radar observations involves the following steps: (1) the establishment of theoretical relations between radar reflectivity and the statistics of the particle-size distribution; that is, D_0 is the median volume diameter; N_t number concentration, and spectrum breadth; (2) the measurement of these statistics at the surface by actual sampling of the rain or snow; (3) bracketing the variation with height of N and spectrum breadth according to predictable effects of the various precipitation processes upon idealized particle-size distributions; or when possible, reducing the problem to two unknowns by relating the variation of N_t to that of D_0; and (4) using the measured variation of reflectivity with height to compute the mass of the median volume particle as a function of height. Because we use the limiting conditions for the vertical variation of particle number and distribution breadth, the computed growth curves represent the boundaries between which the actual growth curve falls.

Of the assumptions involved in the basic technique and in the computations, the following are the most important: (1) Since the radar cannot follow the same set of particles from their point of generation to the ground, it is assumed that the generating cloud continues to release the same size distribution of particles for periods of the order

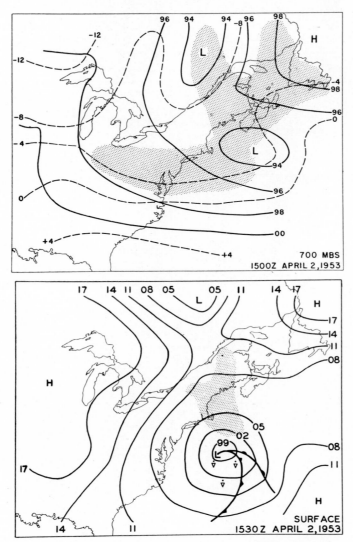

Fig. 1—The synoptic surface map for 10h 30m and 700-mb map for
10h 00m, April 2, 1953

of a half to one hour. (2) The atmosphere is horizontally homogeneous in time and space over the distance traversed by the generating element between the time the generator passes overhead and the time it released the first particles observed at the ground at the radar site. (3) In order to allow for turning of the wind with height, the generator is assumed to have length in a dimension perpendicular to its direction of motion and to be uniform in its generating properties along that direction. (4) In order to compute snow distributions, each raindrop is assumed to have originated from a single snowflake with no break up occurring between the peak of the 'bright band' and the level of complete melting; the flakes themselves may be aggregates of many crystals. (5) In order to com-

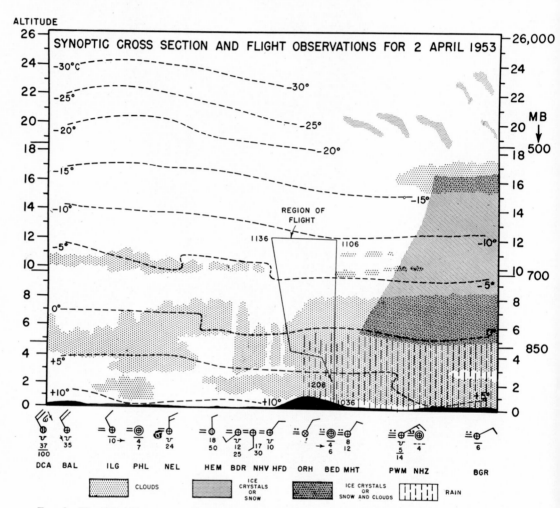

FIG. 2—The SW–NE cross-section based on the 10h 00mm soundings and the aircraft observations for the period 10h 37m to 12 h 20m, April 2, 1953

pute growth in the melting zone, corrections for deviations from Rayleigh scattering are assumed to be approximately the same for the raindrops as for the large wet flakes or crystals from which they originated (that is, the Mie scattering corrections are assumed to be more dependent on particle mass than size).

Assumption (5) is subject to the greatest doubt because large snowflakes are comparable to the 1·25-cm wavelength, and the scattering theory for such large non-spherical particles is not known. Thus, our deductions of growth through the melting zone are subject to question when we have reason to suspect the presence of large flakes. With this much background we proceed to the individual cases.

Storm of April 2, 1953—The radar and aircraft observations were made in the northwest sector of a more or less continuous region of light to moderate precipitation

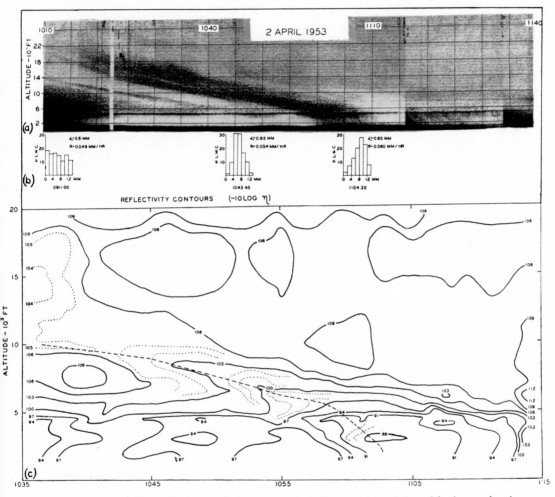

FIG. 3—Storm of April 2, 1953; (a) time-height radar facsimile record; variation of background noise level with altitude is due to sensitivity time control circuit; (b) distributions of liquid-water content with drop size at the ground; (c) reflectivity contour map for streamer seen in 'fax' record at top

associated with a slow-moving low centered approximately 300 mi south of Boston (Fig. 1). The flight made from 10h 36m–12h 20m (all times shown are Eastern Standard or 75th meridian time) (Fig. 2) showed that the upper decks were just clearing; solid stratus water clouds were observed up to 8500 ft (−4·5°C) with the 0°C level at 5800 ft and no visual change in the stratus cloud across this level. Broken cirrostratus were observed off to the east and above. The last streamer from the cirrostratus deck to pass over the radar was studied in detail (Fig. 3a). Precipitation at the ground was like drizzle with maximum drop size of 1·4 mm, but a low concentration of 255 drops/m³; rain intensity was only 0·06 mm/hr. Distributions of liquid-water content with size in the rain are shown in Fig. 3b.

Fig. 3c shows the reflectivity contour chart with solid contours drawn for increments of three db in $-10 \log \eta$ (a factor of two in reflectivity, η). Although the start of the streamer was not studied, the record indicates a slight maximum at about 15,000 ft, but no real growth until the ice crystals approached the top of the stratus water cloud. Growth along the streamer may be seen by following the heavy dashed curve which was drawn through the apices of the contours. Growth continues right down to the maximum reflectivities at 3000 ft. The decrease in reflectivity below 3000 ft is believed to be erroneous. (This is due to large possible calibration errors in about the first 2000 ft of record.) Some slight growth probably continues right down to the ground (note the stratus deck with tops at about 1500 ft on the facsimile record, Fig. 3a).

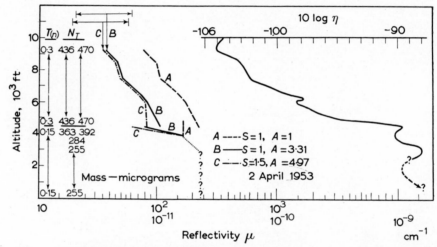

Fig. 4—(Right) Reflectivity versus height along the axis of the streamer seen in Fig. 3; (left) mass of the median volume diameter versus height for various assumed conditions.

In Fig. 4 are shown the reflectivity-height curve along the core of the streamer (on the right) and three computed growth curves for the median-volume particle. The dotted section of the mass curve between 3000 and 4000 ft shows growth of the median-volume particle by a factor of 1·4, due to cloud accretion. Between 4000 and 4500 ft, just below the peak of the bright band, there is a tremendous growth computed along curves B and C, but this is subject to question at the moment. Curve A considers the possibility that both B and C are wrong in this region, and that there was zero growth in this layer. We shall come back to this point later. The discontinuities in all three curves at 4500 ft are mathematical only, and represent the fact that the size distribution shifts abruptly when melting occurs; that is, the larger particles accelerate by a larger ratio than the smaller ones, thus reducing the median volume mass in the rain.

Between 6000 ft (the 0°C level) and 4500 ft, the increase in reflectivity may be attributed partly to growth, and partly to a known wetting effect and an estimated shape effect. If the shape effect is assumed large ($S = 1 \cdot 5$ along curve C), then the growth factor is small; along curve B there is no shape effect ($S = 1 \cdot 0$) and growth must therefore account for a larger portion of the increase in reflectivity. This growth is due primarily to cloud accretion; clumping of the particles is believed to be negligible because of the small size of the final drops at the ground. Between 6000 and 10,000 ft, growth is primarily by diffusion in the slightly supercooled stratus cloud. Riming is believed to be negligible because the computed fall velocity along the streamer is the same at 8000 ft as it is at 14,000 ft, namely about 70 cm/sec. This fall velocity corresponds roughly either to spatial dendrites or slightly rimed crystals. The horizontal double-headed arrows near the top represent the limits within which the growth curves B and C may be bracketed, based on limiting conditions for the variation of total number concentration and spectrum breadth with height. The growth curves would be pivoted about the points computed at the 6000-ft level. The numbers listed under N_t at the left represent total number concentration per cubic meter with 470 m^{-3} corresponding to curve C. Such a concentration is remarkably low, particularly along the core of the streamer. Values under $T(n)$ represent spectrum breadth coefficient which are treated in the thesis cited. Along curve C above the 0°C level the rates of growth (for particles falling at 70 cm/sec) vary from about 1 to $5 \cdot 5 \times 10^{-8}$ gm/sec in reasonably good agreement with HOUGHTON'S [1950] theoretical values for growth of plane dendrites at water saturation. Although the particles are growing at water saturation, they do not deplete the cloud rapidly because of their low number concentration. In fact, the total contribution of the layer between 6000 and 9000 ft is less than $0 \cdot 01$ mm/hr; thus, it would take only a fraction of a cm/sec updraft to balance the rate of removal. This is undoubtedly the reason for the observation of a water cloud in the presence of ice crystals.

Let us return now to the melting layer. The large growth computed along curves B and C is deduced as a result of the absence of a normal decrease in reflectivity η below the peak of the bright band; that is, if the particles melted and accelerated without growth we should expect a decrease in η by a factor of about four for this rain intensity. (The expected decrease in the case of curve C is about six, since this assumes a shape of $1 \cdot 5$.) The difference between the expected decrease and the actual decrease is attributed to growth. In this case, the scattering theory cannot be seriously questioned because the particles in the melting zone are probably still small relative to the wavelength.

The resulting rate of growth is about $0 \cdot 7 \times 10^{-6}$ g/m of fall along curve C, and $0 \cdot 6 \times 10^{-6}$ g/m along B. Only a small fraction of this growth can be ascribed to condensation on the cold melting particles. A somewhat larger fraction of the growth can be attributed to cloud accretion if the particles are assumed to retain their large collection areas for at least part of the 500 ft. However, it is then difficult to account for the formation of the peak of the bright band, since it is generally assumed that the particles collapse to spherical raindrops below the peak. In short, it is difficult to account for the computed growth with presently known growth processes.

Although this might lead us to question the radar observations, we should not be too hasty in discarding them. We know that growth in the melting zone is a complex problem. In the presence of cloud, the large collection areas of the ice crystals and flakes would be expected to result in rapid growth followed by a sudden decrease in growth rate upon collapse to raindrops. Condensation also enhances the growth slightly in the melting zone and suddenly decreases when melting is completed. In addition, if electrical

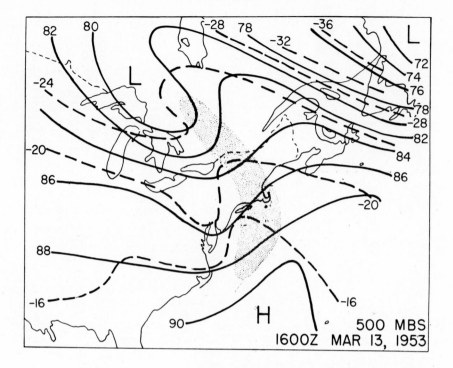

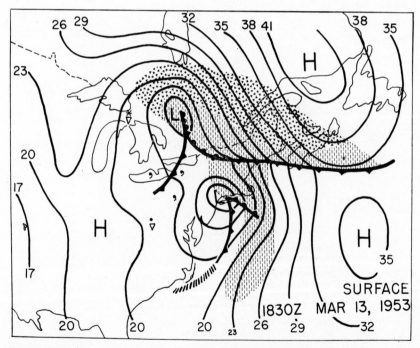

FIG. 5—Synoptic surface map for 13h 30m and 500–mb map for 10h 00m, March 13, 1953; the shaded area on the 500–mb map represents the region where the air is saturated with respect to ice; the coarse shading on the surface map represents snow; the dashed shading, rain

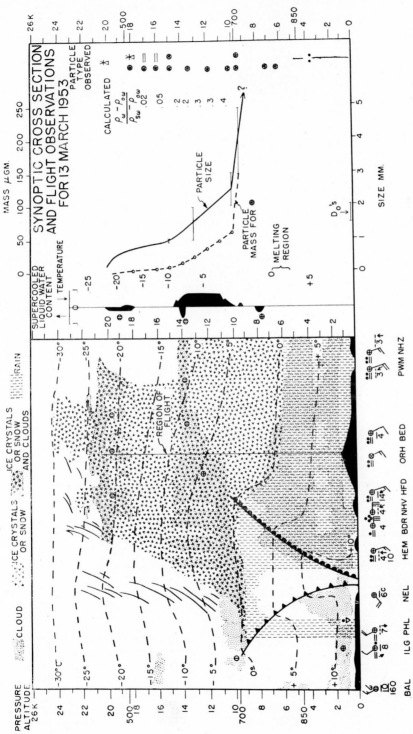

Fig. 6—SW–NE cross-section for 11h 00m and aircraft observations for the period 12h 15m to 16h 19m, March 13, 1953; ascent made from 12h 15m to 14h 15m; descent from 14h 44 m to 16h 19m; particle types are: spatial dendrite ⊛; graupel △; column ▭

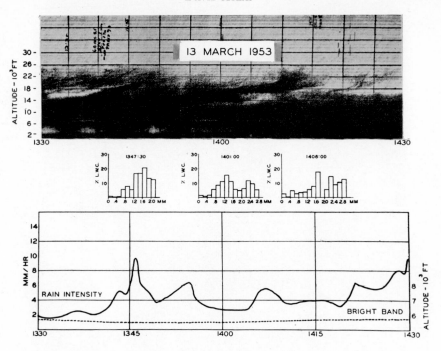

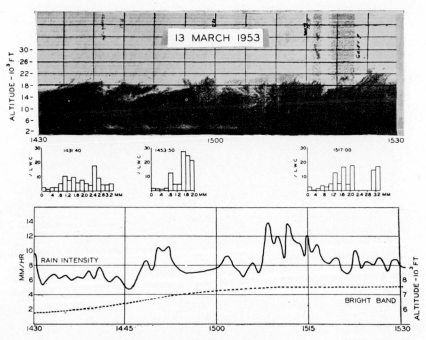

FIG. 7—Time-height radar facsimile record, surface dropsize distributions, rain intensity, and height of the bright band (dashed curve)

effects are to act anywhere, the melting zone seems a likely place. Thus, there seems adequate reason to expect important growth in the melting layer. Unfortunately, however, the present radar data are open to enough doubt and are too scanty to be conclusive in this regard. We shall consider this problem further in the next case.

Storm of March 13, 1953—This case has been treated briefly by CUNNINGHAM and ATLAS [1953]. It is considered here from another viewpoint and with additional data. The observations were made in the most active sector of a coastal cyclone (Fig. 5) with moderate to heavy continuous rain. The flight cross section prepared by Dr. Cunningham's group (Fig. 6) is dominated by an extensive ice-crystal cloud mass in which are embedded active cumuliform layers (18,000–22,000 ft, 0·2 g/m³; and 10,000–14,000 ft, 0·1 g/m³). Major low-level convergence gives rise to a dense cloud mass which extends right up to the zero-degree isotherm below the frontal surface. Particle types are primarily spatial dendrites, although some graupel and columns were observed aloft. Particle masses were derived from the diameter-mass relation of NAKAYA and TERADA [1935] for spatial dendrites, with diameters being observed visually. The quantity $(\rho_w - \rho_{0w})/(\rho_{sw} - \rho_{0w})$ represents the relative value of the ambient humidity with respect to water (1·0) or ice (0) saturation. The sudden increase in particle size at 10,000 ft corresponds to clumping, but this is not representative of the air above the radar where large numbers of individual spatial dendrites were observed down to 7000 ft. Nearer the radar clumping probably occurred at lower levels. In the computations, we start clumping at the 0°C level, which is at 6500 ft over the radar.

Fig. 7 shows the radar facsimile record, the raindrop samples (diameters up to 3·4 mm) and the rain intensity trace (up to 14 mm/hr). Note the fine structure of the rain-intensity trace after 14h 30m. The reflectivity contour maps for two intervals of the radar record are shown in Fig. 8. The uppermost precipitation is streamer form, with relatively high reflectivities (−89 db at 14,000 ft may be compared with the highest value of −88 db near the surface in the April 2 case). The corresponding precipitation rate of 12,000 ft is calculated from the radar measurements at about 0·1 mm/hr setting the scene for high rainfall rates at the surface. In the early contour map, the contours become very uniform in time below 12,000 ft, suggesting that the upper streamers may have seeded the observed supercooled clouds, causing the release of ice crystals over a much wider area than is covered by the streamers themselves. In the later contoured section, the intensity of the upper streamers is slightly greater and the variability in the lower levels is also greater. The numerous reflectivity cells in the melting zone indicate the presence of cellular cloud masses contributing to growth.

In both contour maps, the reflectivity continues to increase right through the melting layer instead of decreasing normally and forming the conventional bright band. This can be seen better in the reflectivity plot on the right of Fig. 9, which is the average of the first three minutes of Fig. 8. (The curve of η versus height in Fig. 9 has been corrected for rainfall attenuation at 1·25 cm.) The lack of a decrease in η below the 'peak' is undoubtedly due in part to growth through and below the melting zone, where we have dense clouds set up by the intense low-level convergence. However, it is probably also due in part to the peculiar scattering habits of large, wet, non-spherical particles at a wavelength of 1·25 cm. Some of the observations at MIT on the same day at a wavelength of three cm also fail to show the normal decrease in reflectivity to be expected

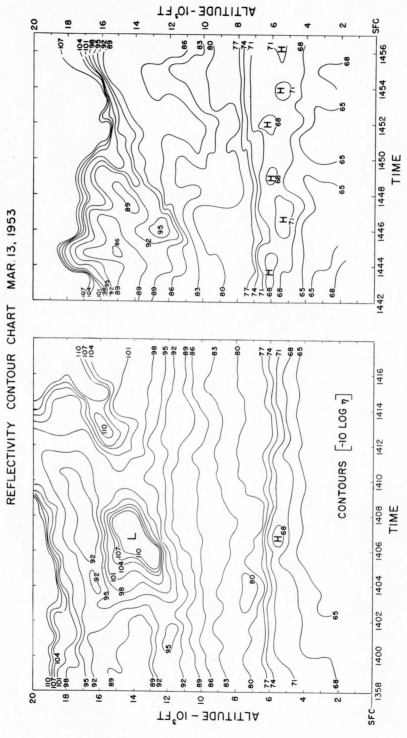

FIG. 8—Reflectivity contour maps for 13h 58m to 14h 17m and 14h 42m to 14h 56m, March 13, 1953

below the bright band, while others have decreases approaching normal. Thus, the large computed growth in the mass height curves (*left*, Fig. 9) from 5000 to 5500 ft must be left open to further consideration. (The two alternatives in growth in this layer depend on the shape factor, the larger growth being associated with the larger shape factor, $S = 1.5$ along curve C.) We shall return to the problem of the reality of this region of large growth later.

In the layer from 5500–6500 ft (0°C level), growth is caused by both aggregation and cloud accretion, the different growth possibilities in Fig. 9 resulting from two different shape effects and a possible variation in the size distribution as a result of clumping. Above the 0°C level, growth is almost entirely by diffusion (curves ABC). Curve D shows the outside limit which would have resulted if growth had proceeded entirely by

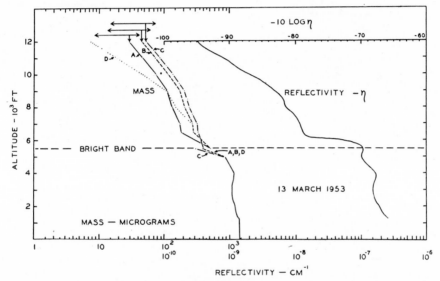

Fig. 9—(Right) Reflectivity versus height averaged over 13h 58m to 14h 00m, March 13, 1953 and corrected for rainfall attenuation; (left) mass of the median volume diameter versus height for various assumed conditions

aggregation from 12,000 ft down to the 0°C level. The horizontal double-headed arrows at the top of A, B, and C represent outside limits due to possible variations in number concentration and spectrum breadth between 12,000 and 6500 ft, the curves being fixed at the lower level. The actual growth is probably bracketed between curves A and C.

Along curve B, the computed median volume mass is 34×10^{-6} gm at 12,000 ft as compared with estimated sizes of 35×10^{-6} gm from the aircraft. Of course, the curves show a possible range from ten to 75 micrograms at 12,000 ft. The corresponding number concentration is 15,300 per cubic meter along curve B, a tremendous number compared to the value of 470 m^{-3} in the previous case. Above the 0°C level growth rates along curve B (for particles assumed to be falling between 0.5 and 1.0 m/sec) are comparable to Houghton's theoretical values for plane dendrites growing at water saturation and exceed the visually observed rates indicated by Fig. 6. This suggested that the snow-filled air between 6500 and 12,000 ft is closer to water saturation than the previous calculations indicated, that is, the values $(\rho_w - \rho_{0w})/(\rho_{sw} - \rho_{0w})$ in Fig. 6. However, there is no water cloud in most of this zone because the large number of particles probably use up the moisture as fast as it is being supplied by the vertical currents. The vertical velocities required to supply sufficient water to balance the rate of removal range from five to ten cm/sec above the 0°C level.

We may return now to consider the large growth reported in the layer from 5000 to 5500 ft, the zone just under the peak of the bright band. This would correspond to growth of the median volume particle at a rate of $3 \cdot 2 \times 10^{-6}$ g/m of fall. If this growth occurred entirely at the expense of water in the atmosphere, the average rate of removal of moisture through the 500-ft layer would be 14×10^{-4} g/m³ sec, corresponding to an increase of about 0·75 mm/hr in precipitation rate. Actually, part of the growth in this layer is probably due to continued aggregation of the melting particles, so that less than 14×10^{-4} g/m³ sec has to be supplied by the environment. As noted earlier, there was some doubt as to the reality of this growth because of the questionable accuracy of the scattering theory for large wet particles at a wavelength of 1·25 cm, and because some of the three-cm observations at MIT on the same day failed to show a corresponding reflectivity structure.

At the time of the Conference, I noted that additional doubt was cast upon the reality of this large growth because the dynamics of the situation could supply water at a rate equal only to about one-third of that at which moisture would be required. However, a re-examination of the moisture supply mechanisms now leads me to the conclusion that the required moisture could realistically be furnished by the atmosphere, and therefore, that the surprising results of the radar computations might be valid indeed. Because of the importance of this aspect of the measurements, further discussion seems desirable.

The original computations of moisture supply were based on the continuity equation for vapor and cloud-water content. The most important terms in this equation are the vertical transport terms: (1) $V_z \partial(\rho q)/\partial z$, representing the rate of condensation with ρ designating air density, q, the saturation mixing ratio, and V_z, the vertical velocity; and (2) $V_z \partial M/\partial z$ representing the vertical advection of cloud liquid water, M being the liquid water content. Smaller contributions to the moisture supply are also made by: (3) condensation on the melting snow, and (4) horizontal cloud advection. These considerations assume that the precipitation process is in a steady state; that is, particularly that local changes in cloud liquid-water content are small and that the precipitation is feeding only on the excess cloud being advected into the region and being formed there by the updraft. This is reasonable, since the cloud was observed to exist in essentially the same form throughout the duration of the flight and the precipitation continued with equal or higher intensities all afternoon.

In determining the vertical transport terms, the vertical velocity could be computed only approximately from the convergence measured on the 14h 30m surface map. The calculated value was 25 cm/sec, a high but not unreasonable value in the center of an intense isallobaric area. This value probably should be reduced to perhaps 15 to 20 cm/sec, since it pertains to the center of the isohyetal region which did not reach the radar site until an hour after the time corresponding to the growth computation. The corresponding rate of condensation at the 5000-ft level would be between 2·4 and $3 \cdot 2 \times 10^{-4}$ g/m³ sec.

Computation of the vertical advection of cloud water depends in addition to V_z upon the vertical gradient of cloud liquid water. Noting that the water cloud was abruptly topped at the 0°C level (6500 ft), it was realized that the gradient of liquid water was strongly negative, corresponding to a large upward advection of water. However, the gradient $\partial M/\partial z$ was greatly underestimated in my original calculations. If we consider that the difference in the saturation mixing ratios between 1000 and 5000 ft was 2·7 g/kg, the water content at 5000 ft would be approximately 2·7 g/m³, provided, of course, that the excess cloud was carried upward and not washed out by the rain. Since $M = 0$ at 6500 ft, $\partial M/\partial z = -5\cdot9\times10^{-3}$ g/m³ per meter in the layer of interest. This is almost 24 times the gradient originally estimated. Thus, with a vertical velocity of 15–20 cm/sec, cloud would be advected into the layer above 5000 ft at a rate of approximately 9 to 12×10^{-4} g/m³ sec. Even if we arbitrarily reduced the cloud content at 5000 ft by a factor of two to allow for some low-level wash out, the minimum rate of vertical cloud advection would be about $4\cdot5\times10^{-4}$ g/m³. The sum of all the water-supply components listed in Table 1 would then range from about 8 to 16×10^{-4} g/m³ sec, the smaller value corresponding to the lower limits of both the liquid water content and vertical velocity at 5000 ft. Thus we see that the atmosphere might reasonably supply the required moisture of 14×10^{-4} g/m³ sec computed as a result of the radar measurements. Because of the necessarily rough approximations required in the latter computation, it is felt that the agreement is rather good. If anything, the radar computed growth appears to be a bit on the high side. Of course, the agreement is even better if one assumes that part of the growth was due to continued aggregation, and did not depend on water from the environment.

Table 1. *Components of the rate of moisture supply in the 500-ft layer below the peak of the bright band*

Component	Approximate value
	10^4g/m³sec
Condensation by lifting ...	2·4–3·2
Vertical cloud advection ...	4·5–12
Horizontal cloud advection ...	0·4
Condensation on melting snow	0·6
Total	7·9–16·2

It is important to note also that the radar-computed rate of growth of the median volume particle in this interesting layer is $3\cdot2\times10^{-6}$ g/m of fall. If the growing particles are considered to be spherical with effective density of 0·05 g/cm³ and collection efficiency of 0·5, in falling through a cloud of density 1·35 g/m³ (half the maximum possible value) they would collect cloud at a rate of about $3\cdot4\times10^{-6}$ g/m. Thus the rate of accretion alone could adequately account for the computed growth rate. We cannot treat the accretion problem more quantitatively because of the possible variations in the effective density and collection efficiency from those selected.

There is, in addition to growth by accretion, a small additional growth due to condensation on the cold melting particles. Furthermore, upon completion of melting and collapse to raindrops, the smaller size of the heavier drops (880×10^{-6} g at 5000 ft) would cause a sudden reduction in the accretion rate to a value of approximately 1·2

$\times 10^{-6}$ g/m for the cloud density of 1·35 g/m³. This growth rate comes close to the average rate of $0·9 \times 10^{-6}$ g/m computed for the raindrops in the layer between 4000 and 5000 ft (where the cloud density would normally be expected to be somewhat less anyway). Indeed, the computed growth rate in the 4000–5000-ft layer may be taken as evidence of the presence of a cloud of the order of one g/m³ in that region and somewhat higher above. Such a cloud density is consistent with the lower estimates made earlier for the layer 5000–5500 ft, and therefore, provides further support for the reality of the large growth deduced in the latter zone.

In summary, therefore, we see that although the radar measurements in the melting zone were subject to question, the reliable measurement of the growth of rain just below the melting zone indicates a cloud content at 5000 ft exceeding one g/m³, a value which is consistent with the sounding. Independent observations from the aircraft show no water cloud at 6500 ft, the 0°C level, while the strong low-level convergence indicates a fairly substantial updraft. It is to be emphasized, therefore, that the meteorological observations alone testify to a very efficient cloud removal process in the vicinity of the melting region. Indeed, the magnitude of the rate of water supply deduced from the meteorological conditions is consistent with that computed from the radar observations. Furthermore, the rate of growth of individual elements as computed from the radar measurements is also in satisfactory agreement with the rate of accretion which might be expected for the relatively large melting particles. Thus, although the radar computations through the melting zone might still be questioned with respect to detail, they can hardly be doubted in essence.

Of course, further verification of the observations are required before final conclusions are drawn with respect to the importance of growth in the melting zone. However, it is suggested that this process is probably important in the forward central region of an active cyclone when the melting level is at an intermediate height, that is, between perhaps 4000 and 10,000 ft. Under these circumstances, the vertical velocities and cloud liquid-water contents may reach substantial values at the same heights at which the precipitation growth process is quite efficient. The process is of more than casual interest to the precipitation forecaster, for it demonstrates that while the rain may be inadequate to remove all the water generated in the lower levels, the melting snow may do the job nicely.

One further point is worthy of additional comment. This is the fact that the vertical velocities required to balance the computed rates of growth above the 0°C level ranged from about five to ten cm/sec; whereas, the updrafts deduced from the low-level convergence were found to be about 15 to 20 cm/sec just below the 0°C level. Although one should not attribute too much significance to the difference in these values because of the approximations required in their computation, the question deserves some attention. If the actual velocities in the snow region exceeded the balancing updrafts of five to ten cm/sec, as might be inferred from the higher values computed at 5000 ft, one would expect to find water cloud mixed with the snow. Since this is not the case, one wonders whether there is indeed a sudden decrease in vertical velocity above the melting layer. Could it be that the low-level updraft is driven in part by the thermal forces associated with the cooling by the melting snow? FINDEISEN [1949] has shown how this effect is responsible for the formation of the 'instability' clouds so frequently found below the melting level. However, one tends to regard these clouds as convective in origin, and therefore, the associated vertical motions are not generally believed to make an average contribution to the large-scale updraft or to the average rain intensity. The validity of this belief has considerable bearing on the nature of the precipitation process as well as on the accuracy of rainfall forecasts. The answer is by no means obvious and awaits further study.

Summary—Above the 0°C level, radar-computed growth rates in two stratiform situations are in general accord with those expected from HOUGHTON's [1950] theory. In the less active storm (April 2, 1953), although growth of the individual particles proceeded at water saturation, their low number concentration (470 m^{-3}) permitted the co-existence of a water cloud. In the deep active storm (March 13, 1953) on the other hand, the crystal number concentration was so high (about 15,000 m^{-3}) that no water cloud existed through a deep layer, despite the fact that their computed growth rates were very close to water saturation. The great difference in ice-crystal concentration in these two cases may be related to the synoptic situation; the high concentration having occurred in the deep active sector of a cyclone, the low concentration at the rear side of a weak storm.

Below the melting level, substantial growth is due to accretion by rain of low-level cloud masses, particularly in the region of intense convergence just ahead of an active cyclonic system (March 13, 1953).

In the melting layer the radar measurements in the cases of April 2 and March 13, 1953 suggested quite substantial growth of the particles in falling through water clouds. However, it is in this region that the measurements are subject to greatest question because the scattering theory for electrically large, wet, non-spherical particles is only poorly defined. In addition, it was originally estimated that the large 'observed' growth could not adequately be attributed to accretion of cloud.

The doubt in the reality of the large growth in the melting layer was further compounded in the March 13, 1953 case by the computed inability of the atmosphere to supply water to the melting layer at the rate apparently required. However, both the latter objections have been removed since presentation of this paper at the Woods Hole Conference by the realization that the cloud-water content in the melting zone was very much greater than originally estimated. This fact, in combination with the abrupt topping of the cloud at the 0°C level, indicates that water is being removed from the melting layer at a rather large rate. Indeed, this rate is in reasonable accord with that previously estimated from the radar measurements, although this is not to suggest that these measurements are without question. Thus it is concluded that there is, in fact, a major growth zone in the melting layer when active cloud masses are being formed and advected up into that zone. What excess cloud cannot be removed by the rainfall from the lower levels may very well be collected by the melting snow above, although complete wash-out as in the case of March 13 must be fortuitous.

Acknowledgments—This paper is a summary of part of the results of a doctoral dissertation in the Department of Meteorology, Massachusetts Institute of Technology [ATLAS, 1955]. Details of the measurement and computation techniques, further elaboration on the results, limitations, and a general summary of the 'stratiform' precipitation process are given in that thesis.

x

REFERENCES

ATLAS, D., The radar measurement of precipitation growth, D.Sc. thesis, Dept. of Met., Mass. Inst. of Tech., June, 1955.

CUNNINGHAM, R. M. and D. ATLAS, Growth of hydrometeors as calculated from aircraft and radar observations, *Proc. Toronto Met. Conf.*, R. Met. Soc., London, pp.276–289, 1953.

FINDEISEN, W., Die Enstehung der O.C—Isothermie und die Fractocumulus Bildung unter Nimbostratus, *Met. Zs.*, v.57, pp.49–54, 1949.

HOUGHTON, H. G., A preliminary quantitative analysis of precipitation mechanisms, *J. Met.*, v.7, pp.363–369, 1950.

NAKAYA, U. and T. TERADA, Simultaneous observations of the mass, falling velocity, and form of individual snow crystals, *J. Fac. Sci., Hokkaido Univ.*, ser.2, v.1, pp.191–200, 1935.

DISCUSSION

Dr. Pauline M. Austin—We had two measurements at MIT on the first occasion that you have discussed, but not on the same streamer. Measurements were taken point by point, down the streamer. Although the streamer looked fairly uniform on the scope, intensity measurements revealed levels where the intensity increased rapidly. We had no access to airborne measurements at the time, but when we saw your results we realized that our regions of rapid growth were exactly those in which water clouds had been observed. This radar evidence of rapid growth would be a useful source of information for pilots, if it could be obtained without delay.

Dr. David Atlas—You must be very careful in using rapid growth as evidence of icing. If snow (and thus echo) is general at the level of rapid growth, I would say there is probably no icing. If, on the other hand, there are regions of no echo at the level of rapid growth in adjacent streamers these echoless regions are likely to contain icing cloud.

Dr. Austin—Then the growth pattern does point out the level at which the water cloud exists.

Dr. James E. McDonald—A principal problem remaining is that of accounting for the heavy growth near the freezing level. Would not the Vierhout mechanism that you mentioned work only with very closely spaced particles? Then surely it will not give you a microgram per meter out of drops that are relatively far apart and falling at quite different speeds.

Dr. Atlas—The particle is falling through a cloud of, say, 500 droplets per cubic centimeter. There is a diffusion field going to the melting particle, and plenty of droplets in that field. However you can better assess the importance of the Vierhout process than I. In the second case cited, that process could still not account for the very rapid growth, because the growth went on for at least three hours. All that I could account for dynamically by taking maximum convergence and so forth was about one third of the supply that was necessary.

(In the light of the revised findings which were reached after the Conference, the latter comments are no longer pertinent. The new and larger liquid-water content found in the melting layer permits us to account for the rate of growth by a single accretion process, and for the required rate of moisture supply, by the existing convergence and updraft. These points are discussed in the text of my paper.)

Dr. Raymond Wexler—Cases of little or no drop in echo intensity at the bottom portion of the bright band are infrequently observed with the CPS–9 radar at MIT. As Dr. Atlas has suggested, some of the difference may be due to the use of different wavelengths. In addition, there may be some difference due to the method of observations in that his antenna is directed toward the vertical, requiring large corrections in range and sensitivity time control (STC), while observations at MIT were made at distances of about ten miles, requiring little or no correction. (Dr. Atlas has replied in private conversation that the range and STC corrections could not account for the observed difference particularly in the case of March 13, 1953.)

Dr. Helmut Weickmann—I would like to recall a paper by FINDEISEN [1949, see References at end of paper]. In snowfalls he always observed an isothermal layer starting at and extending below the freezing level, which he explained as follows. After passing the freezing level, the melting snowflakes take up heat and establish an isothermal layer at 0°C. In this layer the larger crystal aggregates still persist but they have a wet film and are therefore good reflectors. The longer the snowfall persists, the deeper will be the layer. At the base of such a layer there must be a steep lapse rate, leading to convection and the typical fractocumulus or fractostratus clouds. It appears that this isothermal layer at 0°C is identical with the bright band.

Dr. Atlas—I considered that mechanism, but it is difficult to use it to account for the continuous rate of supply that is required.

Dr. L. J. Batten—You have indicated ice above the freezing level, water below. How did you know that there were no water droplets above the freezing level?

Dr. Atlas—The regions where I have indicated no water droplets are those where the icing rate measured by the airplane was zero. Higher up, there were cumuliform water clouds within the snow.

THE MELTING LAYER

RAYMOND WEXLER

Blue Hill Meteorological Observatory, Harvard University, Milton, Mass.

Abstract—The increase in fall velocity of a spherical melting snowflake is derived from the assumption that melting occurs from the outside leaving the inner low-density ice portion intact. The depth of the melting layer (in the atmosphere) may then be determined as a function of the lapse rate, the raindrop size, and the initial and final fall velocities. The theoretical calculations for a sphere appear to underestimate the depth of the melting layer. The combined effects of changes in the scattering cross section and in fall velocity of the melting snowflakes on the location of the peak echo intensity in the melting layer are evaluated. The observed location of this peak in the lower portion of the melting layer is attributed to the larger drops, although the nonspherical shape of the melting snowflakes may also contribute to this effect.

Introduction—Because of the spectacular character of the radar-bright band at the melting layer and the manifold importance of its height, the melting layer has been the subject of considerable research during recent years. It has been apparent that the melting layer undergoes changes due to the effect of the melting precipitation on the air in addition to larger-scale synoptic conditions. The lowering of the melting layer due to cooling by melting snow has been discussed by WEXLER, REED, and HONIG [1954]. The melting layer is also frequently observed to rise, due to the advection of warm air. The significance of the melting layer in creating a region of stability and wind sheer, and causing the development of a stratocumulus deck below, has recently been discussed by BEMIS [1955]. These changes are generally relatively slow, and the melting layer frequently remains at a constant height over a period of several hours. The melting layer may therefore be considered as a quasi-steady state. Its depth will depend on the lapse rate and on the sizes and fall velocities of the melting snowflakes.

A melting snowflake, falling through air with temperatures warmer than 0°C, maintains its temperature at 0°C until completely melted. In saturated air, the snowflake receives heat by conduction and by condensation from its surroundings. Some rough calculations of the melting layer depth, neglecting the latent heat of condensation, were made by AUSTIN and BEMIS [1950]. More recently, in unpublished calculations, Dr. Atlas, using a mean fall velocity for the melting snowflake, determined the depth of the melting layer in saturated air. In this paper the change in fall velocity of the melting snowflake will be determined theoretically and the depth of the melting layer in saturated air will be computed for different size drops. From these calculations an attempt is made to evaluate the role of coalescence.

The computed change in fall velocity of the melting snowflake will also be used to determine the echo intensity profile in the melting layer to be expected due to this factor and the change in radar cross section of a melting snowflake. Other factors influencing the echo intensity, such as shape and coalescence, will be evaluated.

The fall velocity of melting snowflakes—Few measurements of the fall velocities of melting snowflakes are available. It was assumed by AUSTIN and BEMIS [1950] that the change in fall velocity is slight until melting is almost complete. Measurements of the terminal fall velocities of unmelted snowflakes of different types and sizes were made by LANGLEBEN [1954]. Equations relating the fall velocities with the diameters of their equivalent raindrops were derived for different types of aggregates.

A snowflake, consisting of an aggregation of ice crystals, has dimensions which are large and a fall velocity which is small compared to those of the raindrop resulting from its melting. As melting occurs, the dimensions decrease and smaller resistance is offered to the air flow, so that the fall velocity increases. If melting proceeds from the outside of the snowflake, leaving the inner ice portion intact, then the melting of a relatively large percentage of the mass is accompanied by a much smaller decrease in its dimensions. As a result the increase in fall velocity may be much smaller than would be expected from the amount of melting. For the purpose of computing the increase in fall velocity, we shall assume that the melting snowflake is spherical and that the melted portion is absorbed within the ice portion until its diameter is equal to that of the raindrop. Results will be approximately the same if it is assumed that the water collects as a concentric layer outside the ice portion, because the thickness of this layer is negligible until a considerable portion of the ice has melted. Although a melting snowflake, in a saturated environment increases in mass by about six per cent due to condensation, this small increase is neglected and it is assumed that the mass of the melting snowflake remains constant. This assumes, too, that no significant water is present in the melting zone so that growth by accretion is inappreciable. If we let F be the fraction of the snowflake mass that is melted, then the diameter D of the ice portion is given by

$$(1-F)D^3_0 = D^3 \tag{1}$$

where D_0 is the snowflake diameter before melting. This equation is valid until almost complete melting.

As the snowflake melts and water is absorbed within the ice portion, the diameter decreases, and smaller resistance is offered to the airflow, so that the fall velocity increases. The terminal fall velocity V of a sphere of mass m and diameter D is given by

$$mg = \frac{\rho V^2}{2} \frac{\pi D^2}{4} C \tag{2}$$

where ρ is the air density. This equation defines the drag coefficient C of a falling body. In general C is a function only of the Reynolds number. Since the product DV is also proportional to the Reynolds number, we find from (2) that a sphere of constant mass but variable density has a constant Reynolds number; so that for the shrinking snowflake

$$DV = D_0 V_0 = \text{constant} \tag{3}$$

(This assumes that the snowflake is always at its terminal velocity, a condition which is approximately true when the change in velocity is gradual.) This equation would also hold for a disc, provided that a constant orientation is maintained; it would not apply to the zig-zag motion characteristic of large snowflakes. MAGONO [1953] suggests a different form of (2) in that he supposes that a snowflake receives an aerodynamic resistance proportional not only to its area but to its volume, since some of the air passes through the snowflake. Some measurements of the fall velocities of snowflakes appear to support his assumption. However, (2) may still apply to a melting snowflake if the water collects on its outer portion, thus preventing the passage of air through the snowflake.

Substituting (3) in (1)

$$V = V_0(1-F)^{-1/3} \tag{4}$$

which is valid until $V = V_r$, the fall velocity of the raindrop. If the melting snowflake were in the shape of a disc of constant thickness, the equation corresponding to (4) would be

$$V = V_d(1-F)^{-1/2} \tag{5}$$

where V_d is the fall velocity of the disc-shaped snowflake.

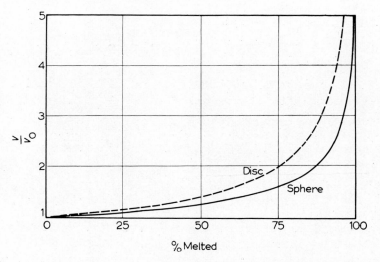

FIG. 1—Increase in fall velocity of a melting snowflake

Fig. 1 shows the increase in velocity of a melting snowflake for both the sphere and the disc. It indicates that the terminal fall velocity of the snowflake increases gradually until almost complete melting has occurred. The type of curve is similar to that assumed by Austin and Bemis for the change of velocity with height. The fall velocity increases by a factor of two when the spherical snowflake is about 90 per cent melted and when the disc-shaped snowflake is 75 per cent melted. Thereafter just prior to complete melting, it rises sharply to the fall velocity of the raindrop. The fall velocity of the melting snowflake is probably similar to that of the disc in the early stages and to that of the sphere in the late stages.

Preliminary measurements by Langleben indicated velocities of wet snowflakes of three to four m/sec, 'the precipitation still having the general characteristic of snow but being quite wet'. It is difficult to judge the percentage of melting of these snowflakes but since the temperature of the air during these measurements was 35°F, then for any reasonable lapse rate the top of the melting layer must have been at least about 300 m above the ground. It will be seen in the next section that this depth implies a snowflake that is fairly close to complete melting. Observation appears to indicate that the snow-flake shape is maintained until almost complete melting has occurred. A velocity of three to four m/sec would fit the theory only if the snowflake were more than about 90 per cent melted.

Depth of the melting layer—The rate at which a spherical ice particle melts in a saturated environment is given by

$$L_i m \frac{\mathrm{d}F}{\mathrm{d}t} = 2\pi ckD\Delta T + 2\pi cKLD\Delta\rho \tag{6}$$

where L_i and L are the respective latent heats of fusion and condensation, c is a ventilation coefficient, k is the heat conductivity, and K the diffusivity of water vapor in the air, ΔT is the temperature difference, and $\Delta\rho$ the vapor density difference between the saturated ambient air and the melting snowflake with temperature at 0°C.

Between 0°C and about 3°C $\Delta\rho$, in g cm^{-3}, is related to ΔT, in °C, by the approximate expression

$$\Delta\rho = 0\cdot35 \times 10^{-6}\Delta T \tag{7}$$

Substituting in (7) and letting $\Delta T = \gamma Z$, γ being the lapse rate and Z the distance below the 0°C level, we find, with the aid of (4) that

$$\frac{3mV_0^3\mathrm{d}V}{V^2} = 2\pi A\gamma CDVZ\,\mathrm{d}Z \tag{8}$$

where dZ has been substituted for Vdt and

$$A = \frac{k + 0\cdot35 \times 10^{-6}LK}{L_i} \tag{9}$$

The coefficient c depends only on the Reynolds number which is constant. The values of c measured for raindrops by KINZER and GUNN [1951] may therefore be used. Substituting $DV = D_r V_r$ where the subscript r refers to the raindrop, and integrating the left-hand side between the limits V_0 and V_r, we find an expression for the melting depth

$$Z_s^2 = \frac{3mV_0^3}{\pi A c\gamma D_r V_r}\left(\frac{1}{V_0} - \frac{1}{V_r}\right) \tag{10}$$

From (4) it is seen that the sphere is more than 99 per cent melted when $V_r = 5V_0$.

Langleben summarized the results of his measurements of the terminal fall velocities of snowflakes by the formula

$$V_0 = kD_r^{0.31} \tag{11}$$

where V_0 is in cm/sec and D is the melted diameter in cm. The coefficient k is 160 for snowflakes consisting of dendrites and 234 for combinations of columns and plates. These relationships have been used to compute the values of V_r/V_0. For a one-mm drop it is found that V_r/V_0 is 3·5 for columns and plates and 5·1 for dendrites. The values of V_r and other constants in (10) were taken from Smithsonian Meteorological Tables (6th ed.).

Fig. 2 shows the melting layer depths for different drop sizes, lapse rates and snow-flake types. For a three-mm drop, which may be considered as a maximum for continuous stratiform rain, the melting distances range from 800 to 1200 ft for a lapse rate of 6°C/km, and 1050 to 1480 ft for 4°C/km.

If the snowflakes were disc-shaped throughout melting, similar calculations show that the melting depths for these snowflakes are about 25 per cent higher than for the spherical snowflakes. This is primarily due to the greater rate of increase in the fall velocity of a melting disc.

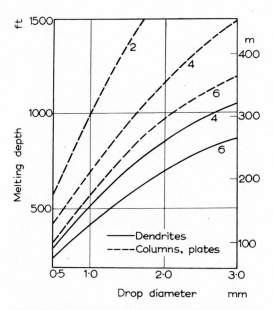

Fig. 2—Theoretical melting depths for snowflakes consisting of dendrites, and of columns and plates; the number on each curve is the lapse rate in °C/km; the 2°C/km curve for dendrites coincides with the 4°C/km curve for columns and plates

It is difficult to compare these theoretical melting-layer depths with observation, since in most cases the melting depth cannot be determined with sufficient accuracy from radiosonde data and radar measurements. In addition, the drop-size distribution is generally not known. Hooper and Kippax [1950], using a vertically pointed 3·2 cm radar with an accuracy of about 150 ft, reported the peak of the bright band to lie, on the average of ten occasions, 330 ft below the 0°C level. They also reported the thickness of the bright band to be about 750 ft, which would indicate a melting depth of about that order. For normal lapse rates between 4 and 6°C/km, this melting depth would indicate maximum drop diameters less than two mm, in agreement with the kind of rain common in England. Austin and Bemis made measurements in Cambridge, Mass. with a ten-cm radar to an accuracy of about 500 ft, and reported the average distance between the 0°C level and the peak of the bright band to be 830 ft. Since the thickness of the bright band was about 1000 ft, a melting layer of about 1300 ft is indicated. For their average lapse rate of 5·5°C/km, Fig. 2 would indicate an aggregation of dendrites with maximum melted diameters between 2·5 and 3 cm.

More recent measurements with a 3·2-cm radar in Cambridge show a melting depth of 1500 ft, accurate to within about 150 ft, for a lapse rate of about 5°C/km. This value is somewhat higher than would be expected from Fig. 2 but is within the theoretical depths for a disc. The curves in Fig. 2 probably represent a lower limit to the melting depth while those for a disc are an upper limit.

If a raindrop is made up through coalescence of several melting snowflakes, then it is evident that the melting depths will be smaller than that indicated in Fig. 2 for one snowflake. For example if a one-mm drop is derived from a coalescence of eight melting

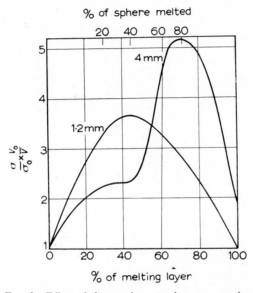

FIG. 3—Effect of changes in scattering cross section and fall velocity of melting snowflakes, with melted diameters of 1·2 and 4 mm, on the echo intensity profile of the melting layer for 3-cm radiation

snowflakes, each equivalent to an 0·5-mm drop, then the actual melting depth would be intermediate between that of the 0·5 and 1·0-mm drops.

Echo-intensity changes—The increase in fall velocity of the snowflakes as they melt causes a spreading out of the precipitation in the vertical, thus reducing the number of particles per unit volume. Since the radar echo is proportional to the concentration of particles, it is thus inversely proportional to the fall velocity of the particles in the melting layer. This factor is believed to be chiefly responsible for the sharp drop in echo intensity at the base of the bright band.

The sharp increase in echo intensity at the upper portion of the bright band is attributed to the variation in the scattering cross section of a melting snowflake. The theoretical scattering cross section of a melting ice sphere, consisting of an inner ice core and an outer concentric layer of water, was computed by LANGLEBEN and GUNN

[1952]. Although this model may not resemble a melting snowflake, their results give a good qualitative indication of the echo intensity change in the melting layer.

Fig. 3 shows the combined effects of the scattering cross section, as taken from the work of Langleben and Gunn, and the fall velocity, as taken from the curve for a sphere in Fig. 1, on the echo intensity of the precipitation in the melting layer as would be detected by a three-cm radar. The echo intensity of the 1·2-mm drop for which Rayleigh scattering applies, reaches a maximum of 3·6 at 40 to 45 per cent of the melting layer (see below for a discussion of the scales). For the four-mm drop, which is outside the Rayleigh region, a maximum of 5·2 is shifted to between 70 and 75 per cent of the melting-layer distance. According to observation with three-cm radiation, the peak of the bright band is most frequently at the lower portion of the melting layer, an effect which Fig. 3 would attribute to large drops. The echo intensity of the rain is about equal to that of the snow for the Rayleigh case, but is greater by a factor of 1·6 for the four-mm drop. The echo intensity at the peak of the bright band exceeds that of the rain by about the same factor of 3·5 for both cases.

It is seen in Fig. 3 that the percentage of the sphere melted is on a non-linear scale along the top, while the percentage of the melting layer is on a linear scale along the base. These comparative scales were matched with the aid of (4) and (10). The matching depends somewhat on the ratio of the fall velocity of the raindrop to that of the snowflake, but the scales are accurate to within two per cent for any reasonable ratio. The scales show that the percent of the sphere melted at first lags behind the percent of the melting layer depth, but then after about 50 per cent it exceeds the melting-layer depth.

Another effect that influences the echo intensity of the melting layer is the shape of the precipitation particles. The echo intensity from randomly orientated particles in general increases as the shape deviates from that of a sphere. The effect is small for ice particles, but may be quite large for water drops or water-coated ice particles. The magnitude of the shape effect may be determined by measuring the amount of depolarization in a precipitation echo [see LABRUM, 1952, or ATLAS and others, 1953]. Recent measurements made at MIT in Cambridge, Mass. with three-cm radar, indicate that, on the average, the shape effect is responsible for an increase in echo intensity of the peak of the bright band by about 40 per cent over that of snow or rain. On rare occasions an increase by as much as a factor of three could be attributed to shape. A few measurements indicated that the shape effect was at a maximum slightly below the elevation of the peak of the bright band. A theoretical interpretation of their results would indicate that the shape of a melting snowflake, insofar as it influences the echo intensity in the bright band, may be approximated to an oblate spheroid with an axis-diameter ratio of 0·4 or 0·5.

Conclusion—The calculations of the melting depth were made on the assumption that the melting snowflakes are spherical. Although there is evidence that melting snowflakes deviate in shape from that of a sphere, it is believed that the assumption does not lead to serious error in heat transfer problems. However, it may lead to an underestimate in the rate of increase in the fall velocity of melting snowflakes, which may account for some underestimate in the depth of the melting layer. Similarly, calculations for a disc-shaped snowflake may over-estimate the melting depth.

The calculations of the two most important effects on the echo intensity profile of the melting layer: the rates of change of the radar cross section and of the fall velocity of a melting snowflake, were made for melting ice spheres in the Rayleigh region (raindrop diameters less than 1·25 mm for three-cm radiation) and for a larger drop-size (four-mm raindrop for three-cm radiation). These profiles indicate that the larger sizes are responsible for a shift in the echo intensity maximum to the lower portion of the melting layer. The deviation of melting snowflakes from a spherical shape may also contribute to this shift. An extension of the work of Langleben and Gunn to other large drops outside the Rayleigh region would be helpful in evaluating the role of the large snowflakes in the melting layer.

Acknowledgments—An expanded version of this report is given in Harvard University Meteorological Radar Studies No. 3. This research is supported under Contract No. 19 (604)–950, with the Air Force Cambridge Research Center.

REFERENCES

ATLAS, D., M. KERKER, and W. HITSCHFELD, Scattering and attenuation by non-spherical atmospherical particles, *J. Atmos. Terr. Phys..*, v.3, pp.108–119, 1953.

AUSTIN, P. M. and A. C. BEMIS, A quantitative study of the 'bright band' in radar precipitation echoes, *J. Met.*, v.7, pp.145–151, 1950.

BEMIS, A. C., The role of melting snow in the atmosphere, *J. Met.*, v.12, pp.186–188, 1955.

HOOPER, J. E. N. and A. A. KIPPAX, The bright band—a phenomenon associated with radar echoes from falling rain, *Q. J. R. Met. Soc.*, v.76, pp.125–132, 1950.

KINZER, G. D. and R. GUNN, The evaporation, temperature and thermal relaxation time of freely falling water drops, *J. Met.*, v.8, pp.71–83, 1951.

LABRUM, N. R., The scattering of radio waves by meteorological particles, *J. App. Physics*, v.23, pp.1324–1330, 1952.

LANGLEBEN, M. P., The terminal velocity of snowflakes, *Q. J. R. Met. Soc.*, v.80, pp.174–181, 1954.

LANGLEBEN, M. P. and K. L. S. GUNN, Scattering and absorption of microwaves by a melting ice sphere, McGill Univ. Sci. Rep. MW—5, 12pp., 1952.

MAGONO, C., On the growth of snowflake and graupel, Sci. Rep., Yokohama Nat. Univ., sec.1, no.2, 40pp., 1953.

WEXLER, R. R., R. J. REED, and J. HONIG, Atmospheric cooling by melting snow, *Bul. Amer. Met. Soc.*, v.35, pp.48–51, 1954.

DISCUSSION

Dr. James E. McDonald—Your theory depends on the product of diameter times velocity remaining constant, and hence on the constancy of the drag coefficient. This I doubt.

Dr. Raymond Wexler—I am assuming that as the snowflake shrinks it remains spherical; the drag coefficient for a given spherical mass is constant, no matter what variation there may be in density.

Dr. McDonald—Probably the main difference between a complex non-spherical flake and a sphere is the greater surface of the former. As its outer surface melted, its drag coefficient would go down very rapidly.

Dr. Wexler—My assumptions are not in agreement with Japanese considerations of the fall velocities of dry snowflakes, but I am assuming that when the snowflake begins to melt a water film forms on the outside and acts as a barrier until the flake is almost completely melted. In other words, it acts as a solid sphere.

Dr. M. P. Langleben—It is quite likely that with the holes that exist through an aggregate the drag coefficient is very different from that for a solid sphere. I have measured the fall velocities of snowflakes fairly close to the melting point. You could still see the crystal structure, so that you would expect the increase in velocity over that of a dry snowflake to be small, but velocities of three and four meters per second were measured. This, incidentally, would give you an increase in the depth of the melting layer, which is what you want.

Dr. Wexler—The theory of the bright band involves an increase in signal due to water collecting on the outside of the snowflake. The signal remains fixed at its increased value until the increase in fall velocity occurs, then decreases sharply. Your early increase in fall velocity does not agree with this picture.

Dr. Langleben—Agreed.

Dr. Helmut Weickmann—It would be interesting to have a comparison of Findeisen's theory, which involves rate of precipitation, and yours, which is concerned with particle size. (See comment in discussion of preceeding paper by Dr. Atlas.)

Dr. Vincent J. Schaefer—Is the instrumentation such that radar can observe a bright band with its lower part touching the ground? This would permit sampling by an observer on the ground.

Dr. Wexler—Yes, that could be done. But existing observations provide conclusive evidence that the bright band consists of melting snow.

Dr. Schaefer—I am led to this suggestion by observations around Schenectady of huge snowflakes falling at the same time as very thin hexagonal columns, and falling with the same speed. (**Dr. Plank** noted, and Dr. Schaefer agreed, that the huge flakes do not always fall slowly; they sometimes fell much faster than single crystals.) When these huge flakes occur it is noted almost invariably that the flakes are in process of melting. I certainly urge that observation of these processes be made right in the field.

Dr. R. M. Cunningham—I have considered this possibility and foreseen one difficulty. When the melting layer approaches the ground, this process of cooling can operate through a greater depth, because there is no air coming up from below. Thus aggregation can operate over a greater depth, leading to larger snowflakes. I am not sure that you would observe flakes anywhere near as big in the free atmosphere. Incidentally, they wouldn't be perfect spheres.

Dr. Wexler—The presence of giant snowflakes strengthens the possibility of breakup upon complete melting. Atlas has observed flakes which if they melted without breakup would form raindrops of diameter much more than six mm.

THE SNOW CRYSTAL AS AEROLOGICAL SONDE

HELMUT WEICKMANN

Abstract—Since snow crystals carry their life histories with them and since our knowledge about their formation has considerably increased during the past years, they can be used as aerological sondes. Continuous snowfall sometimes is characterized by a systematic modification of the crystal forms. Observations are analyzed which have been made during the winters 1947–49.

WHEN the first reports of artificial rainmaking spread from this country to Europe the author was in charge of a mountain observatory of the German Weather Service. At that time and still nowadays, our basic knowledge of precipitation processes was too limited in order to be able to judge completely the potentialities of rainmaking. It was clear that somehow we had to learn more about the formation of precipitation and one way appeared to be a study of the forms of snow crystals since they carried their life history with them as a natural document. This paper presents a first but by far not complete analysis of these investigations which we carried out during the winters from 1946–47 to 1948–49.

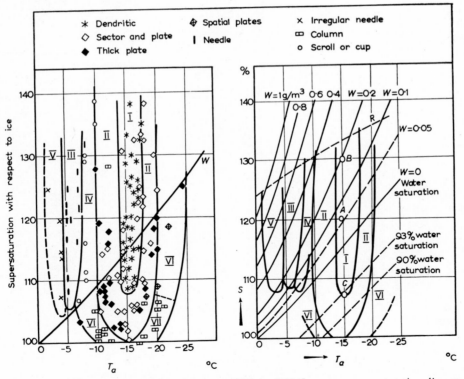

FIG. 1—Formation of snow crystals acording to Nakaya [1954]; temperature-saturation diagram at left showing condition for formation of various types of snow crystals; and curves of equal water content in the region above supersaturation with respect to water

Within the last ten to twenty years our knowledge of the formation and growth of ice crystals has advanced sufficiently in order to use them now as an aerological sonde which not only can tell us in what temperature interval the crystal has formed but also about layers of water clouds which it has passed on its way to the ground. The ice crystal thus becomes significant for several reasons: (1) It helps us to understand the mechanism of precipitation. (2) It can be used in winterly or arctic conditions as an indicator of heights of clouds and of icing conditions in these clouds.

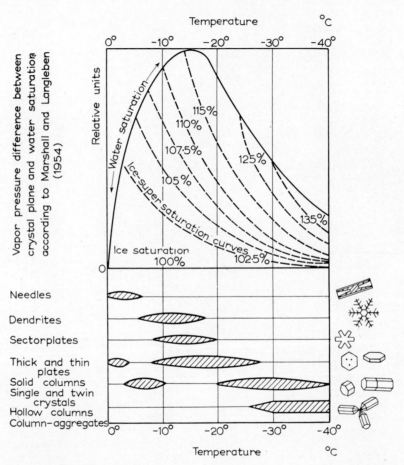

Fig. 2—Relationship of crystal form to temperature and vapor-pressure difference

The basis of such analysis must be a physical classification of ice crystals. Such classification has to take into consideration the factors which lead to the observed crystal form. In the following we will discuss five such factors which influence the crystal on its voyage through the troposphere. These factors are: (1) the temperature at which the crystal forms, (2) the humidity at which it grows, (3) the water content of the cloud in which it grows, and (4) the degree of riming which it experiences. A last factor (5) is the number of crystals; this is determined by the number of freezing nuclei.

From observations in nature and in the laboratory we know that the snow crystals are subject to considerable changes of shape, depending on the temperature where they form. Diagrams over almost the entire tropospherical temperature interval have been

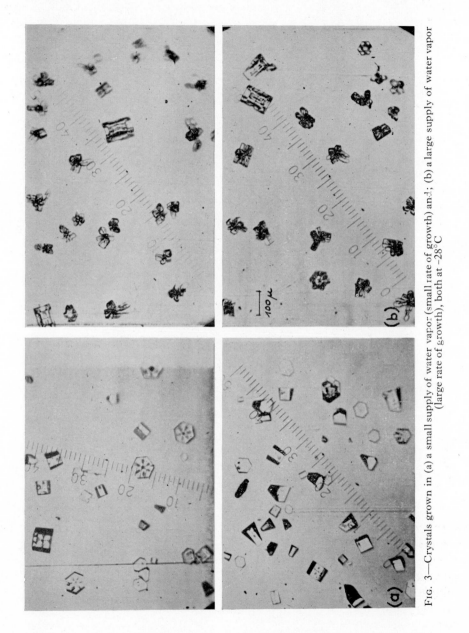

FIG. 3—Crystals grown in (a) a small supply of water vapor (small rate of growth) and; (b) a large supply of water vapor (large rate of growth), both at −28°C

presented first by WALL [1947], then by NAKAYA [1954] and his associates, WEICKMANN [1948], and AUFM KAMPE, WEICKMANN, and KELLY [1954]. These observations are essentially in agreement and have been confirmed by GOLD and POWER [1952] and

MASON [1953]. Nakaya's diagram of snow crystal forms versus temperature is given in Fig. 1, one of the author's in Fig. 2. It is to be noted that in both diagrams temperature and humidity appear. The ordinate in Nakaya's diagram is in units of relative humidity; in Fig. 2 the vapor-pressure difference between water and ice saturation is plotted. Furthermore, AUFM KAMPE, WEICKMANN, and KELLY [1951] emphasize that their studies of the temperature dependence of snow crystal forms were carried out at water saturation. For low temperatures (-28°C) the author showed that the form of the crystals

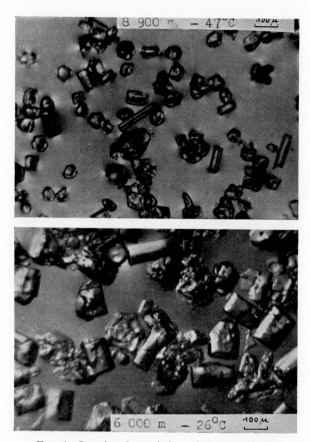

FIG. 4—Samples of crystals from cirrostratus clouds

changed with the supply of water vapor. Fig. 3a shows crystals which have grown in a small supply of water vapor, whereas Fig. 3b shows crystals grown at the same temperature but in a great supply of water vapor. AUFM KAMPE [1952] showed theoretically for conditions in cirrus clouds that ice saturation as well as water saturation may occur and persist depending upon the relative magnitudes of number and size of particles on one part and the moisture supply due to different updraft velocities on the other part. Low humidity is present in cirrostratus leading to fully grown single crystals (Fig. 4). High humidity occurs in the convective type of cirrus clouds and leads to skeleton forms (Fig. 5). Note the similarity of these natural crystals with the artificial crystals of Figures

3a and b. It is possible that even supersaturation with respect to water may occur at times in convective cirrus clouds. This permits some interesting conclusions regarding the growth of crystals. There is no doubt that ice saturation is present at the crystal plane all the time and that also the molecules are bound in the lattice with the same energy as long as the temperature does not change. The only difference would be that in the supersaturated case a greater number of molecules arrives at the growing crystal plane than during the growth near ice saturation. This is an important conclusion since it must be possible to increase the number of molecules arriving at the crystal plane by placing little water droplets in the immediate neighborhood of a growing crystal plane.

FIG. 5—Samples of crystals from cirrus clouds (a) March 15, 1943, top of ci-layer, depth 3500 m, height 8000 m, –44°C; (b) April 17, 1943, cirrus 6300–8000 m, height 7300 m, –32°C; (c) May 6, 1943, ci filosus 6700–7400 m, height 7500 m, –30°C; (d) August 25, 1943, top of ci-layer 7000–9400 m, height 9400 m, –38°C (round dots are air bubbles in cushioning lacquer)

These water droplets may belong to a water cloud in which the crystal grows. They represent an additional vapor source and may therefore influence the crystal's growth in the direction of supersaturated conditions. Thus, with Nakaya and Hanajima, [NAKAYA, 1954] we may recognize the water content of the water cloud in which the crystal grows as a third important factor influencing its form. It appears debatable however, if it is justified to express the water content, as these authors do, in per cent of supersaturation with respect to water. The water content cannot alter the basic form of the crystal, prism, or plate, but it may determine the formation of supersaturation forms. Dendrites may form instead of hexagonal plates or sector stars. This modification generally occurs when the surface diffusion of the molecules in the growing crystal plane becomes deficient.

Y

Such deficiency may be caused by too great a number of condensing molecules or by a certain poisoning of the crystal plane through adsorption of foreign molecules. The surface diffusion becomes unable to distribute the molecules to their proper positions in a fully grown crystal plane, and the molecules stick where they arrive at the plane, that is, preferably at the corners. Therefore, dendritic branches form along the secondary axes. As we have shown elsewhere [WEICKMANN, 1950] dendrites are very sensitive indicators of humidity changes to which the crystal may have been subjected.

FIG. 6—Central crystal with droplets at its edges

Most cloud droplets evaporate in the neighborhood of the crystal. Some, however, are deposited on the crystal plane either through collision before they evaporate or because they were taken along in the stream of water molecules toward the growing plane. It is difficult to separate both effects. Evidence of the second effect is shown in Fig. 6 where the center crystal has collected all droplets at its points and edges, that is, at the places to which the greatest flux of vapor occurs. Riming can occur over quite a large temperature interval, roughly between freezing and −20°C. Riming causes special modifications of the crystal form and is thus the fourth factor to be considered in our physical snow-crystal classification. We have observed on Mt. Hohenpeissenberg that rime if formed at temperatures below −8 to −9°C has a marked crystalline structure: all the thousands of droplets frozen together behave like the surface of one mirror. This indicates that they have grown to little crystals after their deposition and that these crystals have the same orientation. The same happens with rimed snow crystals. Sometimes a star is completely covered with frozen droplets and yet they reflect the light like one surface. At lower temperatures these little crystals may become the center of a new branch or crystal. Droplets collected at −10 or −15°C become little branches or plates, whereas droplets collected at −5 to −8°C become little prisms or needles. (This explains the peculiar bundle-like aggregates of needles which are quite frequently observed.)

At temperatures warmer than −8°C the crystalline character of the rimed cloud droplets is no longer apparent. This may be due to the fact that at warmer temperatures the crystals acquire a thin film of water on their surface so that the droplets flatten out after their deposition. This has been observed by NAKAYA and MATSUMOTO [1953] to occur down to temperatures as low as −7°C. It is possible that this effect plays a role in certain structural characteristics of dendrites. These quite often have air bubbles irregularly lined up along the middle ridges of the six rays. Air bubbles form if water freezes. It is therefore likely that the branches of these dendrites have collected cloud droplets near the freezing level. These droplets merge with the wet surface film of the ice crystal whose subsequent growth after riming must proceed partly from the water phase.

For steady-state conditions the source of water vapor is the updraft and the sink is represented by the ice crystals or cloud droplets. Thus, the crystal concentration becomes a determining form factor. A great number of crystals will consume much water and it may happen that the updraft just can maintain ice saturation for the steadily growing crystals. Only simple forms and no dendrites will then be observed. For the same conditions but a smaller number of ice crystals the liberated water vapor is not consumed immediately and the relative humidity increases. Then the individual crystal will be larger than before and its form will be more of the supersaturated type, that is, dendrites in the plate region. If the humidity reaches water saturation and freezing nuclei are present, crystal forms typical of this temperature range will be added to the other ones.

Special form variations occur if crystals which have originated in great altitudes fall through lower layers and find growth conditions. As long as they are in a homogeneous altostratus consisting of ice crystals only, they grow bigger but retain their original shape as prisms. If they meet, however, supercooled water clouds on their way, their rate of growth is increased and their growth proceeds in the form characteristic of the supercooled cloud. Then we have the well-known prism forms with endplates or endstars.

For the physical classification we arrived at we have used symbols of snow crystals as they were proposed by Nakaya in his general classification (Fig. 7). Figures 8 and 9 show on their left side the forms of snow crystals which we have adopted in our physical classification. The ordinate shows two columns of crystal forms in their dependence from the temperature. Column 1 shows forms typical of small supersaturation. Column 2 shows forms which are typical for growth at or near water saturation. Also the number of freezing nuclei takes part in the determination of crystals of either one of the columns. Crystals of column 1, for instance, can either be formed during a weak updraft mechanism and a small number of crystals, or during a strong updraft and a great number of crystals. A strong updraft, combined with a small number of crystals would tend to produce crystals of the column 2, and a still smaller number would result in rimed crystals. Nature thus displays a great flexibility in maintaining a steady state rate of precipitation and in smoothing out discontinuities.

In this connection, special attention is called to one group of crystals which can be

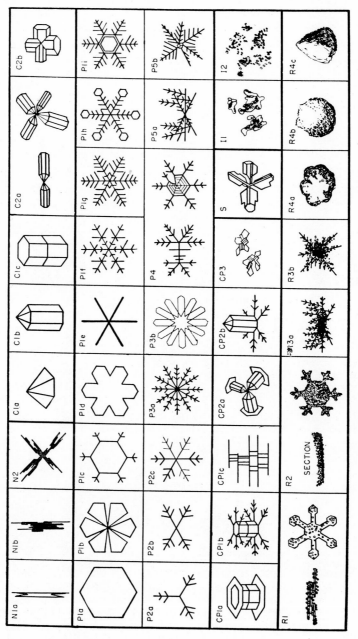

Fig. 7—Sketches of all types of crystals in the general classification

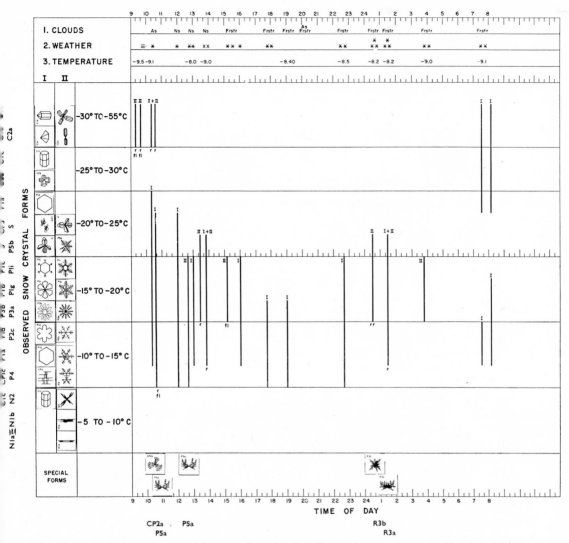

FIG. 8—Crystal types observed by the author showing distribution on February 19, 1947; Hohen-peissenberg, Germany

found in almost any large-scale precipitation. It is the group of spatial aggregates of plates and dendrites which form around temperatures of -20 to $-25°C$. This group, as we have shown elsewhere in these Proceedings, is most efficient in collecting cloud droplets and is therefore able to adjust steady state conditions to a wide variety of warm-front mechanisms.

Figures 8 and 9 present some analyses of snowfalls which seemed to be characteristic. The precipitation starts with prisms and prism aggregates and proceeds during hours to crystals which have been formed at subsequently warmer temperatures.* This indicates that the generating level of the snow descends from high altitudes to lower ones which

* I and II refer to the corresponding crystal columns; r and fl denote "rimed" and "flakes".

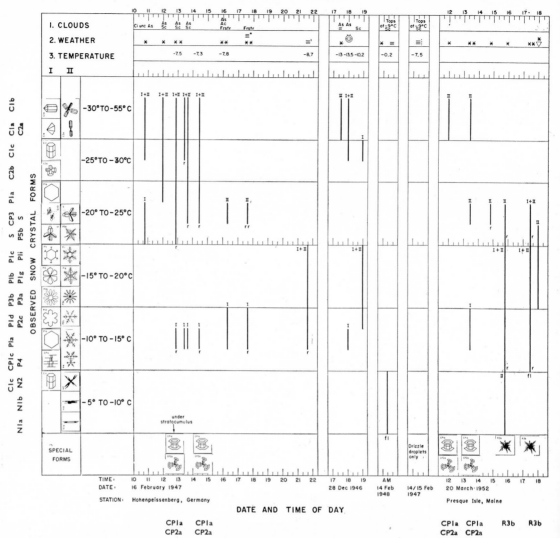

FIG. 9—Crystal types observed by the author showing distribution; various dates and locations

must also be true for the cloud tops. Usually an intensification of the rate of precipitation goes along with the lowering of the generating level of snow accordingly to the greater amount of liberated water as the convergence mechanism spreads to lower levels. During this phase of precipitation the cloud base descends also as has been shown by GOLD-MAN [1951]. It may be more than coincidence that simultaneously the crystal form changes to types which are most efficient in collecting cloud droplets. Thus, nature takes care to maintain a steady-state rate of precipitation and to smooth out discontinuities of the concentration of crystals, that is, of the concentration of freezing nuclei. These are observations rainmakers should be concerned with.

The above-mentioned sequence of the crystal forms indicating a lowering of the generating snow level as the warm-front process continues appears to be typical. We not only found it in Germany but also in observations in this country and, last but not least, it is also reported by DOBROWOLSKI [1904] from the Antarctic. Of course, there are other sequences too. Sometimes forms which are typical of all temperature intervals fall simultaneously indicating that a strong mechanism of convergence has involved the whole troposphere. Sometimes only the altostratus forms precipitate and sometimes they are missing and the crystals are spatial aggregates of plates and dendrites. These latter forms are typical of polar-air instability showers and are as such the characteristic forms of the heavy snowfalls in the snow belt along the Great Lakes.

The needles are another interesting form. They form at temperatures warmer than $-10°C$, that is, at temperatures where not many natural freezing nuclei are present. Fig. 9 also shows two very similar weather situations, the one occurred on February 14, 1947 and the other on February 14–15, 1948. Typical in both cases was a low strato-cumulus deck with tops at the $-10°C$ level. In one case, needles in great numbers combined and fell as large flakes. In the other case only drizzle droplets fell in spite of an abundance of industrial nuclei. Actually, the snow that had fallen previously was discolored by the amount of industrial aerosol that was precipitated with the drizzle droplets. Generally, however, needles seem to occur more frequently over towns than over the open country which seems to indicate that the artificial aerosol over towns is enriched with nuclei active at these high temperatures. It is interesting that Dobrowolski describes snowfalls of needles also in his observations of the Antarctic where artificial sources of nuclei are at a minimum.

It appears that we can learn much about precipitation processes if such observations are carried out systematically. The Signal Corps, therefore, has made a contract with the Mount Washington Observatory with the aim of studying the relations between snow crystals and the weather.

Acknowledgment—Credit is due to H. Bichlmaier and M. Klotz, weather observers on Hohenpeissenberg, who took part in these observations.

REFERENCES

AUFM KAMPE, H., Feuchtigkeitsverhältnisse in Cirruswolken und die daraus resultierenden Formen der Eiskristalle, *Berichte Deut. Wetterd.* US Zone, Weickmann-Heft, no.38, pp.298–302, 1952.

AUFM KAMPE, H., H. WEICKMANN, and J. J. KELLY, The influence of temperature on the shape of ice crystals growing at water saturation, *J. Met.*, v.8, pp.168–174, 1951.

DOBROWOLSKI, A., La neige et le givre; resultats du voyage du S.J. *Belgica* en 1897–1899, *Rap. Sci. la Met.*, 1904.

GOLD, L. W. and B. A. POWER, Correlation of snow crystal type with estimated temperature of formation, *J. Met.*, v.9, p.447, 1952.

GOLDMAN, L., On forecasting ceiling lowering during continuous rain, *Mon. Wea. Rev.*, v.79, pp.133–142, 1951.

MARSHALL, J. S. and M. P. LANGLEBEN, A theory of snow-crystal habit and growth, *J. Met.*, v.11, pp.104–120, 1954.

MASON, B. J., The growth of ice crystals in a supercooled water cloud, *Q.J.R. Met. Soc.*, v.79, pp.104–111, 1953.

NAKAYA, U., *Snow Crystals*, Harvard Univ. Press, 510pp., 1954.

NAKAYA, U. and A. MATSUMOTO, Evidence of the existence of a liquid-like film on ice surfaces, Res. paper 4, Snow, Ice, Permafrost Res. Est., Corps of Eng., Wilmette, Ill., Nov. 1953.

WALL, E., Ueber die Entstehung der Schneekristalle, I, *Wiss. Arb.* Deutsch. Meteor. Dienst–ZFO, v.1, pp.151–179, 1947.

WEICKMANN, H., *The Ice Phase in the Atmosphere*, Ministry of Supply, Millbank, London, S.W.1, 95pp., 1944.

WEICKMANN, H., 'Biologie' der Schneekristalle, *Die Umschau* 50, pp.116–119, 1950.

DISCUSSION

Dr. Ukichiro Nakaya—I would like to say that now I am trying to investigate the effect of the aerosol in the air on crystal formation. We are using the old instrument, and growing the crystal under the same conditions as before, but in air which is free from aerosols. We filter the air with a thermal precipitator and see whether pure water and pure air can make this crystal or not. In the first experiment we found stellar crystals but the shape is different. Also the rate of growth was about one half of that in air containing aerosols.

Dr. K. L. S. Gunn—Radar observation would be an extremely valuable supplement to this type of analysis. One thing that worries me is your interpretation of the observations as the dropping down of the level of formation. I think in both of the diagrams the column type of crystals you show at -10 to $-15°C$ could have been formed at -25 or $-30°C$ because of the symmetry in Nakaya's diagram. You have chosen to put them at $-10°C$.

Dr. Helmut Weickmann—Yes, there is an ambiguity. But after long consideration I thought it more consistent to assume they come from the lower level.

Dr. David Atlas—You said that usually an intensification of the precipitation goes along with a lowering of level of snow generation, because the convergence mechanism spreads to lower levels. I think this is contrary to some observations. As the center of convergence approaches, the depth of the convergence region increases and the generating levels are frequently higher for intense snow than for light snow. Of course there is no single storm model which will fit every case. Along with the observations of crystal types, it is also important to measure the intensity of the snow as a function of time.

Dr. Weickmann—Maybe at times the cloud expands upward, but I think in most cases the cloud goes downward. In the lower layers you have much more water liberated. This is the reason you get a stronger precipitation. An analysis of the Boston rainfall has been made [GOLDMAN, 1951, see list above] which indicated that the precipitation increases with the lowering of the cloud base level and I think the lowering of the base level is more important, because of the greater water content, than the rise of the top of the convergence layer.

There are some cases where one gets particles from different heights and temperatures at once. You see needles, dendrites, prisms, everything. But I believe it is more typical when you get first the cirro-stratus, and then the other stratus, and as it starts to snow you get the prisms, and so forth.

Dr. J. Kuettner—Does the structure of the ice crystals indicate the level where they have mostly developed, or the level where they have been generated? For instance, your diagram may not be a complete proof that the generating level was lowered. Probably it indicates that the level of greatest growth lowered.

Dr. Weickmann—Crystals which are generated at one level and have significant growth in another environment would be included in the category of special forms. For example, a crystal, which has been generated in the cirrus level, falls and then starts to grow considerably faster in a lower layer, usually builds end plates or dendrites onto its original form. It is usually possible to tell whether a crystal has modified its form considerably or still retains the form into which it was born.

PHYSICAL INVESTIGATIONS OF SNOW FLAKES

UKICHIRO NAKAYA

Hokkaido University, Sapporo, Japan

Shadow photography and its application to the study of snow flakes—This work was carried out by K. Higuchi using a simple method devised for taking a shadow photograph of snow crystals without using any lens Fig. 1. A glass plate, with many snow crystals on it, is placed on a photographic paper in a dark box, and illuminated for a short time from above. The clear image of snow crystals is thus obtained (Figures 2, 3a, and 4a). The variation in the size distribution or frequency of occurrence of various types of snow crystals in one snowfall can be studied almost continuously by this method.

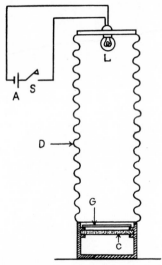

FIG. 1—The apparatus of shadow photography without using any lens; L = light source, D = dark box, G = glass plate holding snow crystals, C = film holder containing photographic paper, A = dry cell, S = switch (Higuchi)

FIG. 2—Shadow photograph of snow crystals taken without using any lens (full size, Higuchi)

After taking a photograph, the crystals are melted on the glass plate (Figures 3b and 4b). This glass plate has previously been treated with silicone oil D.C.200. Accordingly the melted water makes a hemispherical droplet on the silicone film. Taking another shadow photograph of these droplets, the mass distribution is also obtained. The distribution of the size of crystals and that of the mass can be studied at an interval of several minutes during one snowfall.

The coalescence of two crystals was studied as an application of this method. From

327

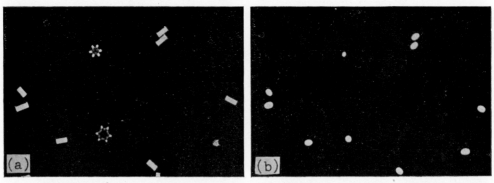

FIG. 3—Shadow photograph (a) capped columns, size distribution; (b) melted droplets, mass distribution ($\times$ 2.7, Higuchi)

FIG. 4—Shadow photograph (a) columns and dendrites, size distribution; (b) melted droplets, mass distribution ($\times$ 3.8, Higuchi)

the size distribution of crystals, the probability of coalescence between two crystals of the same size and that between different sizes was studied with respect to a snowfall consisting of plane dendritic crystals.

Nature of snow flakes—Many snow flakes were photographed while falling (Figures 5 and 6) and after falling on a glass plate during the winters of 1951–1954 in Japan, by C. Magono. It was found convenient to classify the characteristic of snow flakes in three ways; (1) the degree of metamorphic processes, (2) the difference in shape in falling stage, and (3) the variety of types of component crystals. The metamorphic state of snow flakes is changed in the similar process to that of the deposited snow. Aerodynamically, the shape and fall velocity of snow flakes are grouped into three kinds, according to the types of component crystals. As for the types of component crystals, it has been considered that a snow flake usually consists of similar types of crystals. It was found, however, that any two or three kinds of crystals can make coalescence to form a snow flake.

It is expected that a snow flake receives, while falling, an aerodynamic resistance proportional not only to the cross section, but also to the volume, because a part of air

FIG. 5—Successive stages of falling
state of a snow flake of tabulate type
(× 3, Magono)

FIG. 6—Successive stages of falling
state of a snow flake of oblate type
(× 2, Magono)

passes through the snow flake. In the terminal state, the gravitational acceleration of
snow flake is balanced by the drag force of air.

$$\frac{4\pi}{3}r^3(\sigma-\rho)g = \tfrac{1}{2}\rho u^2(A\pi r^2+B\pi r^3) \tag{1}$$

where r = radius

g = gravitational acceleration

u = fall velocity

σ = density of the snow flake

ρ = density of air

A, B are coefficients determined by the shape and structure of snow flake

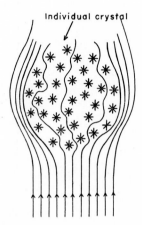

Individual crystal

FIG. 7—Model of a snow flake which shows two resistances proportional to cross section and volume respectively; this model gives the terminal velocity (Magono)

B is considered to be a function of σ. From two observed data (see Fig. 7) the numerical values of A and B are determined, and the fall velocity u of snow flake is obtained as a function of σ and ρ.

$$u = \sqrt{\frac{8}{3}\frac{\sigma-\rho}{\rho}\frac{rg}{0\cdot35-3\sigma+(1-20\sigma)r}}\ \text{cm sec}^{-1} \qquad (2)$$

The velocity calculated from this formula agreed well with the observed data (see Fig. 8).

The mass distribution of raindrops and solid precipitation elements produced by the northwest monsoon was observed by the photographic method in the midwinter of 1953. It was found that the distribution of raindrops or small snow particles is exactly represented by Marshall and Palmer's formula, but that of snow flakes is quite different from their formula. In the case of the precipitation which is made of individual snow crystals and snow flakes, the distribution of small precipitation elements was smaller than that shown by Marshall and Palmer's formula, but on the contrary that of large snow flakes was much larger than that represented by their formula. Many snow flakes, the equivalent diameter of which was larger than 4 mm, were measured. All raindrops observed in this period were smaller than 2 mm in diameter. From these results, it is suggested that the large snow flakes would split into several particles before they melt into raindrops.

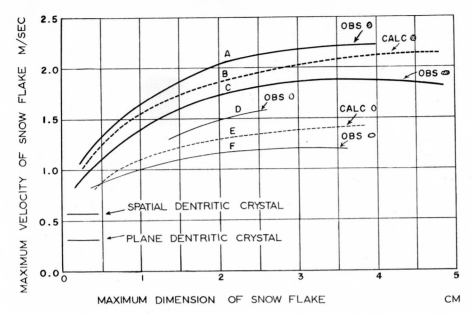

FIG. 8—The relation between fall velocity and size of snow flakes of various types; $A =$ rimed oblate type, obs., $B =$ rimed spherical shape, calc., $C =$ rimed tabulate type, obs., $D =$ unrimed oblate type, obs., $E =$ unrimed spherical shape, calc., $F =$ unrimed tabulate type, obs. (Magono)

THE GROWTH OF ICE CRYSTALS

G. A. WOLFF

Chemical Physics Branch, Signal Corps Engineering Laboratories
Ft. Monmouth, N.J.

Abstract—The problem of the formation of ice crystals having different habits is discussed in detail. The growth of the ice from the vapor phase is analyzed for equilibrium conditions and in cases where equilibrium on the crystal surface has not been established. The equilibrium forms and the growth forms of ice result in the two cases mentioned. There is the possibility that the equilibrium form of ice crystals grown in an electric field changes radically, producing a pronounced needle-like habit. In certain cases when the crystals have macroscopic size, it is conceivable that the equilibrium form may not be obtained even though the vapor phase is saturated. The role of diffusion in the growth process of snow dendrites from the highly supersaturated vapor phase is considered. A possible mechanism with respect to the formation of cubic ice is proposed.

Introduction—The life history of snow crystals is reflected in their habit and form which are dependent upon many factors, as for instance, the temperature of the cloud in which the crystals have been formed, the fall velocity of the crystals, the vertical temperature gradient within the cloud, and so on. It is natural, therefore as WEICKMANN [1956] suggests, to regard snow crystals as aerological sondes which inform us of the atmospheric conditions prevailing in the cloud whence the crystals originated. In trying to evaluate habit and form in this way, we are faced with the fact that we know very little about the factors governing the growth of snow and ice crystals, even though we possess many empirical data on a great variety of snowflakes and ice crystals [NAKAYA and SEKIDO, 1936; AUFM KAMPE, WEICKMANN, KELLY, 1951]. It is the purpose of this paper to give a general outline on ice-crystal growth.

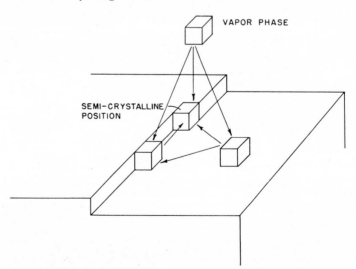

VAPOR PHASE

SEMI-CRYSTALLINE
POSITION

FIG. 1—Schematic representation of the successive and simultaneous
stages of an elementary growth process of a crystal

Factors determining the growth of a crystal—The following processes which are demonstrated in Figures 1 and 2 must be considered when analyzing the growth of a crystal. (For the inverse process, or evaporation, see STRANSKI and WOLFF [1951] and KNACKE, STRANSKI, WOLFF [1951].) A general model of a growing crystal is shown in Fig. 1, while Fig. 2 represents the basal plane of a hexagonal close-packed crystal which can be used for demonstrating crystal growth. The very first process which actually occurs during growth is the diffusion of vapor molecules to the vapor layer adjacent to a crystal plane, that is, within the mean free path distance; we then have the adsorption of the molecule onto the surface; next, the molecule diffuses to a position along the ledge

FIG. 2—Model demonstrating the growth conditions on a crystal surface; the basal plane of
a hexagonal close-packed crystal is shown

boundary and from there to the semi-crystalline position, or growth position, or else the molecule migrates directly from the surface to the semi-crystalline position. Correspondingly, the atoms or molecules also transfer directly from the vapor phase to the semi-crystalline position, or to a position along the ledge boundary. The combination of all these processes occurring successively and simultaneously, determine the growth of a crystal. Furthermore, we should consider the two-dimensional nucleation which precedes the beginning of each new layer, until it attains nucleus size, and the influence of certain surfaces defects, such as spiral dislocations, which lower the two-dimensional nucleation energy. Thus, we see that crystal growth appears as a complex problem.

It can be seen, therefore, that in order to give a complete analysis of crystal growth, only the boundary cases can be given full consideration, and in so doing, we must always keep in mind that the conditions on the surface of an ice crystal are not as ideal as shown in Fig. 2, where we see a close-packed crystal. This crystal has practically no surface distortion and we have no real difficulty in describing surface diffusion. The diffusion on the surface of a close-packed crystal can be described as a transfer of an atom or molecule from a clearly defined potential well to the neighboring potential wells, through so-called saddleback positions. How, then, can we possibly explain and calculate diffusion on the surface of an ice crystal where we have no close packing, but rather lattice cavities and potential wells which are difficult to determine?

The easiest case to consider is that of the crystal in equilibrium with its vapor phase where we rely upon thermodynamical or statistical data only, regardless of the fact that many different processes are actually taking place. Two difficulties must be pointed out, however: (1) A crystal does not increase its size when in equilibrium, and it is growth only in which we are interested. (2) Unless the crystal is of submicroscopic size, it will never assume its equilibrium form, according to I. W. Gibbs. We can show, however, that in reversible growth conditions, or even in quasi-equilibrium, any crystal will develop equilibrium planes corresponding to the supersaturation of the mother phase, though the dimensions of the planes differ from the theoretical values. (Quasi-equilibrium in any process is established when the rates of both the forward and reverse process are great as compared to their difference. This means that, in our example, the number of molecules leaving the crystal (evaporating) and the number of molecules falling upon the crystal (condensing) are great as compared to the number of molecules being permanently integrated into the crystal.)

According to the evaporation experiments of TSCHUDIN, 1946, it may be concluded that in evaporation, the rate-determining step is the transfer of the molecule from the surface to the vapor phase, but for the inverse process (the condensation or growth of ice from the vapor phase) this transfer is in a stationary equilibrium. We have no other information concerning the growth or evaporation of ice, but this result and considera-tion of evidence in general, supports the idea of a quasi-equilibrium which determines the growth of ice.

The equilibrium form can be derived in two ways: (1) by varying central distances of all possible crystal faces, until they are proportional to the specific surface energy of the corresponding planes (Wulff's law); (2) by removing from a crystal form, which is composed of a minimum of low indexed planes, all molecules which are more loosely bonded than are the molecules in the semi-crystalline position. In other words, if for equilibrium conditions, the evaporation probability of a molecule in a corner position is higher than the evaporation probability of a molecule in the semi-crystalline position; the corner molecule will evaporate and leave the corner position empty. In this way, after the next layer is removed, we obtain a new plane belonging to the equilibrium form [STRANSKI, 1949]. Both these methods lead to an equilibrium form of ice consisting of the basal plane (0001) and the prismatic plane ($10\bar{1}0$), when only the interaction between the first nearest oxygen neighbors is taken into consideration, and the slight deviation from an ideal tridymite-type structure is neglected. KRASTANOV [1943] arrived at the same conclusions. The height of the resulting six-sided prism is about 0·8 of its dia-metrical dimension. A study of the influence of the second nearest neighbors reveals the additional ($10\bar{1}1$), ($11\bar{2}0$), and ($10\bar{1}2$) planes which should appear at lower supersatura-tions, that is, for instance, when the ice crystal grows at temperatures close to 0°C. These planes were observed and were reported in the literature [DANA, 1920, 1955]. Occurrence of the (4041) plane, likewise reported in the literature, or other planes may be the result of vicinal growth. A crystal having the different planes is shown in Fig. 3.

If, however, equilibrium at the surface is not established, that is, one of the processes occurring at the surface is rate-determining, kinetic aspects of crystal growth have to be considered. In fact, the value $\frac{1}{2} \times k \times L$ represents the two-dimensional nucleation energy, where k is the specific boundary energy of the nucleus, and L is its perimetrical dimension. In a first approximation, however, the adsorption energy of a water molecule

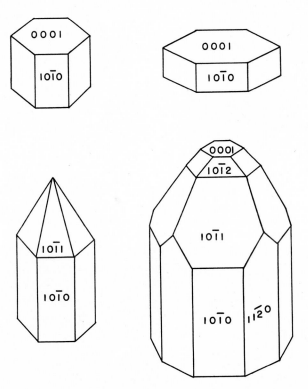

FIG. 3—Schematic representation of different habits of snow and ice crystals

can be taken as a measure of the growth rate of the considered plane. Low adsorption energy results in a slow-growing plane. We find, in this way, that any plane appearing first in the following sequence is a preferred one: (0001), (10$\bar{1}$0), (10$\bar{1}$2), (10$\bar{1}$1), (11$\bar{2}$0). These results are, practically, confirmation of results obtained before, with one basic difference, however; the plane (11$\bar{2}$0) has the fastest rate of growth and the least probability of appearance, of all the planes mentioned. Therefore, at high supersaturations, ranging between −8°C and −20°C, we can expect crystal forms having (0001) and (10$\bar{1}$0) only, but with dendrites along [11$\bar{2}$0]. Vicinal planes may also appear.

In summarizing, it may be said that for normal equilibrium conditions, as well as for growth conditions, the sequence of the planes is about the same. The habit only changes,

z

from the short hexagonal prism, with approximately equal axial and diametrical dimensions, to the flat plate or flake. MASON [1950] assumes prismatic growth which is in contradiction to our results. He assumes the growth-rate of the basal plane (0001) to be greater than the growth-rate of the prismatic plane (10$\bar{1}$0), because the adsorption energy of a water molecule on (0001) is less than on (10$\bar{1}$0). This is just the reverse of what one should expect.

It can be shown that the diffusion rate on the closely packed (0001) plane of an ice crystal is identical for all directions and is high in comparison to the diffusion rate on other planes. The diffusion rate on (10$\bar{1}$0) in the 0001 direction is, very probably, lower than the diffusion rate on (0001), but it is still comparable. These results also imply the growth of flakes. At high supersaturations (about $-8°$ to $-20°C$) when the diffusion in the vapor phase and the dissipation of the heat of condensation are rate-determining, dendrites appear. At very low temperatures ($< -35°C$), the surface diffusion is negligible and growth should result in an equimetrical habit.

The occurrence of hollow forms or 'beakers' indicate ionic forces. Two-dimensional nucleation then originates on corners and edges and, for small diffusion rates, beakers or prismatic hour-glasses appear.

The polarity of ice—One important point is to be considered. The ice lattice is held together by hydrogen bonds, with an energy of about 6 kcal/mole. The hydrogen-oxygen distances are close to 0·99 and 1·77 A, corresponding to covalent bonds and to hydrogen-bridge bonds, respectively. There are many configurations of the hydrogen atoms possible in the lattice [PAULING, 1950; BJERRUM, 1951; RUNDLE, 1955]. According to Pauling, the different configurations can be transformed into each other by rotation of the water molecules. This might be facilitated by lattice defects. Still another way is by mutual transfer of the protons from one molecule to the other through a transition state, where the proton is in the center of two oxygen atoms ('proton jump'). Therefore, if an electric field is applied to an ice crystal, parallel to the c axis, or an ice crystal grows in an electric field, the structure becomes polar. As a consequence, the entropy is changed, the surface energy of (0001) is increased, and similarly, the growth rate is increased in this direction, thus when growing from the vapor, the ice crystal habit is changed to a prismatic needle or to a prismatic pyramidal needle. When growing from water, the polarity is induced by the electric double layer at the solid-liquid interface, particularly when there is selective ionic absorption (NH^+_4, F^-) as found by Workman and co-workers. The resulting ice crystals should, likewise, form prismatic needles when the crystals continue to grow in the vapor, but crystals growing in water may assume a plate-like habit, because the (0001) interface energy is lower in water than in the vapor. Needles in water with [1120] as a needle axis could be expected at high supersaturations.

Cubic ice—Ice having a cubic appearance was observed and reported upon very early. KOENIG [1944] succeeded in proving, by electron diffraction that cubic ice of the cristobalite type existed. He succeeded in obtaining cubic ice from the vapor phase at temperatures below $-70°C$ which were transformed, at higher temperatures into the hexagonal tridymite-type. Similar results were reported by RAU [1944]. From his calculations, BJERRUM [1951] concludes that cubic ice would be unstable at low temperatures, but comparatively stable, with respect to tridymite ice, at high temperatures. There is another point of view which might be advanced. The non-existence of a nucleus, or a sub-nucleus, with a hexagonal diamond structure of a prismatic habit can satisfactorily be explained by the hypothesis that the surface energy of a cubic diamond structure nucleus or sub-nucleus of octahedral habit is less than the surface energy of a hexagonal diamond structure nucleus or subnucleus of prismatic habit. Applying similar calculations to ice, it can be shown that the interface energy, crystal-vapor, or surface energy is smallest for the cubic form. For hexagonal ice, it can be assumed, however, that due to the presence of an electric double layer at the water-ice interface and the polarity thus induced in the upper reticular layers, the interface energy is, in this case, lower for the resulting hexagonal platelets. Therefore, growth from water should favor the hexagonal form. Since homogenous nucleation of ice from water occurs below $-40°C$, cubic ice is to be expected below this temperature only, when nuclei could appear and grow in the vapor phase.

In making his experiments, Koenig had a special arrangement consisting of two walls of different temperature, thereby inducing continual evaporation and condensation. Thus, he might have succeeded in transforming cubic ice into hexagonal ice at temperatures above $-70°C$, but still the question remains whether or not cubic ice is stable or metastable above this temperature.

The existence of snow-flakes having three-fold symmetry is some evidence of the existence of cubic ice above $-70°C$. It is not necessary to assume that these snow-flakes are entirely cubic but rather they are hexagonal with numerous cubic layers of molecular dimensions. The explanation for this is the fact that while ice of the cristobalite type has a sequence of ABCABC ... of double layers of oxygen atoms in the [111] direction, the corresponding sequence in ice of the tridymite structure in the [0001] direction is ABABAB. ... It is reasonable to think that certain defects, or slipping, cause multiple deviations from the normal hexagonal sequence of layers, which may result, for instance, in a sequence such as AB(ABC)BC. . . BC(BCA)CA. . ., and so on. Twinning in diamond-type crystals can be considered as an analogous process. The sections shown above in parenthesis, correspond to cubic sections of molecular dimensions within the hexagonal crystal; sufficient concentration of such cubic intersections could, possibly, affect the hexagonal habit by superimposing the threefold axis of the cubic structure on the sixfold axis of the hexagonal structure. This would result in snow-flakes with a threefold symmetry.

Acknowledgement—The author wishes to express thanks to H. K. Weickmann for his interest in this work and for helpful discussions.

REFERENCES

AUFM KAMPE, H. J., H. K. WEICKMANN, and J. J. KELLY, The influence of temperature on the shape of ice crystals growing at water saturation, *J. Met.*, v.8, pp.168–174, 1951.

BJERRUM, N., Structure and properties of ice, Klg. Danske Videnskab Selskab, Math.-Fys. Med., v.27(1), pp.3–56, 1951, also *Science*, v.115, pp.385–390, 1952.

DANA, E. S., *The System of Mineralogy*, John Wiley & Sons, 6th ed., 1134pp., 1920, and 7th ed., v.1, 834pp., 1955.

KNACKE, O., I. N. STRANSKI, and G. A. WOLFF, Zur Theorie der Verdampfungsgeschwindigkeit, *Zs. phys. Chem.*, v.198, pp.157–185, 1951.

KOENIG, H., Eine kubische Eismodifikation, *Zs. Krist.*, v.105, pp.279–286, 1944.

KRASTANOV, L., Ueber die Bildung und das Wachstum der Eiskristalle in der Atmosphare, *Met. Zs.*, v.60, pp.15–26, 1943.
MASON, B. J., The formation of ice crystals and snowflakes, *Centenary Proc. R. Met. Soc.*, pp.51–58, 1950.
NAKAYA, U. and Y. SEKIDO, General classification of snow crystals and their frequency of occurrence, *J. Fac. Science, Hokkaido Imp. Univ.*, ser.II, Physics, v.1, pp.243, 1936.
PAULING, L., *The Nature of the Chemical Bond*, Oxford Univ. Press, 450pp., 1950.
RAU, W., Gefriervorgaenge des Wassers bei tiefen Temperaturen, *Schr. Deut. Akad. Luftfahrtforschg*, v.8, pp.65–84, 1944.
RUNDLE, R. E., The structure of ice, *J. Phys. Chem.*, v.59, pp.680–682, 1955.
STRANSKI, I. N., Forms of equilibriums of crystals, *Disc. Faraday Soc.*, v.5, pp.13–21, 1949.
STRANSKI, I. N. and G. A. WOLFF, Vapor pressure and rate of evaporation, *Research*, v.4, pp.15–24, 1951.
TSCHUDIN, K., Die Verdampfungsgeschwindigkeit von Eis, *Helvetica Physica Acta*, v.19, pp.91–102, 1946.
WEICKMANN, H. K., The snow crystal as aerological sonde, this publication, pp.315–326.

DISCUSSION

Mr. Anderson—Results which Mason (England) and I obtained in nucleation measurements indicated that the supersaturation for the growth was more or less a constant over the temperature range involved. Yet it did seem to be strongly influenced by temperature. I wonder where the temperature dependence would come in?

Dr. G. A. Wolff—The work of formation of the two-dimensional nucleus is increased with decreasing temperature for constant supersaturation. One also has to take into consideration temperature dependence of the edge energy. Furthermore I might mention that in a more thorough discussion, many points have to be considered. The matter is quite complex. I did not consider, for instance, the energy which is necessary to integrate a molecule from the vapor into an ice crystal of nuclear size. In ice, this term might be small. Last, but not least, we have to consider the influence of dislocations in ice.

Mr. Anderson—How about the length of the two-dimensional nucleus. Would it be temperature dependent?

Dr. Wolff—It is mainly a function of temperature and supersaturation.

Dr. E. J. Workman—With respect to the polarization which you mentioned, we get the impression that this crystal as it grows from some refrigerating surface toward a melt, exhibits on the surface and for many layers under the surface (maybe several, ten, hundred, or thousand) a very high degree of polarization and coordinated orientation of dipoles.

I do not know how else one can explain the electrical effects which we observe in which an ammonium ion, for example, goes into the ice surface against a potential difference barrier of 250 volts, a potential difference which is self-generated. There seem to be some kinds of cells of polarization which we would like to investigate. How to do that, I do not know.

Dr. Wolff—I did not make the experiments, and probably you have thought more about it than I did, but it may be that the interface energy of ice in water is very much lowered because of some kind of an electrical double-layer. When ice grows from the vapor phase it would be quite different. Something like an osmotic effect may come into account.

Dr. Workman—This point may be trivial to this idea, but we need to bear in mind also there is actually a difference in the lattice constant in the c axis direction. Megaw measured an $0 \cdot 03$ per cent difference and Truby found an $0 \cdot 4$ per cent difference in the ratio a/c. The incorporation of fluorine ions can shorten the distance in c direction still further, so there seems to be some connection there.

Dr. Wolff—There is another point I might mention here; that is, the question of occurence of the crystobalite structure in ice. The crystobalite ice is the cubic form of ice, which forms from a vapor phase, as far as I know, at very low temperature. If one calculates the surface energy of the corresponding equilibrium form, then one finds this surface energy to be much lower than that of a hexagonal ice crystal of the same volume, which gives me the idea that the cubic ice crystal is nucleated at low temperatures from the vapor phase as is the case for silicon and germanium. In silicon and germanium one does not obtain the hexagonal structure from the vapor phase nor from any other phase. The hexagonal ice one could get however, from a liquid, because of its polar character. That is only an idea, a suggestion.

Dr. Weickmann—If you work with snow crystals, soon a point is reached where you want to use them as an indicator of the conditions in which they had formed. For this you need some ideas about the factors influencing their growth. There are internal factors, which are pertinent for the growth of any crystal plane, and external or environmental factors. Internal factors which can be different for each crystal plane are, for instance: (1) The formation of two-dimensional or surface nuclei, which is the first step in the growth process of a new surface layer. (2) The local nucleation improvements. This takes care of preferred locations for the formation of surface nuclei on the crystal plane. Such locations may be in the center part of a plane or at the edge or points. This appears to be the determining property for the formation of hollow prisms. (3) The surface diffusion of molecules in the crystal planes. This allows a molecule, which arrives at a crystal plane, to move around and to find a place of growth.

External factors are (see Figure 2, p. 316 of this publication): (1) the temperature; (2) the humidity, relative humidity as well as the absolute vapor pressure difference between the crystal plane and the environment. (3) The temperature affects the hardness and thus the mobility of the molecules in the crystal lattice. The lower the temperature, the harder the crystal gets. The temperature also affects the humidity which is available for crystal growth. The number of molecules available for condensation is proportional to the vapor pressure difference between the crystal plane and the environment. This difference is largest at around $-15°C$ and falls off on both sides. The efficiency of the surface diffusion is affected by this magnitude. For ice crystals, surface diffusion on the more homogeneous base plane is favored over the surface diffusion on the prism plane.

The relative humidity affects the formation of surface nuclei. The higher it is, the more probable is the formation of a surface nucleus. The more surface nuclei are formed, the faster the crystal planes are piled up, and the faster a plane grows vertically to its surface. The surface diffusion which distributes the nucleus in a surface layer affects the tangential growth of a plane.

On this basis, some qualitative explanations can be given for the formation of typical crystal forms, as for instance:

Completely grown prism—The rate of formation of surface nuclei and the rate of condensation of the molecules are in equilibrium for each plane.

Hollow prism—The rate of formation of surface nuclei is too great compared to the rate of condensation of the molecules. The local improvements of surface nucleation favor the edges and points; therefore, the new surface layer starts to grow from outside to inside, and it happens that the plane is not completely finished before a new one already starts to grow from the edges.

Plates—In plates tangential growth of the base plane exceeds its normal growth.

Dendrites—A dendrite indicates a deficiency of the surface diffusion due to too great a number of condensing nuclei, or due to poisoning of the surface through adsorption of foreign molecules. The surface diffusion is no longer able to distribute the nuclei to their proper places.

This can only be regarded as a *tour de force* through the complex process of crystal growth, but certain information consistent with observations can be obtained. Hollow prisms, for instance, form at low temperatures and a humidity close to water saturation (convective cirrus), that is, great supersaturation, but small number of condensing molecules; complete prisms form at low temperatures and a humidity close to ice saturation (cirrostratus), that is, small supersaturation, when the number of condensing molecules is small. Dendrites form where the number of condensing molecules is a maximum.

A FIRST EXPERIMENT ON SNOW-CRYSTAL GROWTH

J. S. MARSHALL AND K. L. S. GUNN

McGill University, Montreal, Canada

Abstract—In analysing the experiments of Nakaya and Hanajima, Marshall and Langleben found the boundaries between the various crystal types to be loci of constant vapor density excess over flat ice equilibrium. In the present experiment, plate needle and column crystals have been grown on a strand of spider silk in a cold box at temperatures from −4 to −20°C. The vapor densities have been measured accurately by measuring the rate of change of diameter of a supercooled water droplet suspended in the working region, and it appears that Marshall and Langleben's estimates of vapour density excess at the boundaries between crystal types are too high by 0.044 gm^{-3}. There is some evidence for an effective equilibrium vapor density of an ice crystal some 0.066 gm^{-3} higher than that for flat ice. Electric fields were applied and modifications in the crystal growth in general accord with Schaefer observed, but there is no evidence of equivalence between effects of charge and vapour density.

Introduction—MARSHALL and LANGLEBEN [1954] interpreted the experiments of NAKAYA [1954] and his coworkers as evidence that snow-crystal habit is determined principally by the excess of ambient vapor density over that at equilibrium with the ice crystal at its own temperature. Changes in crystal type occur when this vapor density excess is sufficient to overcome the inhibitions, first to edge growth and secondly to corner growth, that must exist if the edges and corners have higher surface vapor densities than the flat faces of the crystal. The higher equilibrium vapor densities over the corners and edges of a shaped crystal should make the effective equilibrium vapor density for the particle taken as a whole, somewhat greater than that for flat ice. One purpose of the crystal-growth experiment described here was to determine the effective equilibrium vapor density of a crystal; this is important because the rate of growth of the crystal is proportional to the excess of ambient over this effective density. With the experiment, we also hoped to determine whether electrical charge on the crystal would reduce the inhibitions due to high curvature, as it does in the case of small water droplets.

A sensitive hygrometer for measuring vapor density—The experiment was carried out in a small domestic freezer. Crystals were grown on a two-cm length of spider silk stretched across a wire yoke, and were observed through a binocular microscope, one eyepiece of which was fitted with a micrometer cross-hair. A useful technique was devised for measuring the ambient vapor-density excess or deficit relative to water equilibrium to within 0.002 gm^{-3}. The rate of change of the diameter of a supercooled droplet is a function of known constants and the difference between ambient and equilibrium vapor density at the water droplet. As pointed out by Marshall and Langleben for the case of a growing ice crystal, one must recognize that an evaporating or growing water droplet will be cooler or warmer than its environment, respectively. This point is illustrated in Fig. 1, where a portion of the curve of equilibrium vapor density for water is reproduced. Suppose an undersaturated environment represented by point A. The temperature and equilibrium vapor density for a water droplet in this environment is

340

given by the point B, the intersection of a line of slope K/DL_v with the curve, where K is coefficient of thermal conductivity of air, D is the diffusivity of water vapor in air, and L_v the latent heat of vaporization [MARSHALL and LANGLEBEN, 1954]. The rate of decay of the droplet gives $(\rho_B - \rho_A) = \Delta\rho$, but what is required is the actual vapour density

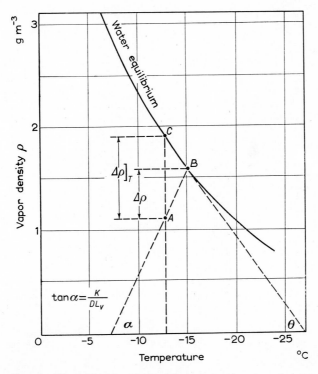

FIG. 1—Illustrating the relationship between the vapor-density deficit for a water drop in an environment at A, $(\Delta\rho)$, and the actual deficit from water equilibrium at that temperature $(\Delta\rho]_T)$

difference from equilibrium at the ambient temperature $(\rho_B - \rho_A) = \Delta\rho]_T$. These are easily shown to be related by

$$\Delta\rho]_T = \Delta\rho\left(1 + \frac{\tan\theta}{K/DL_v}\right)$$

where $\tan\theta$ is slope of the equilibrium vapor density curve at the ambient temperature. The ratio $\Delta\rho]_T/\Delta\rho$ is plotted against ambient temperature in Fig. 2, and so for any measured $\Delta\rho$, $\Delta\rho]_T$ may be determined. It is evident that Fig. 2 applies for supersaturated environments if required. In Fig. 2, the equivalent curve for ice is shown. This gives the factors to be used in computing the actual vapor-density excess $(\Delta\rho)$ between that at an ice particle growing in an environment supersaturated with respect to ice and flat ice equilibrium, from the known vapour density excess at the ambient temperature $\Delta\rho]_T$. (Values from Fig. 2 were used to obtain the loci of Fig. 4, for instance.)

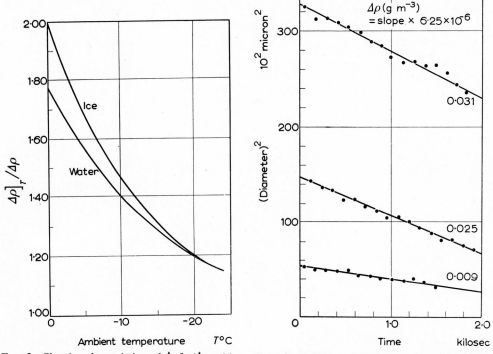

FIG. 2—Showing the variation of $\Delta\rho]_T/\Delta\rho$ with temperature for water and ice spheres.

FIG. 3—Relation of diameter squared and time for three cases of supercooled droplets on the spider silk in the working region

Returning to the 'hygrometer' droplet, for a sphere of radius r, the rate of mass transfer by diffusion

$$\frac{dm}{dt} = 4\pi r D \Delta\rho \tag{1}$$

where D is the diffusivity of water vapor in air, $\Delta\rho$ is the above-mentioned actual vapor-density difference between the evaporating drop and its warmer environment. Also we can write

$$\frac{dm}{dt} = 4\pi r^2 \rho_w \frac{dr}{dt} \tag{2}$$

where ρ_w is density of liquid water.

Equating (1) and (2), and integrating

$$\Delta\rho = \frac{\rho_w}{8D} \cdot \frac{\Delta d^2}{\Delta t}$$

Take $D = 0.2$ cm² sec⁻¹ (at −18°C), $\rho_w = 1$ g cm⁻³, and expressing Δd^2 in (microns)², and Δt in kilosec,

$$\Delta\rho(\text{gm}^{-3}) = 6.25 \times 10^{-6} \frac{\Delta d^2}{\Delta t}$$

A supercooled droplet of say, 100μ diameter is easily obtained by melting the ice crystal under study. Ten minutes' observation is sufficient to determine its rate of change of size, and so $\Delta\rho$ (Fig. 3). Then using Fig. 2, $\Delta\rho]_T$, the actual vapor density difference of the environment from water equilibrium, is obtained.

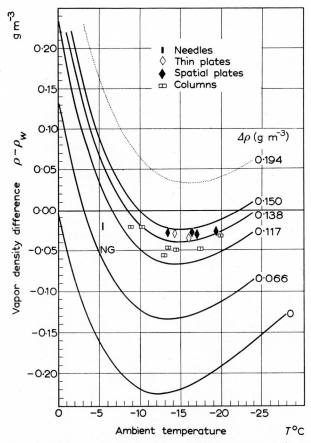

Fig. 4—Various crystal types grown in this experiment shown on a plot of vapor density difference from water equilibrium against temperature; solid curves are loci of constant vapour density excess over that for growing ice

Various attempts at crystal growth—At first, water vapor at 100°C was produced in a five-watt insulated kettle in the cold box. A dense cloud of supercooled droplets was formed, and it was hoped that even momentary supersaturation would exist at some places in the box. Even in the dense cloud the 'hygrometer-drop' evaporated. The highest relative humidity observed was about 99·3 per cent indicating that evaporation from the supercooled cloud could not keep up with diffusion to the cold walls. Thus it appears that visible cloud cannot be taken as sufficient evidence of water equilibrium.

Some crystal growth was observed with this cloud, but the crystal types were obscured by the accretion of supercooled droplets. Instead of the kettle, a water bath on the floor of the cold box was tried; no growth occurred and low vapor densities were measured in the working region.

Finally, vapor was supplied by keeping the ceiling of the cold box wet. With this arrangement, plate, needle, and column crystals were grown readily, but again in an environment below saturation. Again, apparently the supply of vapor from the warm wet ceiling, as from the cloud droplets could not keep pace with the diffusion to the cold walls and the relative humidities in which the needles, plates and columns grew were always between 97 and 99 per cent. There was no cloud and the various crystal types were easily identified (Fig. 4).

Marshall and Langleben assumed that although Nakaya's supersaturation included liquid, values over 100 per cent relative humidity always involved some true supersaturation as well as cloud droplets. Assuming this, they found that loci of constant vapor-density excess over ice equilibrium (for flat ice) gave as good boundaries between Nakaya's various crystal types as his own empirical ones. However, in the present experiment, the crystals were all grown in vapor densities less than water saturation, suggesting that Nakaya's working region must have actually consisted of water droplets in unsaturated vapor.

In Fig. 4, one Marshall and Langleben boundary, that between dendrites and plates ($\Delta\rho = 0.194$ g m^{-3}) is shown dotted. (The opportunity was taken to introduce the notions of Fig. 2 to derive loci of $\Delta\rho$ for ice more accurate than those used by Marshall and Langleben.) To fit their set of boundaries (and notably the plate-column boundary) to our limited data, all their vapor density excess boundary values should be reduced by some 0.044 g m^{-3}; thus the boundary $\Delta\rho = 0.194$ g m^{-3} should be 0.150 g m^{-3} and so on. The various boundary values are presented in Table 1, and the new set of boundaries are also shown in Fig. 4 superimposed on the individual data.

Table 1. *Crystal-boundary values*

Type	$\rho-\rho_i$(g m^{-3})	
	Marshall and Langleben	Values for our present experiment
Dendrites ...	0·194	0·150
Plates	0·182	0·138
Columns ...	0·161	0·117
Needles	0·110	0·066

In this first experiment, no growth was observed for $\Delta\rho$ less than 0.066 g m^{-3}, suggesting that the effective equilibrium vapor density for an ice crystal is 0.066 g m^{-3} higher than that for flat ice. The evidence is not conclusive, but justifies further study.

The influence on electric charge on growth—Various voltages were applied to the metal yoke supporting the spider silk, the silk being generally about one cm from the grounded wall of the cold box. Potentials between about three and 300 volts produced no observable change in type or rate of growth; between 300 and 400 volts, growth was accelerated on all crystal types, but the growth consisted initially of small opaque sprouts all over the crystal which grew subsequently into a jungle of irregular branches of small cross section with no recognizable crystal form [SCHAEFER, 1953]. A voltage applied to the metal yoke was found to produce rapid growth of supercooled droplets (and later crystals) on a new spider silk, which otherwise took some hours of 'breaking in' before crystals would grow on it. A further useful feature of the electric field was that switching it on rotated the crystals (which were usually asymmetric) about the silk, presenting another aspect for observation.

Ventilation—Dendrites were never grown in the undersaturated environment until on one occasion dendritic arms grew rapidly from plate crystals when a 200μ diameter supercooled droplet was nearby, (some two mm along the web). This dendritic growth could always be reproduced at that temperature by having a supercooled droplet adjacent to growing crystals.

Once the dendrite arms were sizeable, their rapid growth could be explained by an overlap of the diffusion fields of the droplet and dendrite. But when the dendritic growth began, the plate crystal was not big enough for a significant overlap of the diffusion fields. Possibly a gentle air flow could alter the diffusion field around the crystal sufficiently. This then raises the point of the importance of ventilation.

Marshall and Langleben, in their analysis of Nakaya's experiments, neglected the effect of ventilation, but concluded that it was probably slight since it was due to natural convection. At the same time, their analysis indicated that crystals would not grow at 500 mb pressure, since the available vapor-density excess drops off with reduced pressure. While this was obviously untrue, they left the problem open. Possibly, the air flow in Nakaya's experiments was considerably less than the terminal speed of crystals, and in the atmosphere the ventilation effect on a freely falling crystal is sufficiently greater to offset the reduced vapor-density excess.

It would seem that ventilation could be highly relevant to considerations of crystal habit, and even a modest amount of it could vitiate experiments meant to involve diffusion only. We think it is important that quantitative consideration be given to ventilation and that our own experiment should change from a static one to one with controlled ventilation.

Acknowledgment—This work was carried out with the support of Contract AF 19(122)–217 extended by the Geophysics Research Directorate of the Air Force Cambridge Research Center and of the Defence Research Board of Canada through Grant 9511–08.

REFERENCES

MARSHALL, J. S. and M. P. LANGLEBEN, A theory of snow crystal habit and growth, *J. Met.*, v.11, pp.104–120, 1954.

NAKAYA, U., *Snow Crystals, Natural and Artificial*, Harvard Univ. Press, Cambridge, Mass., 1954.

SCHAEFER, V. J., Final report, Project Cirrus Part I, Laboratory, field and flight experiments, General Electric Research Laboratory Rep. RL-785, 1953.

DISCUSSION

Dr. Ukichiro Nakaya—How was the ice crystal suspended?

Dr. J. S. Marshall—On a cobweb which was fastened on a yoke.

Dr. Nakaya—Did you get dendrites?

Dr. K. L. S. Gunn—We did grow a dendrite on one occasion when there was a supercooled water droplet two mm along the web from the crystal.

Dr. G. A. Wolff—I understand you tried to explain the crystal habit by diffusion only?

Dr. Marshall—That's what we attempted to do, but we realize that we have probably neglected some part of the story.

Dr. Wolff—I feel that diffusion is an important process, since it is the first step in growth and it may well be that you can explain dendrite formation as long as you assume a certain corresponding crystal growth direction as being preferred but I am not quite sure whether or not one can explain the formation of all ice crystal forms by diffusion only.

Dr. Marshall—We are aware of that.

Mr. Charles E. Anderson—I was amazed that you can explain all this on the basis of diffusion of molecules on the growing crystal, particularly in view of the fact that you must assume that wherever the molecules land, they begin to grow—also in your explanation of the dendritic growth.

Dr. Marshall—At a temperature around $-15°C$ there will be a much denser cloud of molecules at the corners than elsewhere. It is quite permissible for some of that cloud to take part in surface diffusion (in fact, variation in density over the surface may be the result of a surface flow), but in this temperature range one would anticipate more growth at the corners than at any other place due to diffusion. There surely is a more "microscopic" part to the story which diffusion is unlikely to explain.

Mr. Anderson—I have two comments. (1) In a recent paper by Pound and collaborators they studied the heterogeneous crystallization from vapor. In this case they were metal crystals on substrates. They were interested in determining whether the growth was determined mainly by the surface diffusion of the molecules which have become adsorbed at the surface, or whether or not a direct addition of these molecules from the vapor to, say the advancing step, could be important. In their experimental work they found that the surface-diffusion mechanism gave a rate of 10^2 to 10^3 times as great as the later mechanism.

(2) There is a paper by Shaw and Mason [*Phil. Mag.*, ser.7, v.46, 1955], in which they presented supersaturation data for various crystals grown on a surface. They found that there was quite a scatter; and as I recall, there was apparently no clear relationship between the excess vapor and the crystal habit. But, rather, they felt it was some function of temperature. I just wonder what you have to remark about their work.

Dr. Marshall—One has to wait for a third experiment that will settle the complete conflict between Mason's and our experiment.

DISCUSSION OF THE GROWTH OF ICE CRYSTALS

HORACE B. BYERS, Presiding

Dr. J. S. Marshall—I should like to make the point once more that small changes in humidity may be significant. Nakaya used the name 'supersaturation' for the ratio of mass of water substance per unit volume to equilibrium vapor density. The mass of water substance was known to be made up partly of vapor, partly of water cloud, and the proportions were not determined. When supersaturation defined in this way changes by a large amount, the change in vapor density may be small, and yet be the significant change. It is important that this vapor density be measured with high accuracy, in the immediate vicinity of the growth processes being studied. A small difference between the condition at a wall and at a point ten cm away from that wall can have a marked effect on the processes in the chamber.

Mr. Charles E. Anderson—You mentioned a cut-off point for the growth of snow crystals at $-4°C$. This apparently was something that could explain Dr. Braham's peculiar findings in his seeding work. Do we have any experimental evidence either from the laboratory or from the atmosphere, that you can not form ice crystals at warmer than $-4°C$ in a supercooled water cloud?

Dr. Marshall—The only relevant evidence that I know of lies in the Nakaya-Hanajima diagram, assuming that the blank spaces on that diagram indicate regions where snow crystals would not grow. Taking the diagram in its original form, you will not find ice crystals very close to $0°C$. There may be some similar evidence in our own work as reported here, but our experiment must be carried further before this can be taken as reliable. I think that the existing evidence is good enough to justify further experiments, but not good enough to be accepted as the basis for the development of a theory or the explaining of atmospheric phenomena.

Dr. Roscoe R. Braham, Jr.—Did not Dr. Schaefer succeed in the growth of ice crystals in a cold box at $-4°C$, and find a threshold at $-0.5°C$ or $-1°C$?

Dr. Vincent J. Schaefer—Yes, but the growth was very much slower, and one had to use a great deal more material. There is no doubt that the crystals grew.

Dr. Hans J. aufm Kampe—We obtained growth in this region too; the odd thing was that the crystals that grew were very, very thin and transparent.

Dr. Schaefer—The place for making such studies is in supercooled ground fogs, in the fall or spring. I have done a great deal of work in such situations, with temperatures $-1°$ or $-2°C$, and made beautiful pillars and halos. This [in answer to Dr. aufm Kampe] was with dry ice; with silver iodide under similar conditions I had to wait for supercooling of $-5°C$ or $-6°C$.

Dr. Marshall—I am not satisfied that these were observations of crystal growth, as opposed to crystal formation.

Dr. Schaefer—I start with crystals at a tenth of a micron at the largest and they become diamond dust. I published a few pictures of crystals, 0.3 mm long that grew in a supercooled fog by sublimation. [Then in reply to Marshall suggestion that slight supersaturation with respect to water might exist in some parts of the fog]: These were dessicated clouds, so there is a tendency toward less than water equilibrium. Yet the crystals grew to the point where they were diamond dust.

Dr. Cunningham—When you use dry ice, you have a trail of cold air in back of the bit of solid CO_2. Particles may first grow at temperatures considerably below the ambient, but I understand from you that they continue to grow.

Dr. Schaefer—The easiest way to achieve this effect is to use a cylinder of liquid CO_2. The gas issues from a tiny jet, and within a foot reaches ambient temperature. The expanding gas initiates the crystals which grow to a diameter of at least 0.1 micron by the time they reach the temperature of the supercooled cloud. They then continue to grow as long as they remain floating and within a supercooled cloud.

CRYSTAL GROWTH AND NUCLEATION;
LABORATORY AND FIELD STUDIES

CINEMA ON CRYSTAL GROWTH

DAVID TURNBULL

General Electric Research Laboratory, Schenectady, N.Y.

THIS film and the experiments on which it is based are the work of Jack Newkirk of our laboratory. To explain briefly, the experiment is to saturate the solution with cadmium iodide and cool it down. Precipitation of thin approximately hexagonal platelets occurs. These platelets grow very rapidly laterally without change in interference color; that is they do not thicken even though the solution is supersaturated. Then you will see the catastrophe that leads to the generation of a dislocation with a large Burgers vector.

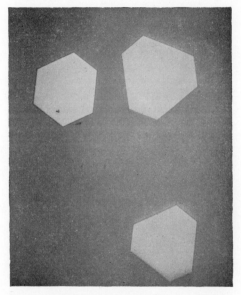

FIG. 1—Three 'one-dimensionally perfect' platelets growing rapidly laterally

Figures 1 through 3 are taken from a cinema made by Dr. J. B. Newkirk of our laboratory illustrating the growth of cadmium iodide crystals from aqueous solutions [see J. B. NEWKIRK, 1955]. The growing crystals exhibit interference colors. Fig. 1 shows three 'one-dimensionally perfect' platelets growing rapidly in the lateral dimensions but not thickening (as evidenced by the constancy of the interference colors). These crystals have no dislocation steps on the broad faces. Fig. 2 shows the dislocation steps that developed in two platelets as a result of a 'growth accident' which was the collision of two growing platelets. The mechanism whereby such an accident leads to dislocation steps has been worked out by J. C. FISHER, R. L. FULLMAN and G. W. SEARS, 1954.

FIG. 2—Dislocation steps in two platelets

FIG. 3—Spiral dislocation steps

Fig. 3 shows the spiral dislocation steps that developed as a result of an unseen growth accident at the edge of the crystal.

REFERENCES

FISHER, J. C., FULLMAN, R. L., and SEARS, G. W. On the origin of screw dislocations in growing crystals, *Acta Met.*, v. 2, pp. 344–346, 1954.

NEWKIRK, J. B., Growth of cadmium iodide crystals, *Acta Met.*, v. 3, pp. 121–125, 1955.

REMARKS ON THE THEORY OF HETEROGENEOUS
NUCLEATION OF CRYSTALS

DAVID TURNBULL

General Electric Research Laboratory, Schenectady, N.Y.

Abstract—The status of the theory connecting crystal nucleating effectiveness with the crystallographic relationship between the nucleating agent and the nucleus is reviewed. In addition to certain crystallographic requirements, an effective catalyst for the nucleation of crystals from dilute fluid solutions usually must have steps in its surface resulting from the termination of screw dislocations therein. Recent experiments have shown that, at least in some instances, such surface steps are also necessary for crystal growth in undercooled pure liquids.

FIRST I shall make a few remarks on the theoretical basis for the importance of crystallographic relationships in heterogeneous nucleation. In the second part of my paper, I will discuss the possible importance of the screw dislocation mechanism in crystal growth from the melt; and whether or not surface dislocation steps may be important in determining the effectiveness of nucleation agents.

A few years ago Vonnegut and I [TURNBULL and VONNEGUT, 1952] attempted to describe the minimum assumptions that have to be made in order to account for the fact that the most effective nucleating agents are generally crystallographically very similar to the nucleus.

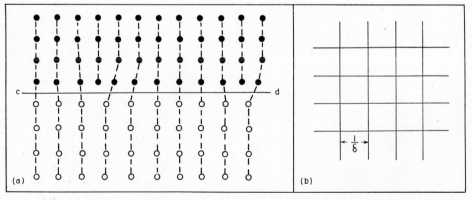

FIG. 1—Dislocation array at interface between two simple cubic lattices

To review our discussion consider first the molecular configuration at the interface between the nucleating agent and the nucleus. It is often possible, as VAN DER MERWE [1950] and BROOKS [1952, p.52] have pointed out, to describe such an interface as an array of dislocations. Fig. 1 shows the interfacial dislocation array that results from putting together two simple cubic lattices with different lattice parameters. It is supposed that the energy of this interface is made up of a chemical and a structural part.

However, in crystallization from the melt, the chemical term is likely to be quite small because, of course, the chemistry of the melt and the crystal are virtually the same so that their 'chemical' interaction with any impurity is likely to be very similar.

The structural part of the interfacial energy is due to the atomic displacements surrounding dislocation cores and increases with the density of dislocations in the interface and hence with the crystallographic disregistry between the nucleus and impurity. The dislocation energy is quite large and when the disregistry is small the nucleus is likely to form coherently on the impurity. That is, the nucleus is strained to an exact crystallographic fit with the impurity on the interfacial planes. (The coherency is two rather than three-dimensional.) (It is required that the impurity be crystallographically similar to the nucleus in two dimensions but not in three.) The elastic coherency energy must be counterbalanced by the driving free energy of transformation. Thus for coherent nucleation

$$\Delta S_v \Delta T = c\delta^2 \tag{1}$$

where

ΔS_v = entropy of fusion/volume
ΔT = undercooling
δ = disregistry at an incoherent interface between nucleus and impurity
c = elastic coefficient of the nucleus

At large disregistries ($\delta \gtrsim 0.04$) the elastic energy becomes so large that it is energetically cheaper for the nucleus to form with dislocations in the nucleus-impurity interface than to form coherently.

Two results emerge from this very crude theory: (1) The undercoolings required for sensible nucleation are in the same order as the disregistries between the nucleus and the impurities on the interfacial planes. (2) For small disregistry ($\delta < 0.02$ to 0.03) the undercooling for sensible nucleation should increase as the disregistry squared with the proportionality constant $c/\Delta S_v$.

At present not much data are available for checking these ideas. However, the minimum undercoolings ΔT_m of water required to nucleate ice on silver iodide [VONNEGUT, 1947] and quartz [SCHULZ, 1951; WEICKMANN, 1951] are in fair agreement with the values calculated from (1) assuming coherent nucleation. Table 1 compares the elastic coefficient of ice calculated by PENNY [1948] with the values calculated from (1) using the undercooling data on quartz and ice. The fact that the two coefficients calculated using (1) are in rough agreement with each other and with Penny's value is consistent with the theory that ice nucleates coherently on silver iodide and quartz.

Now I shall consider the possibility, ignored in the simple theory just discussed, that a nucleating agent may require screw dislocation steps in its surface in order to be operative at small undercooling.

Gibbs recognized that the free energy required to initiate the formation of a crystal plane one atom thick, on an atomically smooth densely packed crystal face, is greater than that required for completing its growth. That is there is a two-dimensional nucleation barrier to the growth of perfect crystals. This barrier is, of course, smaller than that opposing the three-dimensional homogeneous nucleation of crystals. For example, if 40° undercooling is necessary for a sensible rate of homogeneous nucleation of ice in water, about 10° undercooling would be necessary to grow a densely packed perfect ice-crystal face into water at a perceptible rate.

However, in ordinary experience, crystals bounded by well-defined low-index faces grow into fluid media at measurable rates when the undercooling is very small. Until a few years ago this fact was explained by supposing that crystal faces in equilibrium contact with fluid media are very rough. Then BURTON and CABRERA [1951] advanced convincing arguments for the viewpoint that densely packed crystal faces in contact with dilute fluid solutions are virtually perfect. Thus the problem of reconciling the theory of crystal growth with ordinary experience appeared not to have been solved.

Table 1. *The elastic coefficient of ice, calculated on the assumption that ice nucleates coherently on silver iodide and quartz, compared with* PENNY'S [1948] *value*

Nucleating impurity	Disregistry	ΔT °C	c Dyne cm^{-2}	
			From Eq. (1)	Penny's calculated value
	per cent			
Silver iodide*	1·35	2·5	$1\cdot4\times10^{11}$	$1\cdot7\times10^{11}$
Quartz†	3·1	10·2	$1\cdot1\times10^{11}$	$1\cdot7\times10^{11}$

* VONNEGUT [1947].
† SCHULZ [1951].

A new solution of the problem was proposed by FRANK [1949]. He recognized that a step in a crystal face resulting from the termination of a screw dislocation axis therein could not grow out of existence. Therefore, he suggested that most crystals have such steps in them, perhaps as a result of accidents of growth, and that crystal growth from dilute solution, in directions normal to densely packed faces, proceeds by the addition of atoms to these indestructible steps. Frank's theory of crystal growth is now supported by a large body of microscopic and kinetic results.

Burton, Cabrera, and Frank were not able to reach a conclusion on the equilibrium roughness of a crystal in contact with its own melt. Thus the question of whether or not the screw dislocation mechanism must operate in solidification at small undercooling was unresolved.

The possibility that nucleating agents may require dislocation steps in their surface in order to initiate solidification at small undercooling was discussed by Vincent Schaefer and me about two years ago. It was concluded [SCHAEFER, 1954] that some of Schaefer's observations were most simply explained on the assumption that only lead iodide crystals containing screw dislocation steps in their surface could nucleate ice in water at small undercooling. Thus it may be that impurities in order to be good nucleation catalysts in solidification must, in addition to fulfilling certain crystallographic requirements, have dislocation steps in their surface. The presence and number of such dislocation steps is dependent upon the preparation and history of the impurity so that some variability in the catalytic behavior of different lots of the same impurity substance is expected on the basis of the dislocation theory.

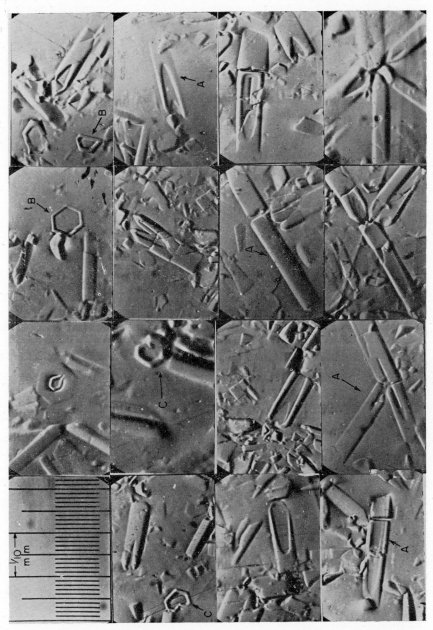

Fig. 2—Imprints of ice crystals taken in cirrus clouds

It is possible that certain catalysts for the nucleation of freezing can only function by the operation of screw dislocations even though dislocation steps might not be required for the crystal growth during freezing. For example the cohesion in an impurity substance might be so great that its surface in contact with the liquid is atomically smooth at equilibrium even though the equilibrium interface between the liquid and growing crystal is rough under the same conditions.

However, there is now some experimental evidence which indicates that the screw dislocation mechanism for growth from the melt must be seriously considered in some instances, at least. Thus investigators from several laboratories [see, for example, Sears, 1955] have now resolved by microscopic techniques growth spirals on the surface of crystals grown from the melt. Recently Hillig and Turnbull [1956] concluded that the dependence of the velocity of crystal growth during freezing upon undercooling in several systems, including ice-water, may be explained most simply if the screw dislocation mechanism operates. The arguments will be described fully in the publication.

In conclusion the degree of crystal perfection of a nucleating impurity must be very important in crystallization processes in dilute solutions and this perfection also may be decisive in controlling the nucleation of freezing of pure liquids.

REFERENCES

Brooks, H., Theory of internal boundaries, in *Metal Interfaces*, pp.20–65, American Society for Metals, Cleveland, 1952.

Burton, W. K., N. Cabrera, and F. C. Frank, The growth of crystals and the equilibrium structure of their surfaces, *Phil. Trans. R. Soc.*, v.243, pp.300–358, 1951.

Frank, F. C., Crystal growth, *Disc. Faraday Soc.*, no.5, pp.48, 67, 1949.

Hillig, W. B. and D. Turnbull, Theory of crystal growth in undercooled pure liquids, *J. Chem. Phys.*, v.24, p.914, 1956.

Penny, A. H. A., A theoretical determination of the elastic constants of ice, *Proc. Camb. Phil. Soc.*, v.44, pp.423–439, 1948.

Schaefer, V. J., Silver and lead iodides as ice crystal nuclei, *J. Met.*, v.11, pp.417–419, 1954.

Schulz, G., Der Einfluss von Fremdkörpern auf die Unterkühlungsfähigkeit des Wassers, *Met. Rundschau*, v.1, p. 237, 1948.

Sears, G. W., Screw dislocations in growth from the melt, *J. Chem. Phys.*, v.23, pp.1630–1632, 1955.

Turnbull, D. and B. Vonnegut, Nucleation catalysis, *Ind. Eng. Chem.*, v.44, pp.1292–1298, 1952.

Van de Merwe, J. H., On the stresses and energies associated with intercrystalline boundaries, *Proc. Phys. Soc.*, v.63A, pp.616–637, 1950.

Vonnegut, B., The nucleation of ice formation by silver iodide, *J. Appl. Phys.*, v.18, pp.593–595, 1947.

Weickmann, H. K., A theory of the formation of ice crystals, *Archiv. Met. Geophysik, und Biokhim*, v.4A, pp.309–323, 1951.

DISCUSSION

Dr. E. J. Workman—I have never gotten over being worried a little bit about what you call 'precise fits.' During the growth of an ice crystal on another surface there must be a difference in ice as it makes the first two or three hundred layers and when it makes a deep micro crystal unit. There is ample evidence, I think, for dislocations within the ice itself.

Dr. David Turnbull—Yes, if the thin film forms on something that doesn't fit very well, I think that is quite true. The atomic spacing in the surface of a microscopic crystal may be a little different from what you measure with x-rays; however, great differences have not been found.

Dr. Workman—Well, Drost-Hanson and I, at the Meeting of the AGU in Washington last spring, showed some pictures of ice growth from the melt which shows evidence of strain well into the crystal, and indeed we interpreted a hexagonal pattern over the micro crystal units as being dislocation phenomena.

Dr. Turnbull—Well, that's all right. You are saying that you get plastic deformation of ice. But you can have dislocations in the crystal without altering the lattice parameter much.

Dr. Helmut Weickmann—Does this dislocation appear only on the sub microscopic scale? Fig. 2 shows imprints of ice crystals taken in cirrus clouds on March 9, 1943. The scale is $0 \cdot 1$ mm. Prism planes are indicated by A. B shows imprints of the base planes and since the crystal was hollow you only see the walls, and C is a case where two spirals are facing each other. Now is this some other effect or is this a consequence of a dislocations growth?

Dr. Turnbull—Is this growth from the vapor?

Dr. Weickmann—Yes, they were taken in cirrus clouds at a temperature around $-40°C$. The initial particles form at water saturation and their subsequent growth may proceed from saturated vapor but not from the liquid.

Dr. Turnbull—Well, I think there is very little doubt that growth of the basal plane of ice in direction of the main axis would require a dislocation mechanism. It is sometimes hard to resolve an ice spiral, but I think you would expect to get steps.

Dr. Workman—You would interpret the one in the corner as two, opposite directed.

Dr. Turnbull—Yes, those may be closed loops.

Dr. Workman—Which eventually turn into hexagons?

Dr. Turnbull—Yes, in fact they do. In the movie this afternoon you will see circular loops which then develop into a hexagon due to the slow growth.

Mr. James E. Manson—Is it possible to nucleate on the base plane of the hexagonal prism and then develop rapid growth in the prism directions, that is, perpendicular to the unique axis.

Dr. Turnbull—Yes. As a matter of fact, you will also see that in the movie. I don't know how thin these hexagons were, but you often see rapid lateral growth of hexagonal crystals and no perpendicular growth at all until you get the catastrophy that leads to the dislocation.

Mr. Charles E. Anderson—Are you able to put numbers into the dislocation theory, in so far as say the undercooling temperature with disregistry?

Dr. Turnbull—This has been done roughly for solid state transformations. A similar rough estimate might be made in this case.

Dr. James E. McDonald—The way the crystal habit of ice varies so rapidly with temperatures in snow crystals is very remarkable; and I was wondering where in the theory that underlies this velocity equation you would look for the temperature effect that would shift the dominant growth rate from the basal planes to other faces.

Dr. Turnbull—Well, there are two possibilities. In the first place the interface diffusion coefficient should be a function of the orientation. Second, the number of attachment sites or dislocation steps also should be orientation dependent. Impurities, which are adsorbed differently or different crystallographic planes, probably interfere with crystal growth.

ICE NUCLEATION AND THE STRUCTURE OF NUCLEI CRYSTAL FACES

JAMES E. MANSON

Atmospheric Physics Laboratory, Geophysics Research Directorate,
Air Force Cambridge Research Center, Bedford, Mass.

Abstract—The nucleating effectiveness of hexagonal and cubic silver iodide injected into super-cooled water clouds has been found to be substantially the same. The effectiveness of two modifications of calcium carbonate, vaterite and calcite, has been found to differ widely, vaterite being effective and calcite not effective. A study of the structure of those faces prominently developed on the nuclei particles indicated that the crystallography of nuclei crystal faces is very important in determining effectiveness in seeding supercooled water clouds.

Introduction—In seeding a supersaturated solution or a supercooled melt, some mechanism is necessary to carry a small portion of the system over the hump separating the metastable state from the stable, lower energy state. As applied to cloud physics, this broad problem narrows down to the freezing of supercooled water drops, or at least to the dual problem of the non-freezing of supercooled water drops and the subsequent creation of ice particles by seeding. The explanation of the non-freezing of water droplets has been well summarized by McDONALD [1953]. Attention will be devoted to the subsequent seeding process as carried out by particulate addition without thermal shock. Thus, the field is limited to cloud seeding by smoke or aerosol particles. This paper confirms structural similarity as an important factor in the mechanism of such supercooled cloud seeding experiments.

The structure of ice—Before discussing the work done on the seeding of laboratory clouds, it will be profitable to establish a reference for structural discussions. The structure of ice and many of the peculiar properties of water can be understood by reference to a model of the water molecule consisting of a sphere of 1·38A radius with tetrahedrally oriented zones of positive and negative charge [BERNAL, 1933; EVANS, 1948; PAULING, 1935; RUNDLE, 1953]. The packing of these molecules in ice is shown in Fig. 1. The simple unit cell obtained by ignoring the placement of the hydrogens is outlined, and the dimensions of this cell given. The sixfold symmetry seen in atmospheric ice particles of platelike habit can be recognized in the plan drawing. It is the structure of this plane which determines the sixfold symmetry of snow particles. In the interpretation of cloud-seeding experiments in a cold chamber with illumination from the top, it must be remembered that thin plates have a better chance of being detected than columnar crystals. This introduces a bias into the experiment, favoring positive results under conditions for development of hexagonal plates.

Silver iodide experiments—Silver iodide offers an interesting opportunity to study the influence of the structure of a particular crystal face on the ability of this face to serve as a nucleus. Below 146°C, AgI exists in two stable modifications. One is hexagonal (H) with the zincite structure. This structure is closely related to that of ice. If one

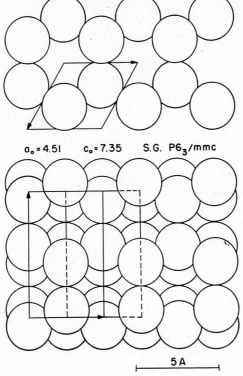

$a_o = 4.51$ $c_o = 7.35$ S.G. P6$_3$/mmc

5 A

Fig. 1—The structure of ice

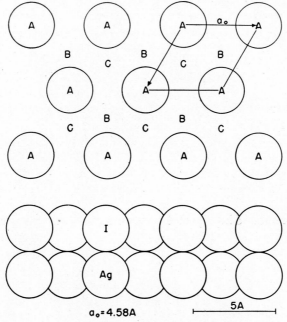

$a_o = 4.58A$ 5A

Fig. 2—Silver iodide layer structure

replaces both the Zn and the O atoms with H_2O molecules, the ice structure results. As has been indicated by VONNEGUT [1947], the dimensions of the unit cell of hexagonal AgI are very close to those of the ice unit cell. The other modification of AgI is cubic (C) with the zincblende structure. The relationship between (H) and (C) can be understood by reference to Fig. 2. In this figure a single AgI layer is illustrated. The plane of this layer is the same crystallographic plane as the hexagonal plate plane of the ice structure. It is referred to as the base plane. If such layers are stacked on top of each other two positions of low energy exist, indicated in Fig. 2 as B and C, A being occupied by the initial layer. Let the atoms of the second layer occupy the B positions. If the third layer then occupied A, and the fourth B, and so on, then the resulting structure is hexagonal. If, on the other hand, the sequence followed is $ABCABC$ . . ., then the resulting structure is face centered cubic. From this it is easy to see how AgI can have two stable modifications below 146°C.

From the point of view of cloud physics, this becomes very important when it is noted that the (H) structure has many crystal planes with structures almost identical to the corresponding ice planes. The (C) structure has only one plane, the diagonal (111) plane, which is close to a corresponding ice place crystallographically. This diagonal cubic plane is parallel to the layer drawn in Fig. 2. This provides a method of determining if the active part of the AgI particle is the face parallel to the base plane. All that is needed is a pair of samples, one cubic AgI and the other hexagonal AgI, in the proper state of subdivision to act as nuclei. It would be advantageous if both samples consisted of particles, each with a well-developed face parallel to the layer in Fig. 2.

A sample was prepared consisting of 70 per cent hexagonal AgI and 30 per cent cubic AgI, with prominently developed base plane faces, as indicated by preferred orientation effects in x-ray Diffractometer data [MANSON, 1955b]. This sample had been reduced to aerosol size by dry grinding, an operation reported [KOLKMEIJER and VON HENGEL, 1934] to increase the proportion of (C). It was possible to prepare a sample of better than 90 per cent (H) before grinding, or to produce a smoke of 95 per cent (H) also showing effects of orientation caused by well-developed base plane faces [MANSON, 1955a]. However, in order to have aerosol samples of comparable sizes and number concentrations the 70 per cent hexagonal AgI sample was used, and called Sample A.

A second sample was prepared consisting of six per cent hexagonal AgI and 94 per cent cubic AgI, after grinding to the proper size range for aerosol production. This sample also had very well-developed faces parallel to the plane of Fig. 2. In the cubic case this is a diagonal plane, the (111) plane. It is emphasized that the evidence for this face being prominent is conclusive, being based on a study of the intensity of reflection of x-rays from specimens of the powder packed in flat samples [MANSON, 1955b] and also settled on flat glass plates. The 94 per cent cubic AgI sample was called Sample B.

The samples were placed in polyethylene bottles fitted with nozzles. The bottles were shaken sideways and then squeezed to eject the fine airborne fraction. Both samples A and B yielded a cloud of nuclei of around four microns diameter, with a range from one to ten microns diameter, as observed by impaction on a greased slide.

The cold-chamber unit used to test these particles is shown in Fig. 3. The temperature indicated by the thermometer on the bottom of the chamber was about 3°C lower than that indicated by the thermometer suspended one-third of the way up the chamber.

Ice formation was usually confined to that part of the cloud between these two thermo-meters. Moist nitrogen was circulated at 5–10 liters per minute.

In the range between —9°C and —11°C both Samples A and B gave positive results. By this is meant that brightly scintillating particles could be observed in the cloud some seconds after introduction of one squeeze of aerosol. Approximately equal numbers of ice particles were observed in each case. In the range between —7°C and —10°C Sample A gave marginal positive results, and Sample B gave negative results. (During a recent trip through Europe, Mr. Birstein of the Geophysics Research Directorate, discovered that Professor Sanger, of the Eidgenossiche Gesellschaft fur Hagelbekampfung in

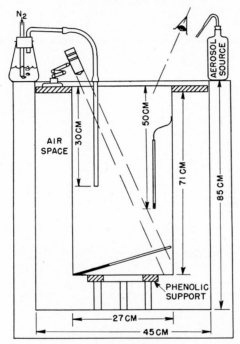

Fig. 3—The cold chamber

Zurich, had obtained this result also, concluding that there was no difference in the nucleating ability of hexagonal and cubic AgI [Pruppacher and Sanger, 1955].)

One interpretation of these results is that nucleation occurs on the hexagonal (0001) base plane, or on the cubic (111) diagonal plane, parallel to the layer drawn in Fig. 2. Another interpretation is that crystal structure has little to do with the activity of AgI, and any well-prepared aerosol of this chemical substance will cause nucleation.

Calcium carbonate experiments—(It is a pleasure to acknowledge Dr. Machta of the U.S. Weather Bureau as the source of the suggestion that the nucleating effective-ness of calcite be tested.) $CaCO_3$ exists at ordinary temperatures and pressures in three modifications, listed in order of increasing stability as: μ (vaterite), λ (aragonite), and β (calcite). Both vaterite and calcite belong to the hexagonal system, whereas aragonite is orthorhombic. Vaterite exists only as thin hexagonal plates or lens-shaped particles

[JOHNSTON, MERWIN, and WILLIAMSON, 1916; GIBSON, WYCKOFF, and MERWIN, 1925], or aggregates of these. The range of conditions under which this modification is precipitated is so narrow that apparently only these two habits exist. This is fortunate for the present purposes, since the small particle size made direct observation of the habit in the

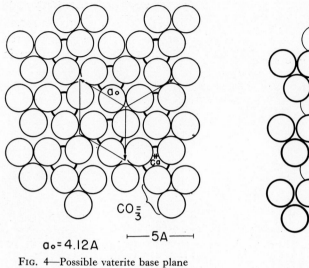

$a_0 = 4.12A$ ⊢——5A——⊣

FIG. 4—Possible vaterite base plane

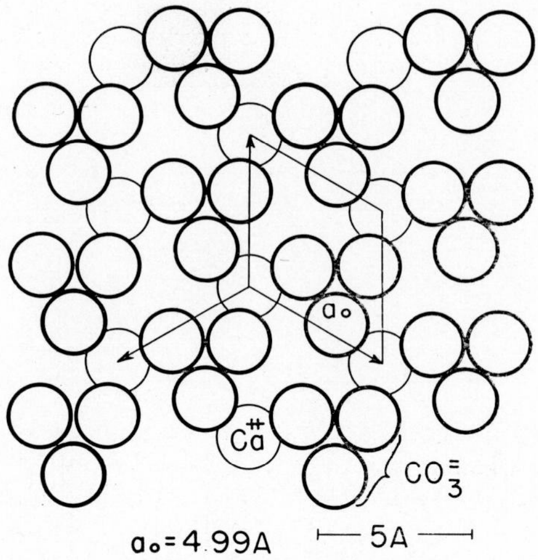

$a_0 = 4.99A$ ⊢——5A——⊣

FIG. 5—Calcite base plane

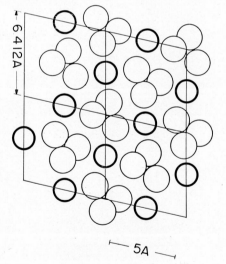

FIG. 6—Calcite cleavage face

electron microscope impossible. In the case of vaterite, therefore, the existence of well-developed hexagonal base plane faces was assumed. OLSHAUSEN [1925] suggested that the calcium and carbonate ions in vaterite occupy the positions of zinc and oxygen in the zincite structure. A plane of this structure is shown in Fig. 4. Unfortunately, this structure leads to very poor agreement between calculated and observed x-ray powder pattern intensities. However, the true structure must contain planes of this spacing, which is seen to differ from that of ice by nine per cent.

The structure of calcite is very well known [WYCKOFF, 1948]. The base plane of calcite is shown in Fig. 5. However, this plane is seldom well developed. The plane which is usually developed, and by which cleaved Iceland Spar is easily recognized, is shown in Fig. 6. A complete lack of hexagonal symmetry is noted. Planes with this atomic arrangement form the faces of the calcite cleavage rhombohedron. In order to run an experiment complementary to the AgI experiment, in which two modifications had an identical face prominently developed, the aerosol of calcite should be prepared with this cleavage face well developed. If possible, no other faces should be developed. In this case, a direct comparison of the nucleating ability of vaterite particles with that of calcite particles would indicate if it is necessary to have a well-developed face with hexagonal symmetry in order to cause ice nucleation.

The source of vaterite for this work was a five-pound bottle of Eimer and Amend calcium carbonate, C.P., precipitated, low in alkalies and heavy metals. This substance proved to be mostly vaterite in a very finely divided state, with perhaps 25 per cent calcite as a coarser fraction. The vaterite was separated by elutriation very effectively in the squeeze bottle nuclei source, and from electron microscope photographs and x-ray line broadening proved to be made up of agglomerates of particles of about 0·08 micron diameter.

When the $CaCO_3$, C.P., was wetted with distilled water and dried at 95°C, it transformed entirely to calcite. The resulting powder yielded a very dense aerosol by the squeeze-bottle technique, and this aerosol was also found to be pure calcite. The electron microscope revealed perfect cleavage rhombohedra in this case, with average linear dimension of about 0·8 microns. Very sharp x-ray lines also indicated this increase in particle size. Although these particles were ten times as large as the vaterite particles, it should be noted that the aerosols were of similar number concentration, and the vaterite particles were largely agglomerated. The calcite rhombohedra were not agglomerated significantly. In any case, the Stokes' fall velocity of a 0·8 micron sphere of calcite in air at −20°C is 0·006 cm/sec. This will not allow fall-out during experimental intervals, which are of the order of ten seconds.

The experimental test was therefore very straightforward, using the cold chamber illustrated in Fig. 3. Vaterite proved very effective at −20°C, causing a dense shower of ice particles in the lower third of the chamber. Marginal results were obtained in the range of −13 to −15°C. Calcite proved ineffective as low as −25°C.

These results were checked in BIRSTEIN's [1955] apparatus. This apparatus provided closer control of the temperature and more complete observation of the cloud. The results were the same. Vaterite had a critical temperature of nucleating ability at about −14°C. Calcite did not cause ice formation in any of the clouds seeded, in this case as low as −20°C. In the tests in Birstein's apparatus the calcite was injected first; the cloud was observed for ten seconds; then the vaterite was injected, and the cloud immediately became full of ice crystals. This consecutive type of test indicates that the first seeding could not have produced a prismatic ice cloud which might escape detection, since then there would be no tendency for the water vapor to deposit on new nuclei. The vapor would be in equilibrium with the ice surfaces. This argument applies only for Birstein's smaller chamber, since in this the entire cloud is seen to transform into ice. In the larger chamber only the lower, colder section turns wholly to an ice cloud.

One further experiment was run with $CaCO_3$. A specimen of Pacific coral, *Pocillopora damicornis* (L.), was ground to a very fine powder. This proved to be the third modification of $CaCO_3$, aragonite. An aerosol consisting of these particles was not effective in causing transformation of a supercooled cloud at $-20°C$; whereas, immediate subsequent introduction of vaterite caused ice formation.

Summary—Both cubic and hexagonal AgI have been shown to be effective as seeding agents for supercooled water clouds. Since the only crystal plane common to both these structures is the basal hexagonal plane of Fig. 2 and this plane is a well-developed face for both samples, the conclusion is drawn that either nucleation occurs on this face or the crystal structure is not the controlling factor in the success of AgI as a nucleating agent.

The complementary experiment of two seeding agents of identical chemical characteristics, but with faces of differing structure, was performed using $CaCO_3$. The vaterite modification, very probably with well-developed basal hexagonal plane faces, was an effective nucleating agent. Calcite, having only rhombohedral faces with no hexagonal structure, was ineffective as a nucleating agent.

The conclusion is that the structure of the faces exposed to the supercooled cloud is very important in determining the effectiveness of a nucleating agent. It can be further stated that the mechanism of nucleation by AgI probably involves growth starting on the hexagonal (0001) face or the cubic (111) face.

Acknowledgments—It is a pleasure to thank Charles E. Anderson, Chief of the Cloud Physics Section, for his encouragement in this work, and for allowing the use of his cold-chamber unit at the cost of a delay in his own work. Mr. Birstein is to be thanked for the use of his cold chamber and cryostat, and Sally Naumann for her aid in operating this unit and for taking the electron microscope photographs.

REFERENCES

BERNAL, J. D. and R. H. FOWLER, A theory of water and ionic solution, with particular reference to hydrogen and hydroxyl ions, *J. Chem. Phys.*, v.1, pp.515–548, 1933.

BIRSTEIN, S. J. and C. E. ANDERSON, The mechanism of atmospheric ice formation, I: The chemical composition of nucleating agents, *J. Met.*, v.12, pp.68–73, 1955.

EVANS, R. C., *An Introduction to Crystal Chemistry*, University Press, Cambridge, England, chap.10, pp.285–309, 1948.

GIBSON, R. E., R. W. G. WYCKOFF, and H. E. MERWIN, Vaterite and μ-CaCO$_3$, *Amer. J. Sci.*, 5th ser., v.10, pp.325–333, 1925.

JOHNSTON, J., H. E. MERWIN, and E. D. WILLIAMSON, The several forms of calcium carbonate, *Amer. J. Sci.*, 4th ser., v.41, pp.473–512, 1916.

KOLKMEIJER, N. H. and J. W. A. VAN HENGEL, Cubic and hexagonal silver iodide, *Zs. Krist.*, v.88, pp.317–322, 1934.

MANSON, J. E., X-ray diffraction study of silver iodide aerosols, *J. Appl. Phys.*, v.26, pp.423–425, 1955a.

MANSON, J. E., Preferred orientation of platelets, in X-ray diffractometer powder samples, *J. Appl. Phys.*, v.26, pp.1254–1256, 1955b.

McDONALD, J. E., Homogeneous nucleation of supercooled water drops, *J. Met.*, v.10, pp.416–433, 1953.

OLSHAUSEN, S., Structure investigations by the Debye-Scherrer (powder) method, *Zs. Krist.*, v.61, pp.463–514, 1925.

PAULING, L., The structure and entropy of ice and of other crystals with some randomness of atomic arrangement, *J. Amer. Chem. Soc.*, v.57, pp.2680–2684, 1935.

PRUPPACHER, H. R. and R. SÄNGER, Mechanismus der Vereisung unterkühlter Wassertropfen durch disperse Keimsubstanzen, I, *Zs. angw. math. Phys.*, v.6, pp.407–416, 1955.

RUNDLE, R. E., The structure and residual entropy of ice, *J. Chem. Phys.*, v.21, p.1311, 1953.

VONNEGUT, B., The nucleation of ice formation by silver iodide, *J. Appl. Phys.*, v.18, pp.593–595, 1947.

DISCUSSION

Dr. David Turnbull—Did you say that silver iodide nucleates at ten degrees? Is that because the particles are very small, and thus are not effective at minus three?

Mr. James E. Manson—In the work that I did, the two crystal forms of silver iodide produced nucleation at $-10°C$. Neither would work at a warmer temperature.

Mr. S. J. Birstein—I think it is a well-known fact that the nucleating temperature depends on particle size. We have found this for lead iodide. Saltzberg, in our laboratory, did it for silver iodide and in Hosler's paper the effect of temperature is also discussed.

I believe that Manson's particles were rather small and that is why he got ice crystal formation at $-10°C$ instead of -4, -6, or $-8°C$.

Mr. Manson—On this particular experiment the particles ranged from one to ten microns. They were produced by grinding and were not formed by a smoke generator. They might fall out more rapidly than the ice can develop to observable size at the warmer temperatures.

Dr. Helmut Weickmann—In the early work of Vonnegut and of you, Dr. Schaefer, you tried to get results with ground silver iodide and lead iodide, and it didn't work. It only works if the iodide crystals are produced by condensation or sublimation.

This nucleating effect depends on the cleanliness of the surface. The surface soon gets saturated with foreign molecules, ions, and other particles which are absorbed and loses its nucleating effectiveness.

Mr. Manson—Well, I think that the surfaces of a ground sample are probably as clean as those made from an acetone mixture.

Dr. Weickmann—But why then did the first experimenters find different effectiveness for samples made by grinding and by vaporizing?

Mr. Manson—Wasn't it earlier reported that chemically precipitated silver iodide did not work at all?

Mr. Birstein—Well, I question this. I was in Switzerland this summer, and Professor Sänger was studying the nucleation properties of a number of chemical. (Work since published; see Manson's References, PRUPPACHER and SÄNGER [1955]). All of their chemicals were ground and introduced into the cloud with a polyethylene bottle. They found silver iodide was effective at minus four or five, in spite of grinding.

Mr. Manson—Well, yes, it was relatively freshly ground. In my work there was no noticeable difference several weeks after grinding.

Dr. Vincent J. Schaefer—I think the point Weickmann is bringing up is that it would work at the warmer temperature immediately after grinding.

Mr. Manson—I think the cleanliness of the surface is more a matter of micro-seconds instead of several days after grinding.

Dr. David Atlas—Is there some greater significance of these observations which you have not mentioned?

Mr. Manson—You mean the work with calcite which was suggested by the Weather Bureau since the composition of Pacific coral atolls is mostly calcium carbonate. This was the instigation of the work on calcium carbonate.

However, the results indicate that vaterite was the only active modification of calcium carbonate and this is an unstable modification which was not found in five samples of Pacific coral which were tested.

Dr. Raymond Wexler—The activity of silver iodide as a freezing nucleus increases as the temperature decreases. Was there any attempt to measure the concentrations at different temperatures in your experiment? Now, I wonder if you measured the concentration at different temperatures, at say below minus ten.

Mr. Manson—In my observations, I was not concerned with this problem. The main point I am making is that I found no difference in the activity of the two modifications of silver iodide. The reason that I used this rather impure hexagonal modification was because it was ground to the same particle size range as the cubic. Before grinding, the hexagonal sample should contain 90 per cent of the hexagonal form. In grinding, it transforms partly into cubic.

I wonder if I could ask a question of Dr. Turnbull. I thought that the prism faces would become active, because of the effect of grinding, which causes partial transformation of either modification. During grinding the base plane may slip and form steps on the prism faces. I wondered if crystal growth is initiated on the steps.

Dr. Turnbull—I am convinced that the crystallization from the melt does require, in many instances, steps which would be an important consideration in the function of silver iodide.

Dr. Weickmann—But, I think it is justifiable to look for substances other than silver iodide because in the basic theory three dimensional similarity is not essential but two dimensional similarity is. So you may have a cubic crystal with no similarity at all with the hexagonal structure of ice and still similarity in one plane is sufficient that the water deposits in the ice crystal structure.

Mr. Manson—Well, that is the thesis of my paper.

Dr. G. A. Wolff—It may well be that, after grinding, there is still some of the vaterite left unconverted and is active as a nucleus. I feel that it will make very little difference, whether or not the resulting vaterite calcite mixtures contain either a small or a large percentage of vaterite since just the presence of very small amounts of active nuclei is sufficient, as has been shown by Tamman and others. Furthermore, there might be seeding action due to the presence of active intermediate states created by grinding. This means that grinding of the vaterite produces, possibly, a frozen-in-varite-calcite transition state which could act as nucleus. I mention the Hedvall effect as an analogy. This effect can be described as the increase in activity and reactivity of a substance, while undergoing a transformation of modification or condition. It would be worthwhile to test the nucleation activity of such an intermediate crystal state.

Mr. Manson—The vaterite wasn't ground and I couldn't get any information from the producers as to how it was made. This sample was taken directly out of a bottle of C.P. calcium carbonate, and the particles were about 800 A across. They gave double the width of diffraction lines than the calcite particles did.

These vaterite particles weren't treated any further and they might have contained some wetting or emulsifying agent. The particles caused the nucleation of the clouds which would indicate the surfaces were clean enough to be active.

(*Added in proof*) Dr. Wolff's remarks appear to me to be a valid criticism of the silver iodide work, where it is true that neither test sample was completely free of the alternative modification. On the other hand, they lend weight to the finding that calcite was not effective as an ice nucleus, even when formed by heavy grinding of cleavable Iceland spar.

THE EFFECT OF CONDENSATION NUCLEUS SIZE AND TYPE ON THE TEMPERATURE OF ICE CRYSTAL FORMATION IN CLOUDS

C. L. HOSLER AND G. R. SPALDING

Pennsylvania State University, University Park, Pa.

Abstract—Eight compounds have been used to determine the role that the size and composition of the nuclei play in regulating the temperature at which ice crystals form in a cloud produced in an expansion chamber. Helium, nitrogen, and air were used as carrier gases. Insoluble nuclei all show an increase in freezing temperature with increased nucleus size. Soluble nuclei show a more complex relationship based on the concentration of the solution formed. The meaning of the results is discussed.

A NUMBER of substances have been tested by cloud physicists to determine their effectiveness in initiating the ice phase in clouds. The substances used in this study were chosen partly because work had been done on them by other investigators, partly because they had been used in earlier experiments by the authors. These earlier experiments involved the testing of aqueous solutions of some of these same compounds to determine their influence upon the freezing temperature of water in capillaries and in droplets on a surface [HOSLER, 1954; HOSLER and HOSLER, 1955; HOSLER and SPALDING, 1955]. The cloud chamber employed has been described previously [HOSLER, 1954]. Briefly, a tubular expansion-type cloud chamber was used to create the cloud. Light transmission through the cloud was recorded and the presence of ice was detected by the character of these records of the light transmission. Water clouds dissipated rapidly due to the vapor-pressure gradient produced by the presence of ice on the chamber walls. Ice clouds persisted for some time, creating a distinctively different graph of light transmission plotted against time. Air, nitrogen, and helium were used as carrier gases. Before nuclei were introduced into the chamber, the gas was tested for freedom from nuclei by cooling by expansion. Aerosols were introduced into the nuclei-free carrier gas by vaporization from an electrically-heated platinum foil and in one case by atomizing an aqueous solution. Control over nucleus size was maintained by regulating the rate of vaporization. Vaporization temperatures were maintained low enough to minimize dissociation or decomposition. Sampling of nuclei was accomplished by a thermal precipitator and electron photomicrography provided a means of measurement of particle size and shape. Electron diffraction patterns were taken to verify the nature of the nuclei themselves and spectrographic analysis was carried out on the compounds used to generate nuclei.

Table 1 shows the results of some of these experiments. The lower limit of nucleus size was less than 0·01 microns. The number of nuclei present was two or more orders of magnitude larger than required to accommodate all of the excess water vapor so that the numbers could vary greatly and the fog intensity and drop size distribution would remain constant. It was simpler to insure an over-abundance of all nuclei than to maintain the number constant at a smaller number.

Table 1. *Temperature at which ice formed as a function of size and type of condensation nucleus*

Nucleus	Size range largest 10 per cent	Temperature at which ice was detected
	micron	$-°C$
AgI	0·011–0·070	11·6
	0·040–0·120	9·1
	0·060–0·140	7·0
PbI_2	0·032–0·130	18·2
	0·052–0·220	14·7
	0·085–0·425	8·0
CuI	0·049–0·135	23·1
	0·089–0·270	18·4
	0·109–0·480	15·9
KI	0·106–0·175	26·5
	0·126–0·260	22·9
NH_4I	0·197–0·500	23·3
	0·312–0·600	25·1
NaCl	0·105–0·215	31·8
	0·300–0·400	31·0
TlI	0·030–0·155	33·2
	0·076–0·185	29·5
	0·093–0·210	27·2
$PbCl_2$	0·021–0·135	33·5
	0·052–0·300	29·2
	0·071–0·500	21·8

A good index of the varying nucleus population for the purpose of this study was the size range of the largest ten per cent of the nuclei. This size range appears in Table 1. The data for Table 1 were obtained using air as a carrier gas. These same chemicals tested in nitrogen and helium yielded comparable results when the size distributions were as indicated in Table 1, and the separate data are not reproduced here. It can be seen that within the size ranges tested, all agents except NH_4I give higher freezing temperatures with increased nuclei size.

In order to explain the reason for this behavior, one would have to know something about the properties of such small particles in water at temperatures below 0°C. The solubility of none of these materials is known for temperatures below 0°C even in bulk quantities. The added difficulty of their small size makes their behavior under these conditions even more vague. By making some simple calculations based on solubility at 0°C as determined for bulk quantities we have a basis for speculation as to what might happen to the various nuclei types and sizes. The volume of the water droplets formed in the cloud chamber was computed from drop-diameter measurements made at a temperature one centigrade degree higher than the temperature at which a given aerosol produced ice. Using this information together with the aerosol size measurements, the several combinations of drops and nuclei can be used to compute the concentrations of the aqueous solutions that might be produced should the nuclei dissolve. Table 2 gives possible molar concentrations for, large drops and large nuclei, large nuclei and mean drops, and small nuclei and mean drops and in the last column the molar concentration of a solution saturated at 0°C.

Table 2. Possible concentrations in cloud droplets

Nucleus	Concentration in moles per liter $\times 10^5$			
	Largest drops nuclei	Largest nuclei mean drops	Smallest nuclei mean drops	Saturated solution at °C
AgI	0·6	1·8	0·007	0·001
	2·0	7·6	0·3	
	2·1	9·8	0·8	
PbI$_2$	2·2	10·1	0·2	95·0
	6·3	37·4	0·5	
	31·5	145·0	1·2	
CuI	8·5	56·6	2·7	4·2
	51·1	286·0	10·2	
	221·0	1350·0	15·8	
KI	31·5	333·0	73·8	767,000
	93·6	780·0	89·4	
NH$_4$I	1050·0	8,470·0	517·0	1,060,000
	1810·0	16,600·0	2330·0	
NaCl	502·0	2,190·0	255·0	610,000
	3220·0	13,200·0	5560·0	
TlI	8·0	102·0	0·7	19·3
	13·6	126·0	8·8	
	123·0	1000·0	12·7	
PbCl$_2$	7·6	100·0	0·4	2500
	61·1	770·0	4·0	
	213·0	1650·0	4·7	

From Table 2 it would appear unlikely that the larger AgI crystals could dissolve completely and that therefore all droplets would contain saturated solutions if indeed the AgI dissolves at all. There seems to be little question that a solid nucleus is present to influence the freezing point. CuI and TlI are also likely to be present as solids. In the case of several of the other salts, it is apparent that they would be totally dissolved if their solubilities are of the same order of magnitude as at 0°C, and if their rates of solution are such as to permit them to be completely dissolved during the lifetime of a droplet. If these salts are totally dissolved, then the mechanism of ice nucleation may be quite different than in the case of AgI and may be the same as for the dilute solutions reported in the three references previously cited.

If so, then the critical factor is not the size of the solid nucleus itself but the concentration of the resulting solution which is of course a function of size of both nucleus and droplet. It has been demonstrated [HOSLER, 1954; HOSLER and SPALDING, 1955] that for the salts $PbCl_2$ or NH_4I, very dilute solutions raised the freezing temperature of droplets by increasing amounts, as the concentration of the solution was increased. This was true up to a point beyond which, if the concentration was further increased, the freezing point was again lowered. Referring to Table 1 then, we see that for $PbCl_2$, as the size of the nuclei increased and the molarity of the possible solution increased, the freezing temperature was raised. Note that the molarity of the solution computed for the largest drops and the largest nuclei (and giving the highest freezing point) is close to the molarity of the solution found to give the maximum raising of the freezing temperature for water in capillaries and in droplets (10^{-3} molar). For NH_4I, the small increase in the nucleus size that was produced, failed to raise the freezing temperature. In fact, it seemed to lower it. Again, data from capillary and droplet experiments showed why this might be expected. The increase in molarity produced a concentration close to that for which a depression of the freezing point was noted in captive droplet experimentation (10^{-2} to 10^{-1} molar). It was not possible to further decrease the nucleus size by vaporization. In order to determine whether a higher freezing temperature might be obtained, smaller nuclei were produced by spraying a fine mist of NH_4I solution to produce nuclei. When this was done and droplets of optimum solution concentration were produced, abundant ice occurred at a temperature of $-15°C$ in contrast to the $-23°C$ required to produce ice when the salt was vaporized. This difference may have been due to the more nearly optimum concentration of NH_4I. The different mode of dispersal, unfortunately, renders the data incomparable.

The inference from this work might be that there are two distinct mechanisms that can be invoked to increase the temperature at which the ice phase appears in clouds, both of which are affected by the size of the nuclei introduced. First, is the well-known effect of silver iodide which in all likelihood acts as a true freezing nucleus, by providing a structure upon which ice can build. VONNEGUT [1949], in addition to being the first to note this, also noted the effect of the size on the efficiency of silver iodide as a nucleus [VONNEGUT, 1948, p.27]. Vonnegut found that AgI particles one micron in diameter initiated ice formation at $-4°C$ and particles 0.01 microns in diameter required a temperature of $-8°C$ to produce ice. The data for AgI in Table 1 give freezing temperature changes of about the same magnitude. BAYARDELLE [1955] also demonstrated the effect of AgI nucleus size on the freezing temperature of water. In this case, AgI particles were suspended in water contained in a silicone-coated glass tube. Table 3 gives a summary of the results of Bayardelle. Note that the dimensions given are the size of the holes in a filter through which the nuclei passed and not necessarily the nucleus size.

The quantitative agreement of these data with the two sets of cloud-chamber observations is poor; however, the same qualitative results were obtained by varying nucleus size in all cases. In the case of solid nuclei the importance of size may stem from energy considerations due to the relatively small amount of new surface that must build up in the case of the larger nuclei. The probability of the existence of suitable surface features would also be a function of nucleus size.

A second group of agents possess the ability, when present as ions in solution, to neutralize the effect of water droplet size in depressing the freezing point and hence can

Table 3. Results of Bayardelle

Filter size	Mean temperature of ice formation
micron	°C
2000	−2·0
65	−3·9
30	−6·7
10	−9·1
0·025	−13·2

lead to a higher nucleation temperature. The concentration of these salts in solution is critical and hence the size of the nucleus determines the temperature of ice formation. The nature of the role these ions play is a very difficult one to understand. If we first answer the question, why do smaller droplets freeze at lower temperatures than large droplets, then we are in a position to investigate the manner in which ions in solution alter the pattern. A great amount of experimental work shows that the radius of the water droplet is the parameter that influences the freezing temperature and the smaller the radius, the lower is the freezing temperature. Volume and surface areas are not critical except inasmuch as they effect the distance from the interior of the water to the surface [HOSLER and HOSLER, 1955; HOSLER and SPALDING, 1955]. It appears to be some property of the water surface or interface which depresses the temperature of nucleation by an amount proportional to the distance from the interior or the center, to the surface. Foreign ions may either alter the surface or the ability of the surface to depress the nucleation temperature. Such an hypothesis would require that surface forces or orientation of the molecules in a water droplet be effective over distances of at least several microns. This is contrary to orthodox thinking; however, any orientation in the surface would decrease with distance and approach zero asymtotically and we are not prepared to state at what distance such an orientation would cease to exert an influence upon the probability that the structure of water at −30°C would assume that of ice. Experiments show that droplets whose radii are less than 50 microns exhibit the property of undergoing amounts of supercooling proportional to some negative power of the radius. This would suggest the order of magnitude of the distances involved.

The practical value of knowledge of the effect of size and type of condensation nuclei on the temperature of ice-crystal formation would be greatest in the field of cloud seeding. If the artificial initiation of the Bergeron-Findeisen process in clouds should be demonstrated to appreciably alter the amount of precipitation from a cloud, then the production of ice at the proper level within the cloud would seem to be very important.

REFERENCES

BAYARDELLE, M., Influence des Dimensions des noyaux de congelation sur la temperature de congelation de l'eau, C.-R., v.241 (2), pp.232–233, 1955.

HOSLER, CHARLES L., Factors governing the temperature of ice-crystal formation in clouds, Proc. Toronto Met. Conf., 1953, R. Met. Soc., pp.253–261, 1954.

HOSLER, CHARLES L., and ROBERT C. HOSLER, An investigation of the freezing of water in capillaries, Trans. Amer. Geophys. Union, v.36, pp.126–132, 1955.

HOSLER, CHARLES L. and G. ROBERT SPALDING, An experimental study of the effects of aerosols of a number of pure chemicals on the freezing characteristics of supercooled liquid droplets, Final Rep. Contract AF19(604)–140, 79pp., 1955.

VONNEGUT, B., Project Cirrus Final Report, RL.140, Schenectady, N.Y., 1948.

VONNEGUT, B., Nucleation of supercooled water clouds by silver iodide smokes, *Chem. Rev.*, v.44, pp.277–290, 1949.

DISCUSSION

Mr. S. J. Birstein—We have done some of that work and somehow have never gotten around to publishing, except on the sea-salt nuclei produced on a hot wire. We also used the upper ten per cent of the size distribution. Now the lead iodide is the one thing we have worked on more carefully and we found the following.

All particles that we could produce below a certain particle size nucleated at $-13°C$. Above another particle size, $-7°C$ was our limiting temperature. Between these two sizes, nucleating temperature was a function of particle size. We could not get ice crystals at above -6 or $-7°C$, no matter how much we increased the size. That is an interesting point which I thought I might present here.

With lead chloride, which we found decomposes quite readily, I wonder whether you could not have had decomposition taking place when you worked with larger particles.

Prof. Charles L. Hosler—This is always a problem when we vaporize these aerosols. I didn't mention it, but we did run these in helium, nitrogen, and air. The results given are those in ordinary air; I didn't present the others, because they are not much different.

Mr. Birstein—Did you do work on all of these particle sizes in nitrogen and helium also?

Prof. Hosler—Yes. The only effect of the helium was that the thermodynamic properties affected particle sizes. With the helium, I think, we got smaller sizes.

Mr. Birstein—Were you able to measure the decomposition of these? When we used ammonium iodide, prepared from melting on platinum foil, no matter what we did, it decomposed.

Prof. Hosler—We experienced that too.

Mr. Birstein—Those are the things I didn't mention because we had a chamber full of iodine when we got through.

Prof. Hosler—That is why we resorted to the spray.

Dr. Raymond Wexler—Those are diameters in microns?

Prof. Hosler—Yes, in the case of Bayardelle, it is the filter size.

Dr. Wexler—You don't compare the diameters of the particles in the two experiments?

Prof. Hosler—No. In all cases, the particles used in the French experiment were smaller than this. Otherwise, they wouldn't have passed through the filter.

Dr. Helmut Weickmann—I'd like to make one remark on the work of Bayardelle and your work, because a large discrepancy seems to exist between a paper I wrote and her results as they were referred here. The thing I want to point out is the following: If you have water, supercooled to about $-3·9°C$, and an ice seed which has a diameter of about 41 A is introduced into this water, then this ice seed should create nucleation of the water. Now, according to the lattice structure of silver iodide it can orient water molecules in the right structure over an area as large as 41 A. This would mean that we would have to have a silver iodide nucleus only as large as 41 A; but as these data show, that is 65 microns. This is 10,000 times larger than would be required.

I would also like to draw attention to a paper of Volmer. He once was concerned with the same discrepancy, during experiments with salt, or something like that, and found that a certain nucleus has a probability of 10^4 possible nucleating places, but only about one place is really active and this may be the solution to the discrepancy.

Here in this nucleus, you have probably many more than 10^4 sites; but active nucleating sites are only one out of 10^4, or maybe one out of 10^6. Is this correct?

Dr. David Turnbull—I agree generally with Dr. Weickmann that the dependence of undercooling on the size of silver iodide particles apparently can't be accounted for on the assumption that an AgI particle is as effective as an ice nucleus of the same size. However I estimate the diameter of an ice nucleus to be about 200 A at $4°$ undercooling.

Prof. Hosler—I want to make one further comment. If someone at some time, demonstrates that the Bergeron and Findeisen mechanism is an important factor in controlling precipitation artificially, then I think those data would become of importance to those interested in seeding clouds; inasmuch as the size they get out of the generators and the height the certain sizes reach might be critical; and also a number of different compounds might be used because it might be disadvantageous to freeze a cloud at the warmest possible temperature. There may be some optimum thickness you'd like to have below the level of ice crystal formation before you initiate the ice phase.

STUDIES ON THE EFFECTS OF CERTAIN CHEMICALS ON THE INHIBITION OF NUCLEATION

S. J. BIRSTEIN

Geophysics Research Directorate, Air Force Cambridge Research Center, Bedford, Mass.

Abstract—Studies have been made in the laboratory and in the field on the use of certain chemicals to inhibit nucleation. It has been found that chemicals of the type that form co-ordination complexes with heavy metals are the most effective in inhibiting ice crystal formation. Methyl amine and ethyl amine, the compounds investigated most thoroughly, both inhibit silver iodide nucleation below −40°C, the temperature of 'spontaneous' nucleation. These two agents appear equally effective on natural type ice nuclei. The results of the 'poisoning' studies are analyzed to gain an insight into the mechanism of the reaction, and it is concluded that specific surface compounds are formed on the nucleating agents and, as the nucleating surface is altered, ice-forming ability is diminished.

Introduction—Studies have been carried out in our laboratory on the effect of certain 'poisons' on the inhibition of nucleation. Because it was found that as a silver iodide surface is reduced by photolysis [INN, 1951], its nucleating effectiveness is diminished, it was decided to try other means of altering particle surfaces and then measuring nucleating effectiveness. VONNEGUT [1948] found that certain substances, alcohols for instance, are effective in inhibiting nucleation.

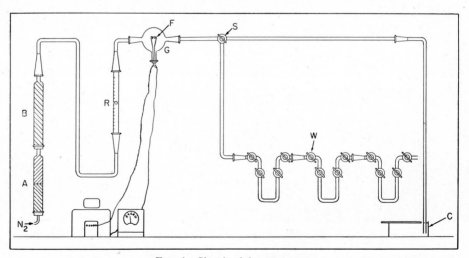

FIG. 1—Sketch of the apparatus

Experimental—The apparatus used in these experiments, Fig. 1, consisted of a hot-wire nuclei generator [BIRSTEIN and ANDERSON, 1955] in which the nitrogen flow and filament current were carefully controlled to assure reproducibility of results. For inhibition experiments the nuclei were passed over the vapor of the poison in saturator W, thermostatted to control the partial pressure of the vapor. The poisoned nuclei were then passed into collector C or directly into the supercooled cloud. As a control, nuclei were periodically diverted from the saturator through three-way stopcocks, and their efficiency checked. Frequent electron-microscope examinations were also made of the nuclei.

Discussion—The first experiments were run on the effect of ammonia on nucleation from supercooled clouds by silver iodide and lead iodide. Silver iodide nuclei were produced in the nuclei generator and passed through the saturator filled with ammonia. The temperature of the ammonia in the saturator and, therefore, its vapor pressure could be varied. Starting with a vapor pressure of 100 microns, the temperature in the saturator was gradually raised; for each temperature increment, a sample of the nuclei which had passed through the saturator was tested for nucleating ability in a supercooled cloud at −20°C. On silver iodide nuclei, nucleating effectiveness gradually fell off until at a partial pressure of seven mm of ammonia, these nuclei were no longer effective.

Lead iodide nuclei were next run through the ammonia-filled saturator and the partial pressure of ammonia was varied. The ammonia seemed even more effective on the lead iodide than the silver iodide and lead iodide nucleation was completely inhibited at an ammonia partial pressure of five mm or higher.

The above experiments were then repeated for sec-butyl amine. On silver iodide nuclei, nucleation was inhibited when the partial pressure of the amine was approximately one mm; on the lead iodide, the sec-butyl amine appeared equally effective in inhibiting nucleation. No ice particles were seen when the nuclei were passed through the saturator in which the amine was thermostatted to maintain a vapor pressure higher than one mm.

Tests were run again using clean-surfaced nuclei as a control and the output of the saturator was monitored by catching the nuclei in the thermal precipitator for electron microscope studies. In all cases, the nuclei output was found to be sufficient to cause ice formation, if active.

Ethanol, which was previously reported to be effective [VONNEGUT, 1948], was found partially effective in inhibiting ice formation, and only at much higher partial pressures than either ammonia or sec-butyl amine. This compound can therefore be classed as ineffective for all practical purposes when pre-adsorbed on both silver iodide and lead iodide. Propylene glycol, contrary to previous reports, was found ineffective.

Other compounds were also tested to check their ability to inhibit ice crystal formation from supercooled clouds at −20°C. These compounds were isobutane, diethyl ether, n-heptane, bromobenzene, and ethylene glycol. None of these compounds appeared effective in inhibiting ice formation.

Because the two best compounds for the nucleation inhibition were found to be ammonia and sec-butyl amine, we decided to study the amines further as nuclei 'poisons'. To be an effective poison, a substance should be fairly volatile and have an appreciable vapor pressure at the temperatures under consideration. It should not condense at the temperature of the supercooled cloud being used. Since the reaction of ammonia and amines with heavy metals appears to be one of co-ordination complex formation, our substance should also form strong co-ordination complexes with the heavy metals.

The two materials which appeared best suited for study as nuclei poisons on the

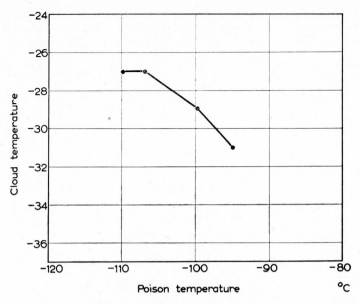

FIG. 2—Inhibition of lead iodide nucleation by methyl amine

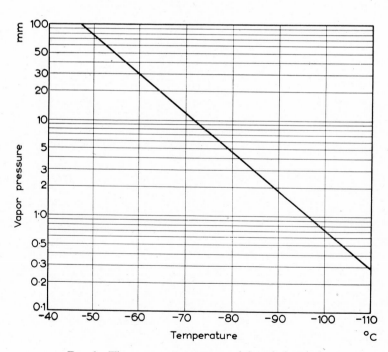

FIG. 3—The vapor pressure curve (of methyl amine)

basis of the above requirements appeared to be methyl amine and ethyl amine, and the investigation of the effect of methyl amine and ethyl amine on the inhibition of nucleation by silver iodide and lead iodide was thus begun. The effect of the two amines on lead iodide nucleation has been studied quite thoroughly. The study on the effect of methyl amine and ethyl amine on silver iodide nucleation has not yet been completed.

Fig. 2 illustrates the results obtained for the inhibition of lead iodide nucleation by methyl amine. If the methyl amine in the saturator is held at a temperature of −110°C, no ice formation takes place in a supercooled water cloud until the cloud temperature is lowered to −27°C. If the methyl amine saturator is thermostatted at −100°C; no ice-crystal formation is seen in the supercooled cloud until the temperature is lowered to

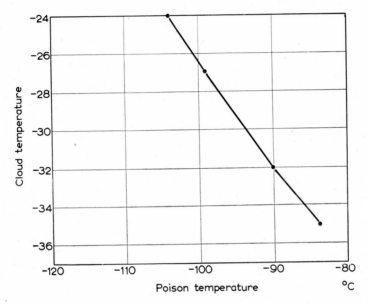

FIG. 4—Results of inhibition of nucleation

−29°C. If the saturator is held at −85°C, one sees no ice crystals forming until a temperature of −31°C is reached. If the methyl amine is warmer than −85°C, no ice crystals can be seen in the supercooled cloud at temperatures as low as −40°C. From an inspection of the vapor pressure curve obtained from values found in the literature (Fig. 3), it can be seen therefore that if the methyl amine is adsorbed on the lead iodide at a vapor pressure of approximately 0·4 mm, this is effective in inhibiting nucleation down to −27°C. If the poison is adsorbed at a pressure of 0·7 mm, the ice-crystal formation is inhibited down to −29°C; with a vapor pressure of one mm of methyl amine, ice-crystal formation is inhibited down to −31°C; and if the vapor pressure of the methyl amine exceeds one mm, no ice-crystal formation can be seen down to the temperature of 'spontaneous nucleation', −40°C.

The results for the inhibition of nucleation on lead iodide by ethyl amine are shown in Fig. 4. Here it is found that if the ethyl-amine saturator is held at −104°C, no ice formation is seen in the water cloud until the temperature is lowered to −24°C; if the amine saturator is kept at −100°C, one must lower the cloud temperature to −27°C before ice formation takes place. If the saturator is held at −90°C, ice formation in the supercooled cloud in the cryostat does not take place until the temperature is lowered to −32°C; when the saturator temperature is held at −84°C, ice-crystal formation does not take place until the temperature in the cloud is −35°C. If the saturator temperature is kept above −84°C, one finds no ice-crystal formation occurring as low as −40°C.

If one inspects the best available vapor-pressure curve for ethyl amine (Fig. 5), again obtained from a number of sources found in the literature, and puts the results obtained

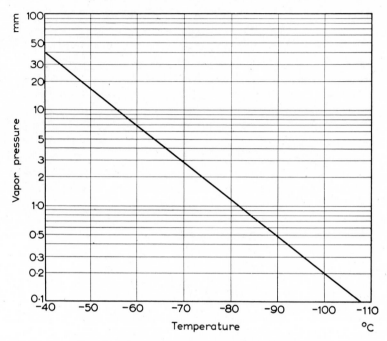

FIG. 5—The vapor pressure curve of ethyl amine

for inhibition in terms of vapor pressure, it is found that if the ethyl amine vapor pressure is approximately 0·14 mm, no ice-crystal formation takes place down to a temperature of −24°C. At an amine vapor pressure of approximately 0·21 mm, no ice crystals are seen in the cloud until the temperature is lowered to −27°C. If the ethyl amine vapor pressure is kept at 0·48 mm, ice-crystal formation is inhibited in the supercooled cloud down to a temperature of −32°C. When the ethyl amine vapor pressure is kept at approximately one mm, no ice crystals are seen down to −35°C, and if the amine vapor pressure is above one mm, no ice crystals can be seen in the supercooled cloud down to −40°C.

In all cases the cloud temperature in the cryostat was measured to a precision of approximately 1°C, and the temperature in the saturator was held within these limits.

Other compounds checked in our apparatus were dimethyl amine and trimethyl amine. These compounds were tested only in supercooled clouds held at −20°C. The amine temperature in the saturator was lowered until lead iodide and silver iodide would just inhibit the nucleation of a supercooled cloud at —20°C. The results shown in Table 1 were obtained.

Table 1. *Results in amine tests*

Amine	Vapor pressure (AgI)	Vapor pressure (PbI$_2$)
	mm	mm
Sec-buty amine	1	1
Dimethyl amine	1	3
Ammonia	7	5
Trimethyl amine	15	40

Because these experiments showed that it was possible to inhibit the crystal formation down to —40°C with partial pressures of ethyl amine and methyl amine of the order of slightly over one mm, we decided to design an experiment to check whether we could inhibit ice-crystal formation below —40°C with slightly higher partial pressures of amine. Since in the experiment run above —40°C, no provision was made for excluding room air, full of atmospheric nuclei, from the cryostat, we finally ran an experiment in which we mixed a stream of nitrogen with a known partial pressure of methyl amine, with another nitrogen stream containing lead iodide nuclei. The amine was introduced into the supercooled cloud together with the nuclei. The cryostat temperature at the start of the experiment was warmer than —40°C, and it was cooled after the amine-nuclei mixture had been introduced. With methyl amine vapor pressures of the order of three mm in the mixed nitrogen stream, we found that it was possible to cool the cryostat below —45°C before ice-crystal formation took place. We did find, however, that if we introduced the amine and nuclei into the chamber simultaneously and then cut off the amine and continued adding lead iodide nuclei, as we increased the nuclei-amine ratio, the temperature at which ice-crystal formation took place was raised. This experiment was then repeated with lead iodide and ethyl amine and essentially the same results were obtained.

Because of the encouraging results on the inhibition of nucleation in the laboratory, we decided that the next logical step was to check the efficiency of nucleation 'poisons' in the atmosphere. In the laboratory, working with known compounds, it is possible to postulate both the mechanism through which ice-crystal formation takes place and the mechanism by which ice-crystal formation is inhibited. In the atmosphere, however, with the great variety of particles of all sizes, shapes, and composition, we know practically nothing concerning which materials are active as ice nuclei and how they act. We felt that if atmospheric ice formation could be inhibited in a manner similar to that employed in the laboratory, a valuable insight would be gained into the entire mechanism of ice-crystal formation in the atmosphere.

The experiments on atmospheric nuclei poisoning were done at the Blue Hill Observatory, where we assumed that we would be less bothered with industrial pollution than in South Boston where we ordinarily work. Runs were made on days when we had a southeast wind. The apparatus consisted of a deep-freeze unit refrigerated with freon 22, in which we placed a black-coated stainless-steel cylinder closed on the bottom; the cylinder measured 11 inches in diameter and 28 inches deep. The can was insulated from the walls and bottom of the unit with bakelite spacers. The interior of the cylinder was viewed through a plexiglass top by means of a beam of parallel light. The temperature in the cold chamber, neglecting the top quarter, could be held to within 1°C. Air was pulled through the chamber by means of a pump located at the outlet line to prevent contamination of the material by the pump. Before making a run, outside air was pulled through the chamber, and it was cooled slowly and the temperature and number of background ice crystals recorded. When the background count has been established, a mixture of air and methyl amine vapor was introduced into the chamber as it was gradually cooled. The vapor pressure of the amine was approximately three mm. Using this apparatus, we were able not only to prevent the crystal formation down to −40°C, but down to −52°C, twelve degrees below the temperature of 'spontaneous nucleation'.

In view of our ability to inhibit ice formation down to −52°C, let us now attempt to explain the mechanism. Many complexes of cobalt, platinum, lead, and silver salts are known, especially with ammonia as the complexing agent. Most of the studies have been with cobalt and platinum halides of the type $MX_n \cdot mNH_3$ where n is the valence of M, the metal and m is almost any integer from one up to the co-ordination number of the metal.

With the silver and lead halides, the number m does not follow this co-ordination number too closely. For instance, BILTZ [1922] gives a series of lead halide-amine complexes and their decomposition points where $P_{NH_3} = 100$ mm. For example

$$PbI_2 \cdot 8NH_3 \qquad T = -51 \cdot 5°C$$
$$PbI_2 \cdot 5NH_3 \qquad T = -3°C$$
$$PbI_2 \cdot 2NH_3 \qquad T = +33°C$$
$$PbI_2 \cdot 1NH_3 \qquad T = +88°C$$
$$PbI_2 \cdot 0 \cdot 5NH_3 \qquad T = 126°C$$

This points up the extreme stability of the amine complexes of the lead salts.

VOSBURGH and McLURE [1943] derive the following constants in water at 25°C

$$\frac{[Ag^+][NH_3]}{[Ag . NH_3^+]} = 4 \cdot 3 \times 10^{-4}$$

$$\frac{[Ag^+][NH_3]^2}{[Ag(NH_3)_2^+]} = 6 \cdot 2 \times 10^{-8}$$

These silver complexes are also quite stable. SIDGEWICK [1950] states: 'The replacement of hydrogen in ammonia by alkyl groups weakens the tendency to form amines; aryl groups seem to have a stronger effect.'

The tendency to co-ordination increases with the basic dissociation constant of the amine in each (primary, secondary, or tertiary) class. BRUEHLMAN and VERHOEK [1948], on the basis of experimental work, came to the conclusion that the affinity for hydrogen ion (normally measured basicity) by amines does parallel the affinity for silver ion (a Lewis acid), but that there is a smaller range of basicity for silver ion than for hydrogen ion. However, there is no single explanation for the formation or stability (or both) of these metal amine complexes. Reasons and theories vary widely.

Studies have been made on the rate and quantity of amine taken up on a silver iodide and lead iodide sample at low temperatures. It has been found generally that the initial reaction on both materials is extremely rapid, limited only by the rate of diffusion of the amine to the solid material. At $-20°C$, the initial reaction in the case of silver iodide appears to be the formation of a monolayer of $Ag(C_2H_5NH_2)_2I$ or $Ag(CH_3NH_2)_2I$.

On lead iodide, too, the diamine compound appears formed on the surface. The compounds are $Pb(C_2H_5)_2I_2$ and $Pb(CH_3)_2I_2$. After the formation of the surface complex, a slow take-up of amine by the interior of the crystal takes place. The reaction taking place, therefore, appears to be the chemisorption of the amine on the nucleus surface with the formation of a heavy metal-ammino complex on the surface. This essentially destroys the silver iodide or lead iodide surface, and the new surface is inactive in ice-crystal formation.

Conclusions—From the above experimental data, it can be seen that it is possible to inhibit nucleation by chemisorbing traces of foreign materials on the surfaces of the nuclei. This reaction completely alters the solid surface and makes it inactive. In the case of silver iodide and lead iodide nucleation, poisoning the surfaces with amines gives the amino complexes $Ag(RNH_2)_2I$ and $Pb(RNH_2)_2I_2$. The fact that methyl amine and ethyl amine are also active on atmospheric nuclei leads one to suspect that the active nuclei in the atmosphere are of a type which can react to form co-ordination complexes with amines, for example, the compounds of most heavy metals.

The fact that it is possible to inhibit ice nucleation below $-40°C$ is a rather significant fact. This would indicate that the $-40°C$ transition is heterogeneous rather than homogeneous nucleation. It would also appear that a distinct class of nuclei becomes active at $-40°C$, and hence the inhibition of these nuclei by the chemisorption of the amines.

That the inhibiting reaction is really chemisorption of the amine on the solid surface, not solution of the amine vapor in the supercooled water droplets with a lowering of the freezing point can be shown from a number of runs in which it was shown that the inhibition of nucleation depends solely on the conditions under which the nuclei were treated, not on the amine-vapor concentration in the deep freeze. If a nuclei sample, after treatment, is diluted with an equal volume of clean nitrogen and one-half this mixture is passed into the supercooled cloud, it is effective at the same temperature as the undiluted material. The reaction of the amines with the nuclei is practically irreversible, and these results would be expected if the condition of the solid surface is the controlling factor in nucleation inhibition.

It is felt that this approach to nucleation studies is an extremely fruitful one and will contribute much valuable information on the nature of the surfaces necessary for nucleation.

REFERENCES

BIRSTEIN, S. J. and C. E. ANDERSON, The mechanism of atmospheric ice formation, I, The chemical composition of nucleating agents, *J. Met.*, v.12, pp.68–73, 1955.

BILTZ, W., Uber die Ammoniakate der Bleihalogenide, Stammverbindungen und Mischverbingungen, *Zs. anorg. u. algem. Chem.*, v.124, pp. 230–247, 1922.

BRUEHLMAN, R. J. and F. J. VERHOEK, The basic strength of amines as measured by the stabilities of their complexes with silver ions, *J. Amer. Chem. Soc.*, v.70, pp.1401–1404, 1948.

INN, E. C. Y., Photolytic inactivation of ice forming silver iodide nuclei, *Bul. Amer. Met. Soc.*, v.32, pp.132–135, 1951.

Sidgewick, N. V., *Chemical Elements and their Compounds*, Oxford Univ. Press, v.1, 51pp., 1950.

Vonnegut, B., *Science*, v.107, pp.621–622, 1948.

Vosburgh, W. C. and R. S. McLure, Lmplex ions; IV, Monammine-silver ion, *J. Amer. Chem. Soc.*, v.65, pp.1060–1063, 1943.

DISCUSSION

Major Currie S. Downie—I'd like to mention that on some of the Air Force flights with the B–47 aircraft and also some of the British flights, temperatures of -50 to $-55°C$ have been encountered [Best, 1952; Bundgarrd and Downie, 1953] with liquid water drops in clouds. That may have some bearing on the work you have been doing.

Mr. S. J. Birstein—Yes. That also substantiates the theory.

Dr. Hans J. aufm Kampe—We had a similar experience in the laboratory, freezing of cloud droplets at $-53°C$; but still we were in a laboratory atmosphere and, although taking all precautions, we were not entirely sure if there were traces of alcohol vapor present. We also repeated Rau's experiments with a little alcohol in the chamber and found as he did, liquid water down to $-70°C$.

Mr. Birstein—Speaking of Rau's experiments, I saw Rau in Germany; he had repeated his experiments, not using alcohol, and got the same results. I haven't been able to understand how he did it, but he says he repeated it.

Dr. aufm Kampe—You probably read the most recent paper by Smith, Hefferman, and Seely. They burned silver iodide with hydrogen, and the effectiveness was reduced by a factor of ten after eight minutes. Then they burned it with kerosene and it was active for fifty minutes.

Mr. Birstein—I have never been convinced that when you burn silver iodide you wind up with a pure compound. It seems impossible. I don't think anybody has actually made a good study of what you get from one of these generators.

Dr. aufm Kampe—I think that should be one of the next things that should be done.

Dr. Vincent J. Schaefer—Just for the record, I would like to emphasize my belief that there is still a homogeneous nucleation temperature at about $-39°C$; and also express my confidence that the Bergeron-Findeisen theory remains important in cloud mechanisms.

Dr. E. J. Workman—I should like to have seen these contamination studies carried out a little more realistically with respect to practical applications for the atmosphere. When you are dealing with concentrations large enough to produce a measurable pressure of ammonia, it is little difficult to tell what you may have dissolved in water films and water drops in the cloud chamber. Certainly we would be inclined to disagree with the notions that ammonia poisons silver iodide as a nucleating agent when it is in small concentrations as in the atmosphere.

As a matter of fact, if one forms silver iodide in such a way as to get very small particles, apparently, and adds just traces of ammonia, I mean traces that are realistic even with respect to the concentrations of the atmosphere, one gets maybe a hundredfold increase in nucleation effect. I think there is no doubt about that effect any more, but with high vapor pressure, as in the present work, you may be poisoning the water.

Mr. Birstein—If you compute the amount that would get into the water as compared to what would stay on the solid surface, it is very little, and I don't think they'd give you the wide spread of the rate of crystallization. If you notice where we take the mean concentration and keep it constant, we still got the same temperature.

Dr. Workman—But the range is off completely.

Dr. Helmut Weickmann—If you have an ion imbedded in a gas which consists of dipol molecules, they have a tendency to gather around this ion. Now if something like this would play a role in one of these experiments, then we could make the following considerations. Let's assume an ion is adsorbed on the nucleus and its size would be just large enough that six H_2O molecules could gather around and would have the right spacing which is needed in the ice lattice. If there are only a few of these ions, they may assist in the orientation of H_2O molecules in order to build up the ice lattice. This won't work if this ion is too large, because you get too many H_2O molecules around. It won't work either if it is too small. You may get only four around and this won't fit the ice structure. So we should try to investigate substances whose ions have a certain size so that we will just get six H_2O molecules around.

In very small quantities, these ions may act as an improving agent for nucleation; but if you have too many then this agent would occupy all the places on the nucleus and would no longer allow the water molecules to get between and get oriented.

So, we could explain Dr. Workman's observation that ammonia is a good means to improve nucleation; and Mr. Birstein's, that ammonia stops nucleation.

References

BEST, A. C., Ice accretion in cirrus cloud, *Met. Res. Com.* MRP 730, 1 May 1952.
BUNDGARRD, R. C. and C. S. DOWNIE, Thunderstorm icing and precipitation USAF Air Weather Service Project Blacksheep BSTC 1, July 1953.

SURFACE NATURE OF ICE CRYSTALS

UKICHIRO NAKAYA

Hokkaido University, Sapporo, Japan

Etching of crystal surface of ice—This experiment was carried out by K. Higuchi at Hokkaido University, Sapporo, Japan. The polished surface of commercial ice was coated with replica film of polyvinyl formal, and was left in the cold chamber. Separated etch pits with geometrical shape were produced on the ice surface (see Figures 1–7), and the shape of the pit figure coincided with a section cut from a hexagonal column with a plane. The figure of a regular hexagon was obtained on the surface parallel to the base plane of crystallization, and the sides of the hexagon were found to be parallel to those of vapor figure; that is, parallel to a-axes. These etch pits can be used as a simple method of determining the orientation of a-axes as well as c-axis.

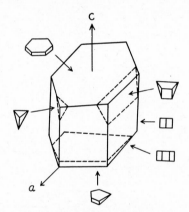

FIG. 1—Schematical sketches of various shapes of etch pits on the surface of ice
(Higuchi)

As etching proceeds, the bottom of the etch pit becomes a plane of mirror finish which is parallel to the base plane. Continuing the etching process further, this surface develops into a stepped structure. The height of the steps was measured by the shadowing method used in electron-microscope technique, and was found to vary between three to 16 microns, the mean having been about five microns. This is another evidence to show the layer structure of ice crystal, the layer being perpendicular to c-axis.

Thermal etch pits of snow crystals—This experiment was carried out by M. Kumai at Hokkaido University in connection with the dislocation theory of crystals.

Experiments on etch pits and dislocations were carried out with aluminium, germanium, zinc, silver halide, alkali halide, etc. The number of etch pits in the subboundary coincided with the number of dislocations. The surface density of etch pits of

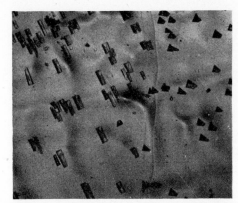

FIG. 2—Etching of ice surface covered with replica film; five per cent solution (× 36, Higuchi)

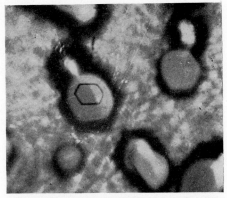

FIG. 3—The sharp figure is a void produced by internal melting; the sides show the directions of *a*-axes; the diffuse hexagon is an etch pit, the side being parallel to *a*-axis (× 41, Higuchi)

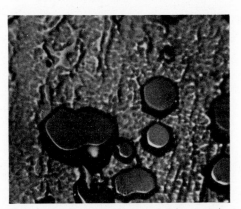

FIG. 4—Basel planes of mirror finish appear in the etch pits (× 37, Higuchi)

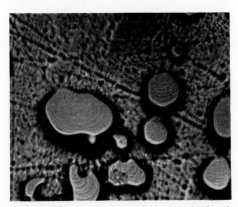

FIG. 5—Layer structure appears in the basal planes in the later stage of Fig. 4 (× 37, Higuchi)

FIG. 6—Two groups of steps start from two corners and the corresponding steps are of the same depth (× 36, Higuchi)

FIG. 7—Shadowing with chromium vapor for the measurement of step heights (× 110, Higuchi)

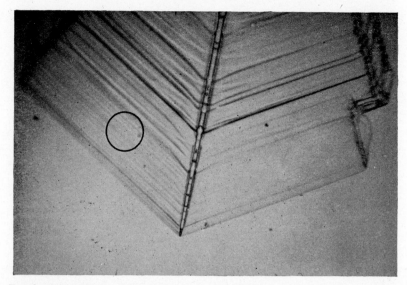

FIG. 8—A branch of an artificial snow crystal of sector type; the circle shows the spot where the replica for the electron-microscope investigation is made (× 80, Kumai)

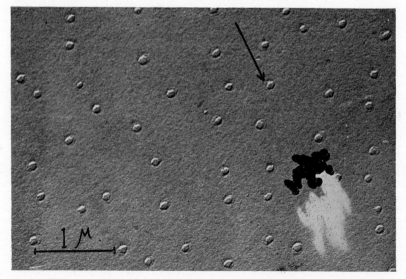

FIG. 9—The thermal etch pits on the surface of a branch of the artificial snow crystal shown in Fig. 8; the group of black spheres is carbon particles showing the direction of shadowing (× 22,000, Kumai)

good annealed pure aluminium is reported to be $10^6 \sim 10^7/cm^2$, and that of NaCl is measured to be $10^5/cm^2$.

Kumai succeeded in taking the electron-microphotographs of etch pits on the surface of natural and artificial snow crystals (see Figures 8 and 9), and observed their shape and density of distribution. As for the artificial snow crystals, a plane crystal of sector type was made, and the thermal etch pits were made on its surface by exposing the crystal to the air in the cold chamber for 10 to 20 minutes. The relative humidity was about 80 per cent. The replica of etch pits was made by using one per cent solution of formvar dissolved in ethylene dichloride. The crystal was put on the mesh of the holder and the solution was poured on the crystal. After the solvent was evaporated, the sample was kept below freezing and the snow crystal evaporated by sublimation. The shadowing was done on the top surface of the replica film with chrome vapor in a vacuum vessel.

The shape of etch pits in (0001) plane is a hexagonal type or a rounded pattern. The density is $10^7 \sim 10^8/cm^2$, being of the same order of magnitude as the case of good annealed pure aluminium crystal. These etch pits show a definite orientation. These results suggest that the etch pits coincide with the dislocations in snow crystals and their arrangement shows the existence of dislocation network in snow crystals.

DISCUSSION

Dr. Helmut Weickmann—Can we be absolutely sure that the holes are in the surface of the ice crystal and not in the film? It may be something which is in the film.

Dr. Ukichiro Nakaya—We believe, up to now, that the circular forms are a real phenomenon and appear in the ice. We made experiments with the film alone but no such network appeared.

Dr. Vincent J. Schaefer—I think I can speak a bit on this subject. I have done a great deal of work with polyvinyl formal replica films and they're absolutely featureless if prepared properly. So I would say anything you saw here today, except possibly a few of the tiny holes which weren't pertinent to what he has been talking about, are real things.

Dr. T. W. R. East—Was the depth of the circular steps five microns?

Dr. Nakaya—Yes.

Dr. East—This has nothing to do with the atomic structure?

Dr. Nakaya—No.

Dr. East—Do we infer from the etch pits of the different kinds of surface that the internal structure of the ice is different?

Dr. Nakaya—Now this is a guess, but in the case of dendritic formation there will be very large crystal defects, or some foreign particles as in any crystal which we would call a dendritic formation. As for the layer structure of the single crystal of ice, I made the experiment by using single crystals of ice which were brought from a glacier in Alaska. The single crystal of ice was about one foot long. We brought about three tons of these single crystals and kept them in the cold chamber, and I used perhaps one ton of them during two years. We found that single crystals of ice have a layer structure perpendicular to the c-axis, small angle boundaries appear at the points of contact with the wedge. The dislocations are concentrated there. The crystal supported on its endings does not show a circular bending, but deforms in a V-shape. The free end doesn't go up. This is due to the gliding between elementary layers.

The thickness of the elementary layer is about 50 microns. We made very sharp parallel marks on the surface in the vertical direction, and these marks remained parallel after the deformation. So it's quite certain that an ice crystal has a layer structure, and the thickness of the elementary layer is nearly constant, about 50 microns.

NOTES ON THE STRUCTURE OF ICE

E. J. WORKMAN

New Mexico Institute of Mining and Technology, Socorro, N.M.

Abstract—Since the second part of this paper deals with work which has been published or is scheduled for publication, a complete report will not be given here.

A LARGE number of surface replicas of ice crystals have been made and the surface features studied with the electron microscope. Our original interest was that of finding structural manifestations of the role of certain ionic impurities incorporated during the freezing process. Single crystals of glacial ice and representative samples of single ice crystals (frozen under controlled conditions of purity and rates of growth) were prepared. After etching and replication all samples studied revealed that single crystals of ice are composed of bundles of hexagonal prisms [TRUBY, 1956].

When the growth of the ice is stopped abruptly and a replica of the surface made, additional structural features become apparent. A hexagonal pattern is again obtained in the basal plane and the dimensions are identical with those found in the basal plane for the etched samples. The surface consists of stepped areas and a central cavity. The step height for pure ice is approximately 500Å and is reduced to about 200Å for ice formed from a 10^{-5}M solution of CsF. Walter Drost-Hansen and I have discussed these observations and if one interprets the steps as evidence of a dislocation mechanism, one may calculate the radius of the central cavity following F. C. Frank. The result is one-tenth micron in excellent agreement with estimates made from the electron microphotographs.

REFERENCES

TRUBY, FRANK K., Hexagonal microstructure of ice crystals grown from the melt, *J. Appl. Phys.*, v.26, pp.1416–1420, 1955.

WORKMAN, E. J. and W. DROST-HANSEN, On the microstructure and formation of ice from liquid water *Trans. Amer. Geophys. Union.* v.36. p.534 1955 (abstract).

DISCUSSION

Dr. Richard Schotland—I was wondering about your first paper concerning the ionic transfer between the impure water and the pure ice crystals. Is not the transfer of ions dependent on the type of contaminent you have?

Dr. E. J. Workman—The charge-transfer mechanism in ice is by protons, regardless of the contaminants. Presumably the contact melts a small portion of the ice, and during a refreezing process we do, in fact, have a great deal of charge separation. Reynolds and his colleagues think this is analogous in some way to the electrical freezing effect.

Dr. Helmut Weickmann—I would like to remark about your first paper that I'm very happy that you found another effect which produces electricity. I was a little afraid that you would run into trouble with the glaze-ice process; since in the case of soft hail particles, we probably don't have spray-off at all which is required for the glaze-ice electrification process.

Prof. Charles L. Hosler—We are at the beginning of a project to determine the temperature limitations of the sticking together of ice crystals on impact, and I wouldn't want to say this is a result, but it seems there is a very sharp cutoff between −7 and −11°C, and I wonder if there might be a relationship between the temperature where they start to stick together on impact, and the point in the cloud where you started to note the charge separation?

Dr. Workman—I think I should say in connection with this remark, and in connection with Dr. Weickmann's remark it just might turn out that these negative charges aren't as high as some of us think they are, in which case we may have to go back to somewhat more moderate temperatures again.

Dr. G. A. Wolff—I would suggest that perhaps there is a polar axis present in ice which may play an important part in the generation of thunderstorm electricity. As a possible method of determination of the polar axis, you could use triboluminescence, that is, place the ice crystal in front of a multiplier and crush the crystal at −10°C, and at lower temperatures. The presence of triboluminescence could, possibly, indicate the polar axis.

Dr. Workman—Do you have any doubt that you will find luminescence?

Dr. Wolff—No, but we have to investigate it further. Triboluminescence has been observed at low temperatures only, I checked it at zero degrees and found no triboluminescence, however the ice was not prepared under the conditions under which you have prepared it, that is, from dilute solutions of flourides or ammonium salts.

OBSERVATIONS OF FREEZING NUCLEI
OVER THE SOUTHWESTERN U.S.

A. RICHARD KASSANDER, LEE L. SIMS AND JAMES E. McDONALD

Institute of Atmospheric Physics, University of Arizona, Tucson, Ariz.

Abstract—Flight observations of numbers of freezing nuclei as a function of temperature were made at 5000 and 15,000 ft over southern Arizona every day from January 3 to January 31, 1955. The dates on which peaks in the nuclei counts occur do not support in any clearly recognizable way the hypothesis that they are associated with meteoritic dustfalls. The average temperature to which collected air samples had to be cooled to obtain given ice-crystal concentrations over Arizona are equal to within about two degrees centigrade, the corresponding values found at similar altitudes over Sydney, Australia, during the same period, thus suggesting a possibly worldwide similarity in nuclei populations. Observations of a remarkable nucleation activity noted on three occasions in air samples taken within clouds containing natural ice crystals are reported briefly but cannot be ascribed to any known physical processes.

DAILY NUCLEI-COUNT FLUCTUATIONS

Introduction—For four weeks during January, 1955, daily flights were made from Tucson, Arizona, by staff members of the Institute of Atmospheric Physics of the University of Arizona for the purpose of observing day-to-day fluctuations in the population of natural freezing nuclei in the free atmosphere. These observations were made in cooperation with the Radiophysics Division of the Commonwealth Scientific and Industrial Research Organization, Sydney, Australia.

The work of BOWEN [1953] on the hypothesis that meteoritic dust may nucleate clouds and thereby influence rainfall amounts received at the ground has made it desirable to seek all possible means of studying the nature of daily variations in nuclei counts. A fairly direct test of this hypothesis should be afforded by flying suitable equipment well above the surface dust layer and counting the numbers of nuclei effective at successively lower temperatures on each of a series of days including several 'meteor days', as we may briefly term those dates falling about 29 days after passage of the Earth through a major meteor stream. To avoid possible bias and error due to any local peculiarities of atmospheric particulates Bowen has sought to carry out such measurements at more than a single place; so the Radiophysics Division built and generously donated to the Institute of Atmospheric Physics a replica of the nuclei counter [SMITH and HEFFERNAN, 1954] which was to be flown in Australia during January 1955. In addition to these Tucson and Sydney flight measurements, observations were made in Hawaii with a simpler device set up at an elevation of about 10,000 ft on Haleakala Crater and operated during the same January, 1955, period. Only the Arizona observations will be described in detail here.

Observational procedure—The Australian nuclei counter consists essentially of a cold chamber having a volume of about 75 liters into which a sample of natural air is introduced and cooled at a rate of about 4°C/min. A beam of light illuminates a ten-liter working volume which is continuously observed by the operator as the cooling proceeds.

A source of water vapor continuously adds fresh vapor to the observation chamber to maintain a cloud of droplets throughout the chamber. Occurrence of freezing in a droplet is made evident by the scintillation of the resultant ice crystal. The operator logs the number of scintillating particles (or spacing between particles) present in the working volume as a function of the steadily decreasing temperature of the cloud. For other details of the procedure, see the original report [SMITH and HEFFERNAN, 1954]. To insure comparability of results, E. J. Smith of the Radiophysics Division spent a month at the Institute of Atmospheric Physics in November, 1954, checking out all flight personnel in the use of the cold chamber.

For the Arizona flights, the nuclei counter was installed in a Lockheed Hudson aircraft with a collection tube projecting from the nose of the aircraft well ahead of the plane of the propeller. A 1·5-inch diameter rubber hose of total length about 15 ft carried the sample to the counter. Ram pressure was sufficient to flush out completely the previous sample and leave a fresh sample in the box in about one minute. A run consisted of observing and counting the ice crystals appearing during the 10–12-minute period required to cool the sample to $-40°C$.

From January 3 to January 31, daily flights to 15,000 ft were made. Two observers went on each flight to permit cross-checks between independent observers. Each observer made one run at the 15,000-ft level and each made one run at the 5000-ft level. One of the two made a single run immediately upon landing, employing an air sample whose collection was completed exactly at the instant of touch-down of the aircraft. The samples taken at 15,000 ft are regarded as free from any contamination due to local dust which in the winter is not known to rise above a few thousand feet above terrain, particularly during the morning hours (10h 00m–12h 00m) during which these flights were almost invariably made. Westerly or northwesterly flow at 15,000 ft prevailed during most of the period, so the air at the 15,000-ft level cannot be said to have been uninfluenced by possible surface sources upwind (in the California area). The observations taken at 5000 ft were made in order to detect, if present, any systematic height variations relating either to surface effects or, on Bowen's hypothesis, to descent of a stratum of nuclei from above. The surface observations were made in order to shed indirect light on the whole question of surface contamination and to extend the basic study of height variations of nuclei counts. During all but one flight, the aircraft flew within about 50 miles of Tucson. On one occasion the flight went to northern Arizona and back, but no significant differences characterized the results of this flight.

Results—For each of the approximately 150 samples taken in the course of the Arizona flights during January, 1955, the temperature at which the number of ice crystals reached a value equivalent to 0·1/L (0·1 crystal per liter), 1/L, 10/L and 100/L was determined. This range of crystal concentrations spans the values customarily regarded as necessary to initiate the Bergeron mechanism of precipitation in clouds (10/L being a commonly suggested concentration).

In Figures 1–4, the results for samples taken at 15,000 ft are presented in detail. As has been cited above, samples taken at this level are believed to be free from local contamination and hence should be fairly representative of the entire southwestern U.S. For each of these figures, the results of each of the two observers' determinations are plotted for each day in order to display the variability inherent in this observational technique.

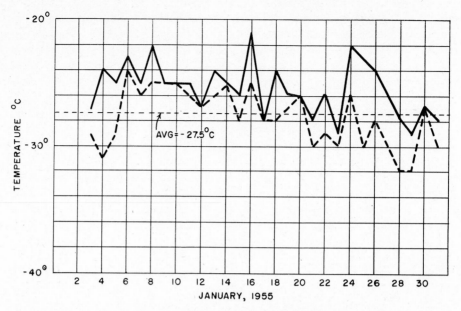

FIG. 1—Daily variation in temperatures at which ice-crystal concentrations reached 0·1 per liter in air samples taken at 15,000 ft over southeastern Arizona; solid curve refers to warmer one of each pair of daily values, dashed curve to colder values; average temperature difference between observers, 2.3° C

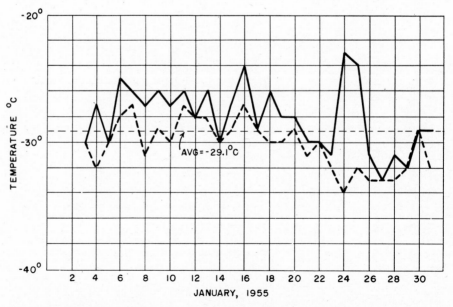

FIG. 2—Daily variation in temperatures at which ice-crystal concentration searched 1 per liter in air samples taken at 15,000 ft over southeastern Arizona; solid and dashed curves as in Fig. 1; average temperature difference between observers, 2·1°C

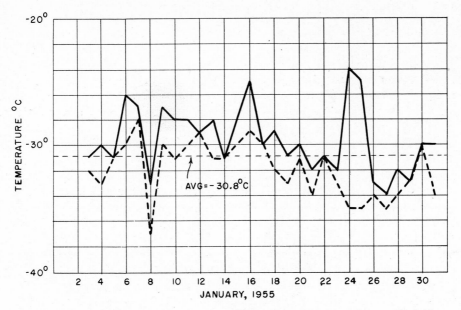

FIG. 3—Daily variation in temperatures at which ice-crystal concentrations reached 10 per liter in air samples taken at 15,000 ft over southeastern Arizona; solid and dashed curves as in Fig. 1; average temperature difference between observers, 2·3°C

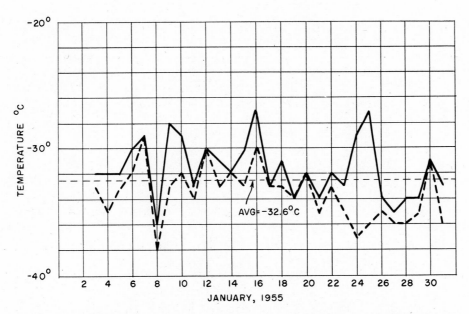

FIG. 4—Daily variation in temperatures at which ice-crystal concentrations reached 100 per liter in air samples taken at 15,000 ft over southeastern Arizona; solid and dashed curves as in Fig. 1; average temperature difference between observers, 2·0°C

Since six persons rotated as observers during these flights, the slight differences resulting from individual observing techniques cannot easily be shown on figures, so the lines joining the points have been drawn simply to connect the points corresponding respectively to the warmer and the colder of the observations for each flight. The average difference, without regard to sign, between the temperatures at which the crystal concentrations rose to each given value are entered on the corresponding graph to provide a measure of the dispersion in results arising from personal differences of technique. It will be seen from Figures 1–4 that this difference averages about two degrees Centigrade, but on one occasion (January 24, concentration 10/L) it was as large as 11°C. It is entirely possible that even so large a difference between observers is a real one due to differences in nuclei populations at points several tens of miles apart on a given flight, though this possibility could only be attested by repeated observations at the air points in question.

These nuclei counts at 15,000 ft over Arizona do not reveal peaks on those dates which would agree with the worldwide meteor days as discussed previously by Bowen [1953]. The Arizona nuclei counts exhibit, in fact, no prominent peaks if we consider averages for both observers on each run. The results of the concurrent observations in Sydney have been described briefly by Bowen (talk to International Arid Lands Symposium, Albuquerque, N.M., 1955) as offering some support for the meteoritic hypothesis and hence differ in this respect from the Arizona data. In particular the Sydney data for concentrations of 1/L exhibit peaks on January 13, 23, and 29 in good agreement with the meteor days. Note that the Arizona curves running through points corresponding to the warmer temperature of each pair of observations display maxima near January 16 and 24–25 and that such maxima are displaced about two or three days from the Sydney maxima and from the meteor days of the Bowen hypothesis. Although so little is known of the vertical air motions in the stratosphere and ozonosphere in particular parts of the world that one must be willing to admit differences of a few days in times of descent of any strata of meteoritic particles incident upon the top of the atmosphere, we cannot find any strong reason for selecting the warmer points of the pairs of observations in question, so we cannot offer these points as indirect evidence for the meteoritic-dust hypothesis. The conclusion, to repeat, is that the Arizona nuclei counts in January 1955 do not seem to support the hypothesis in the way that the Sydney data do.

The observations carried out by personnel of the Radiophysics Division in Hawaii during this same January period appear to support the Bowen hypothesis as well as or better than the Sydney data. Furthermore, some concurrent nuclei counts made by Cwilong in Panama also tend to support the hypothesis, though in a way that is less clear-cut. Hence the Arizona data seem to stand alone as failing to substantiate the suggestion that there may be significant increases in the numbers of freezing nuclei on the days falling about 29 days after passage of the earth through meteor showers. It is clear that more work along these general lines is needed to make final decision possible in this interesting question.

Since the nuclei counts made in Arizona during the past January have considerable interest in themselves all aside from their implications for the Bowen hypothesis, additional results are presented in Figures 5 and 6 and Table 1. In Fig. 5, comparative temperatures at surface, 5000 ft and 15,000 ft for a concentration of 1 per L are shown and in Fig. 6 the same types of curves are given for a crystal concentration of 100 per L.

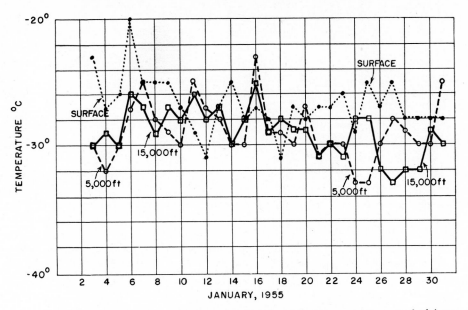

FIG. 5—Daily fluctuations in temperatures at which ice-crystal concentrations reached 1 per liter at surface, 5000 ft and 15,000 ft; curves for 5000 ft and 15,000 ft are for averages of daily pairs of observations

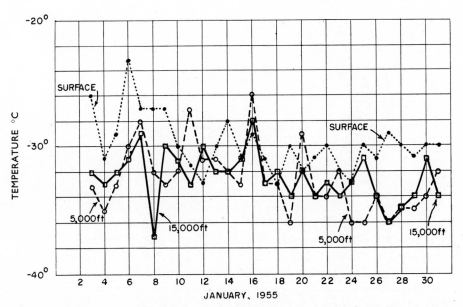

FIG. 6—Daily fluctuations in temperatures at which ice-crystal concentrations reached 100 per liter at surface, 5000 ft and 15,000 ft; curves for 5000 ft and 15,000 ft are for averages of daily pairs of observations

Table 1 summarizes the average temperatures at which the nuclei counts rose to given concentrations at each of the altitudes at which samples were taken. Note that although there is an evident trend towards more active freezing nuclei at greater heights, there is only a difference of a few degrees between the surface nuclei activation temperatures and the 15,000-ft nuclei-activation temperatures at corresponding crystal concentration. Thus, to develop a concentration of one ice crystal per liter, surface air had to be cooled on the average to about $-27°C$ while 15,000 ft air had to be cooled to $-29°C$. This difference is about equal to the average difference between observers, so it may not even be a real difference. In any event, these results provide some small basis for concluding that even surface nuclei counts should give a good first approximation to the upper air nuclei counts in the Arizona area. Daily fluctuations aloft are not, however, faithfully shown by corresponding surface fluctuations, as for example on January 6.

Table 1. *Summary of the average temperatures at which the ice crystal concentrations rose to specified values at three altitudes over southern Arizona during January 3–31, 1955*

Altitude	Ice crystal concentration			
	0·1/L	1/L	10/L	100/L
ft	°C	°C	°C	°C
Surface	-25	-27	-28	-30
5,000	-26	-29	-31	-33
15,000	-27	-29	-31	-33

Finally, note that the Sydney and Tucson data are in remarkably good agreement as to the average temperatures at which nucleation develops a given ice-crystal concentration. Thus, for just the 15,000 ft data one finds that over Arizona cooling to $-29·1°C$ was required on the average during January, 1955, to develop an ice crystal concentration of 1/L, whereas the same figure for Sydney was $-27·4°C$, or only $1·7°C$ warmer despite the large geographical separation of these locales. An equally small temperature difference appears from other such comparisons in these two sets of data, so one is tempted to conclude that freezing nuclei populations may be much the same in all parts of the world. Such a conclusion cannot be drawn firmly, however, until very much more information is available than is presented here.

It is to be noted that the Tucson and Sydney nuclei counts yielded results in substantial disagreement with the conclusions of Aufm Kampe and Weickmann [1951], who suggested that in most air masses natural aerosols should produce ice crystal concentrations of the order of 1/L to 10/L by cooling only to about $-15°C$.

Summary and conclusions—The Arizona nuclei counts of January, 1955, do not exhibit fluctuations that support in any clearly recognizable way the hypothesis that Bowen has formulated to account for certain irregularities in long-term rainfall records. Concurrent counts made in Sydney with the same apparatus and observing techniques appear to support the meteoritic dust hypothesis, as do also concurrent counts taken in Hawaii and Panama. Whether some peculiarity in the high-level airflow over the south-western Arizona could account for a failure to observe such peaks, or whether unrecognized differences in observing techniques are basically responsible, or whether some phenomenon not related to meteoritic dust is in control here is not clear.

It is of considerable interest to learn that the nucleating efficiency of freezing nuclei in Arizona during January, 1955, was nearly identical, on the average, to that of nuclei over eastern Australia, for this poses the possibility that some sort of large-scale uniformity may exist in this regard. The Hawaii and Panama data tend to support this speculation, though those observations were less detailed than the Tucson and Sydney observations.

The work reported here must be regarded as making its principal contribution by virtue of providing free-air observations of the activation temperatures corresponding to a series of different crystal concentrations in air that may be regarded as representative of the southwestern United States in midwinter. In general, it would seem that air must rise to an altitude of between 20,000 to 25,000 ft in winter in the southwestern U.S. in order to be cooled to such a low temperature as to yield crystal concentrations of the order of those currently felt to be necessary to initiate the Bergeron process in super-cooled clouds.

OBSERVATIONS ON EVAPORATION ICE NUCLEI

Introduction—During two of the flights made during January, 1955, a phenomenon of basic interest in the problem of natural freezing nucleation was observed. This phenomenon consisted of an unusually warm nucleation temperature for samples of air taken within ice-crystal clouds. The sampling procedure employed with the Australian nuclei counter consists in filling the chamber, warming to about $+10°C$, and then starting the cooling process that leads to nucleation in the cloud of drops that is created in the chamber. Hence, the ice crystals drawn into the chamber from the cloud and held at above-freezing temperatures for a time of the order of 100–200 sec must have both melted and evaporated. Since air samples taken on the same day and at the same altitude but outside the clouds exhibited no unusual nucleation properties, the observed phenomenon is suspected of being a property of some kind of residues left from the melting and evaporation of the natural ice crystals.

Observations in natural clouds—L. L. Sims, flying as one of the two observers on the January 8 flight, directed the pilot to enter a small cumulus cloud from which snow virgae descended. His objective was to draw in a sample of air from within this cloud, which was one of a small fraction of such cumuli showing evidence of having been naturally nucleated. The clouds had bases at 5000 ft and tops at about 10,000 ft; the sample was taken at 5200 ft at a temperature of $-3°C$. Immediately after admitting the cloud-air sample into the cooling chamber which was at $13°C$, two unusual phenomena were noted. First, there existed a large number of non-scintillating particles with average spacing of only about 0.5 cm. Second, a smaller number (roughly ten per cent as many) exhibited scintillation effects. No water droplet fog was in the chamber at this time. After noting the above peculiarities and waiting about two minutes to detect any changes in the appearance of the sample, fog was added in the normal fashion and the cooling process begun. Immediately after the chamber temperature fell below $0°C$, large numbers of scintillating crystals appeared. At a temperature of $-1°C$ their concentration was already up to about 100/L as estimated from intercrystal spacing. This high concentration was maintained to about −10°C, after which fallout reduced the value to only about 1/L. Not until the chamber reached −25°C did the concentration of scintillating particles rise again to the 100/L value attained at −1°C. By way of comparison, a clear-air sample taken near this cloud showed no scintillating particles at all until −11°C (one lone crystal) and gave a 100/L concentration only after cooling to −32°C, which is close to the month-long average temperature required for 100/L (see Table 1).

It was not possible to secure a second ice-cloud sample on January 8; but on January 9 two more cases of a similar nature were observed, but with less extreme departure from normal. In a cloud at 10,000 ft which contained ice crystals that were clearly discernible as they flashed into the chamber, a sample was taken and held at about 13°C for ten minutes before being cooled. Again a high concentration of dull particles plus a few scintillating particles were found at above-freezing temperatures. On cooling, a few scintillations were observed at −5°C and by about −11°C a concentration in excess of 100/L was observed. These fell out as before and not until about −25°C did the concentration reach 100/L. For comparison, samples were taken on this day in both clear air and in water-droplet clouds, yet neither type of sample displayed unusual characteristics.

The second ice-crystal cloud sampled on January 9 exhibited a high concentration of non-scintillating particles during the above-freezing stage and gave one scintillating crystal at −4°C and 100/L at −14°C. This second cloud was in the vicinity of a smelter at Douglas, Arizona, and only slightly above the level of the smelter smoke plume so it was decided to take a sample well within the plume for comparison. Such a comparison sample taken on January 11 at 8000 ft did in fact show a high concentration of non-scintillating particles at the start of the run (above-freezing temperatures) but did not show any unusual nucleation effects (to get 100/L required cooling to −27°C).

The Australian flight personnel have reported observations of high concentration of non-scintillating particles similar to those described here as seen at above-freezing temperatures; they also describe seeing occasional scintillating particles at such times. They did not observe the peculiar nucleating effects that are reported here for three samples taken entirely inside ice-crystal clouds.

Despite continued search for ice-crystal clouds during the remainder of the period of flight work, no additional observations were possible on this peculiar effect. This is unfortunate in view of the great potential importance of any natural process which might create highly active residues within ice crystals that would retain their nucleating effect even after melting and evaporation of the crystals. The phenomenon becomes of principal interest in connection with its possible relation to natural seeding by cirrus clouds. If residual particles of some unidentified nature could survive descent from a cirrus deck through many thousands of feet of unsaturated air and still yield nucleation effects comparable only to those known to occur with silver iodide, the significance of the process would be obvious. In order to gain further information on this process some laboratory studies have been conducted by L. L. Sims. These will be briefly summarized next.

Laboratory observations—In an effort to duplicate the natural phenomenon just described, Sims attempted to form ice-crystal clouds within the cooling chamber of the nuclei counter by cooling to temperatures of the order of $-40°C$, then warming to above freezing and then cooling again. To maintain the cloud of ice crystals in suspension while carrying them through this cycle, a fan was introduced into the chamber and operated during the initial experiments. No successful laboratory reproductions of the phenomenon were obtained until the fan was removed. On carrying out the process without a fan in operation inside the chamber, residual nucleating effects were found at temperatures as warm as about $-5°C$. At the present time this work is suspended because of other Institute activities, and it is not possible to draw any firm conclusions as to the implications of the laboratory work. Just prior to suspension of the work it was discovered that the early nucleation effect was not then reproducible unless the initial cooling rate in the chamber was about double the rate employed in the flight work, so this point will have to be checked more completely in the near future.

It should be noted that a somewhat similar phenomenon has been found by Gourley and Crozier (unpublished) at the New Mexico Institute of Mining and Technology. Their experiment consisted of evaporating (but not also melting) ice crystals formed by spontaneous nucleation at the $-40°C$ point. Residual nuclei of some unidentified type were left after evaporating the crystals and survived for times of the order of several hours. The physics of this phenomenon was not studied in detail by Gourley and Crozier and so, like the possibly related phenomenon described here, remains to be explained.

Summary and conclusions—The point of greatest importance in these observations seems to be that natural ice-crystal clouds forming in an air mass having no apparently abnormal nucleating properties yielded some type of residues capable of remarkably efficient nucleation. The chemical physics of the phenomenon is completely unknown. It is suggested that others working on nuclei-counting experiments should search for additional evidence of this potentially important phenomenon, both in the free atmosphere and in the laboratory.

Acknowledgments—This paper reports work done jointly by a number of members of the staff of the Institute of Atmospheric Physics; thanks are due to all of them. The generous assistance of the Radiophysics Division of the Commonwealth Scientific and Industrial Research Organization is gratefully acknowledged. E. G. Bowen and E. J. Smith of that organization deserve particular thanks for their part in initiating the work described here.

REFERENCES

AUFM KAMPE, H. J. and H. K. WEICKMANN, The effectiveness of natural and artificial aerosols as freezing nuclei, *J. Met.*, v.8, pp.283–288, 1951.

BOWEN, E. G., The influence of meteoritic dust on rainfall, *Australian J. Phys.*, v.6, pp.490–497, 1953.

BOWEN, E. G., Unpublished talk at International Arid Lands Symposium, Albuquerque, N.M.

SMITH, E. J. and K. HEFFERNAN, Airborne measurements of the concentration of natural and artificial freezing nuclei, *Q.J.R. Met. Soc.*, v.80, pp.182–197, 1954.

DISCUSSION

Dr. Everly J. Workman—How warm could you make the air sample and still have the ice reappear?

Dr. James E. McDonald—The first occasion was about $+13°C$, and the other $+10°C$.

Dr. Workman—We are interested in this problem through the work of Mary Gourley, in our laboratory. She finds a persistent nucleus from clean ice which has been desiccated to the point of invisibility at very high magnification.

Dr. McDonald—Is this at negative temperatures?

Dr. Workman—Yes, we wouldn't expect that it would occur after having been at warmer temperatures. We have not determined the limits of temperature yet.

Dr. McDonald—The Gourley results are as perplexing as ours. Some property apparently persists long after common sense indicates it should have gone. They differ in the respect that your group did the experiments at negative temperatures by dehumidifying the samples, so they would evaporate and not melt.

Dr. Helmut Weickmann—I'd like to offer a possible explanation of this phenomenon. Let's say your observation is correct. You didn't get any contamination from exhaust gas or from anything else. Once a nucleus has acted as a freezing nucleus it has an adsorption layer of H_2O molecules. This adsorption layer adheres to the crystal face and does not evaporate, not even at a low relative humidity. It also persists in temperatures above freezing and, this is important, with its molecules arranged in the right spacing. So, if you cool it down afterwards, you still have the oriented adsorption layer or, in other words, a very good freezing nucleus.

Dr. Edward M. Brooks—I'd like to make one point about these meteor showers. You mentioned that the Sydney and Haleakala Crater data supported the Bowen hypothesis. I think we should remember that meteor showers themselves may last many days, sometimes weeks, and it is very exceptional to find just a strong burst and then have nothing on the previous or following day.

Another thing you have to think of is the thirty-day period you mentioned. Of course, that could allow a little leeway, too. It seems to me you should not expect a sharp peak to verify the hypothesis but rather a gradual rise and fall. It seems that there should be some other explanation for that some day.

Dr. McDonald—The start of all this came from the rainfall peaks which are surprisingly sharp. This was Bowen's first point. One would ask for equally high peaks in the nuclei. But, I agree that from the astronomical and the meteorological aspects one would not expect it.

Dr. David Atlas—I wonder about the significance of these nuclei counts with regard to natural precipitation because of the great difference in the temperatures at which sufficient nuclei are presumably available to initiate the Bergeron process, and that at which actual clouds have been observed to release ice crystal precipitation. Nuclei counts of 10 per liter are not observed above $-28°C$, while observations of *Fallstreifen* by Peppler in Germany and our own radar observations of natural precipitation show a rather strong preference for the initiation of the Bergeron process in the neighborhood of $-15°C$. Can you explain this apparent inconsistency?

Dr. McDonald—If, in fact, there exists a residual property that would suffice to initiate crystal formation, then homogeneous nucleation at the cirrus clouds could be the source. They could fall out of cirrus, into lower clouds.

Dr. James P. Lodge, Jr.—I think all of us tend to underestimate the persistence of crystals. There was some work done in Germany by some of the medical researchers during the war. They were studying the nucleation of carbon dioxide bubbles in liquids. They discovered that a sodium chloride solution which had been made up, filtered, and allowed to stand 15 or 20 minutes still contained particles of something or other, presumably remaining polymolecular aggregates of sodium chloride capable of nucleating the formation of CO_2 bubbles; and only after something like standing for an hour could you pull a vacuum on them without getting bubble formation. Apparently, these crystalline entities, whatever they are, do stick around a lot longer than we think.

Dr. H. J. aufm Kampe—I have a few questions. First, do you have values of the temperature gradient above 15,000 ft, too? And what is the size of these particles if we assume it is meteoric dust that comes down?

Dr. McDonald—Several microns.

Dr. aufm Kampe—Still a particle of ten microns falls only about one centimeter per second if there is no convective action which brings it down more rapidly.

Dr. McDonald—Yes.

Dr. aufm Kampe—I remember our flights in Germany in connection with Professor

Regener's ozone measurements. Since Regener assumed that ozone is brought down from the ozone layer to lower layers by convection, it was important to know the gradient, that is, the instability or the stability of the layers above your sampling layer.

The next question is when you warmed the icebox to 13°C, was there water on the walls?

Dr. McDonald—No, the water all evaporated.

Dr. aufm Kampe—You mentioned two temperatures, at which you have ice crystals, and these are Rau's 'magic' temperatures. In his experiments he found peaks at —4 and —12°C. He said 'What I need as freezing nucleus is not necessarily an ice crystal but any dry dirt.' Therefore my question about the wet or dry state of your box.

I assumed you had cumulus clouds which formed from thermals. So you had air from the ground and with it you would have dust from the desert at least in Arizona. You mentioned, however that you also sampled other clouds that did not show the effect, and for those one would have to find another explanation.

Dr. McDonald—We took samples in water clouds on the same days and levels and they did not do it. It appears that the only differences was that some clouds had gone through the ice phase.

STUDIES ON RE-EVAPORATION ICE NUCLEI

CHARLES E. ANDERSON

Geophysics Research Directorate, Air Force Cambridge Research Center, Bedford, Mass.

Abstract—The critical supersaturation ratio for the formation of ice crystals from water vapor on foreign nuclei was experimentally studied over the temperature range −24 to −44°C and was determined to be below 1·3 over this range. Individual determinations demonstrated conclusively that ice crystal formation can proceed at vapor pressures considerably less than the saturation value with respect to water.

Introduction—In the long-standing controversy about the origin of atmospheric ice particles, two schools of opinion have developed whose basic difference is whether or not ice particles require water saturation as a prerequisite to their formation. As most of you probably know, our experimental group at GRD favors the negative side in this debate, since a great deal of our experimental work [BIRSTEIN and ANDERSON, 1955; BIRSTEIN, 1954] points in the direction of an adsorption-orientation-nucleation process at the surface of an ice nucleus. This type of process need not have the liquid droplet stage, marked by water saturation, to lead to ice crystals.

Since our previous investigations were confined to specific chemical substances, we could not carry over our arguments to the natural case inasmuch as definite knowledge of the chemical nature of the natural ice nuclei is lacking. The experiments to be discussed here were initiated with the view toward obtaining quantitative data on the ice-forming properties of ordinary surface air in the hope that these data could contribute a better understanding of the atmospheric process.

Description of measurements—The primary tool employed was a 0·1 m³ expansion chamber which was expanded at a rate to correspond to a temperature decrease of 7°C/min. This is about the same temperature fall accompanying a vertical velocity of 10 mps as in an active cumulus updraft. Since the chamber walls were cooled simultaneously with the expansion, heat transfer to the test gas from the outside was low enough to allow one to characterize the overall process as quasi-adiabatic.

A carefully calibrated thermocouple measured the air temperature and a similarly calibrated platinum resistance thermometer measured the wall temperature. A transducer converted the test gas pressure into a signal suitable for recording. All three variables were recorded on strip charts. A narrow beam of light traversed the chamber center section which enabled visual monitoring of the test gas from viewing ports located at 10°, 30°, and 90° from the forward direction.

Our experience has been that the eye is the best detector for ice crystals among water drops, and that specular reflections seen at 90° to the light beam offer the best proof of the presence of ice crystals.

To be able to calculate the supersaturation at which ice crystals form, one has to know the actual water vapor pressure at the instant nucleation takes place. We have been unsuccessful in devising an arrangement to directly measure the vapor pressure during expansion, and have had to resort to indirect methods. One way could be to control the initial amount and compute the value at later times from the expansion ratios. This method suffers when the chamber temperature falls below 0°C, since there will exist a gradient of vapor pressure from the test gas to the wall because the wall will tend to remain at the ice-saturation value at the wall temperature. Thus, a loss of vapor to the walls will occur at a rate depending on the gradient. The longer the run, the greater will be the loss to the walls.

We sought to minimize this loss by using extremely short periods between the initial checkpoint and the appearance of the nucleation. This was accomplished by either working from a saturated state at various low temperatures, using a water cloud or ice cloud as the starting point, or by working backwards from the point of occurrence of a water cloud. We assumed throughout that the typical dense water clouds occurred at 100 per cent humidity with respect to water, regardless of the temperature or previous history of the nuclei.

Cosmic-ray cloud chamber studies have shown that nuclei left after the evaporation of a cloud require much lower supersaturations for succeeding cloud formations [WILSON, 1951, p.13]. This is attributed to the failure of the larger droplets to evaporate completely, which are called thus re-evaporation nuclei. Although we felt this phenomenon would not change our assumption that all water clouds formed at 100 per cent relative humidity, we were interested to see if the supersaturation required for ice crystal formation would be lowered if the cloud were re-formed on evaporated ice-crystal nuclei.

The cases where the ice cloud preceded the water cloud during the expansion permitted an exact computation of the supersaturation, since we could work backward to the pressure and temperature where the ice cloud formed. In those cases where this did not happen, we could compute ranges of supersaturation only using the argument that either ice or water saturation prevailed at the moment the new expansion commenced. This moment was as long as ten minutes after the previous ice or water cloud evaporated. During the waiting period, the temperature and pressure of the test gas was kept as near constant as possible.

Results—The supersaturations so computed are shown in Table 1 and Fig. 1. There is no tendency for the re-evaporation ice nuclei to be activated at lower supersaturations. It might be remarked that in nine out of ten cases where a previous mixed cloud evaporated, the new cloud appearing was ice only.

Fig. 1 demonstrates conclusively that ice-crystal nucleation can proceed at supersaturations less than water. The single-starred points are for exactly computed values by the procedure described above. The ranges between maximum and minimum possible values for the other data are shown by the solid lines. Some independent data for critical supersaturation for crystal growth are plotted on Fig. 1 as the dotted lines through the circles [SHAW and MASON, 1955].

Interpretation of results—In addition to the fact that ice-crystal nucleation can occur below water saturation, several other conclusions may be drawn from these data:

(1) The supersaturations for crystal growth are in the same range as the supersaturations for nucleation. This agreement may be more than fortuitous if one argues that the heterogeneous nucleation of ice crystals is through an adsorption-orientation

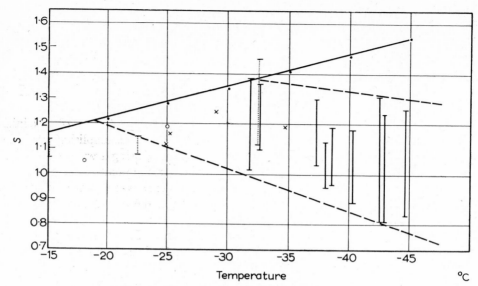

Fig. 1—Supersaturations for ice-crystal nucleation

Table 1. Ice crystal supersaturation for nucleation

Date	Temp.	S'_{min}	S'_{max}	S'_{exact}	Previous cloud
1955	°C				
July 14	−44·6	0·84	1·26	...	ice
Aug. 2	−31·8	1·02	1·38	...	mixed
Aug. 2	−42·5	0·82	1·31	...	ice
Aug. 9	−38·0	0·95	1·13	...	mixed
Aug. 9	−32·6	1·1	1·36	...	mixed
Aug. 9	−40·3	0·89	1·18	...	ice
Aug. 12	−24·9	...	...	1·12	water
Aug. 12	−37·3	1·04	1·3	...	mixed
Aug. 12	−42·9	0·82	1·24	...	ice
Aug. 17	−29·0	...	...	1·25	mixed
Aug. 17	−38·6	0·96	1·19	...	ice
Aug. 18	−25·2	...	...	1·16	none
Aug. 18	−34·6	...	...	1·19	mixed

mechanism, because the important thing here is the formation of crystal nuclei on the surface of the substrate by the proper arrangement of molecules of adsorbed water, a sort of solidification process, which should be independent of supersaturation once the adsorption is accomplished. Thus, the supersaturation will determine gradients in the gas phase, and probably the growth of the crystal seeds.

(2) The data suggest crudely a decrease of supersaturation with temperature. If one draws boundary lines through maximum and minimum supersaturations as done in Fig. 1, a region of possible supersaturation is enclosed which seems to slope away from the line of water saturation and towards lower supersaturations as the temperature

decreases. In the extreme, one could speculate on the possibility of a cross-over temperature above which the required supersaturation for nucleation is higher than water saturation, and below which it progressively becomes lower than water saturation. This would mean that above say $-20°C$, the expected first phase would be water, while below $-30°C$ the first phase would be ice. We actually verified this latter result several times. It should be remembered that these ice nuclei do not seem to be the cloud drop nuclei, since at the maximum they were only about $100/cm^3$, while the subsequent water cloud was $10^3/cm^3$ or above.

Acknowledgment—The help of P. Gustafson of the Cloud Physics Section is gratefully acknowledged. He is responsible for the operation of the chamber which made these data possible.

REFERENCES

BIRSTEIN, S. J., Adsorption studies of heterogeneous phase transitions, *Geophys. Res. Pap.* 32, Air Force Cambridge Research Center, Cambridge, 37pp., 1954.

BIRSTEIN, S. J. and C. E. ANDERSON, The mechanism of atmospheric ice formation, I, The chemical composition of nucleating agents, *J. Met.*, v.12, pp.68–73, 1955.

SHAW, D. and B. J. MASON, The growth of ice crystals from the vapour, *Phil. Mag.*, v.46, pp.249–262, 1955.

WILSON, J. G., *The Principles of Cloud-Chamber Technique*, Cambridge Univ. Press, England, 131pp., 1951.

DISCUSSION

Dr. J. S. Marshall—Since Mr. Anderson is looking at a temperature-sensitive phenomenon and trying to establish more closely its relationship with temperature, is it not worth recognizing that supersaturation itself is a function of temperature? Would it not perhaps simplify the matter if supersaturation were replaced by the excess of the vapor density over equilibrium density, thereby eliminating the equilibrium density itself and dealing in excess density?

Mr. Charles E. Anderson—Most of the theories with which we work go back to supersaturation ratios.

Dr. David Turnbull—The only possibility that I could see why the supersaturation might go down as you decrease the temperature would be the possibility that some of the nucleating agents may have changed structure on lowering the temperature.

Dr. Hans J. aufm Kampe—Did I understand you used dirty air?

Mr. Anderson—Yes.

Dr. aufm Kampe—Did you also use silver iodide?

Mr. Anderson—No.

Dr. aufm Kampe—Figure 1 shows that sometimes ice crystals occurred even below ice saturation.

Mr. Anderson—No, that was below the ranges where we could not compute the exact values.

Dr. aufm Kampe—How accurate is your determination of temperature?

Mr. Anderson—Well, these are within a degree.

Dr. E. M. Fournier d'Albe—You presumably had hygroscopic nuclei present.

Mr. Anderson—Anything that came in from the street.

Dr. Fournier d'Albe—There may be liquid present before you reached the water saturation line.

Mr. Anderson—Quite true.

Dr. James P. Lodge—I'd like to raise the question of just how statistically valid the downward trend might be. Have you made some statistical tests of it? You could draw almost anything from those if you wanted to prove something.

Mr. Anderson—Well, it was impossible to make tests on a statistical basis with the experimental set-up used.

Dr. Turnbull—I wanted to bring up the same point. You could actually picture the first three descending and the last four or five ascending.

Dr. Helmut Weickmann—I'd like to make one remark which is initiated by the title of the paper. The title is Re-evaporation Nuclei, and I'd like to call attention to an observation which was once described by Rau.

At a certain temperature below zero, he started evaporating the water droplets; then, sometimes, the nuclei which were just at the edge of being evaporated started nucleation. I made quite similar observations when I observed the ice formation on freshly cleaved mica. If you breath on a freshly cleaved mica you get a very thin film of water which you can see as colored Newton rings. Crystallization of this film proceeds from two places; (1) on disrupted mica sheets, and (2) at the rim of the thin water film just where everything is in the process of evaporating. This seems to indicate that the process of evaporation is as important a step in the process of ice formation as is the process of condensation.

As long as the freezing nucleus is completely submerged in water, the adsorption or surface forces of the nucleus are probably too weak to orient the bulk water, but as the bulk water evaporates and only a very thing film is left, ice may form similarly as in Birstein's experiments. The molecules in this adsorption film become oriented and if the environment is supersaturated with respect to ice, a crystal starts to grow.

Maybe we should consider this in any seeding or cloud modification experiments because where you artificially evaporate the cloud you give the natural nuclei a chance to act.

Mr. Anderson—We had ten cases where we started with the mixed cloud and allowed it to evaporate and in nine out of ten cases we always got an ice-crystal cloud on the second formation.

Mr. James E. Manson—I'd like to ask a question referring to Dr. Weickmann's comment. Did you make any estimates as to how much cooling occurred on the evaporating surface in the bulk water?

Dr. Weickmann—Yes, this was taken into consideration, since I measured the wet-bulb temperature only.

THUNDERSTORM ELECTRICITY

THUNDERSTORM CHARGE GENERATION

E. J. WORKMAN

New Mexico Institute of Mining and Technology, Socorro, N.M.

Abstract—Laboratory experiments designed to measure the amount and sign of the charge separated by two ice formations in rubbing contact are described. In a simulated thunderstorm environment, it is found that a graupel-crystal collision process can lead to large amounts of charge separation. The experiments demonstrate, in a general way, that the warmer or the more contaminated ice becomes negatively charged. Further experiments indicate that the charge separated during rubbing contact is due to the freezing potential which arises as a result of re-solidification of a liquid layer formed at the point of contact.

FOLLOWING are (1) a brief outline of thunderstorm charge-generating processes as currently viewed by S. E. Reynolds and his associates in our laboratory, and (2) a brief review of some of our research work on ice as grown from the melt.

Reynolds and I [WORKMAN and REYNOLDS, 1950] suggested the possibility that thunderstorm electricity might be produced in a cloud by the freezing of wet ice in the form of hail. Up to that time some of us had been concerned with a description of the gross electrical features of the thunderstorm and we were impressed by the fact that the lower negative charge center appeared to be fixed at elevations in the cloud favorable to the production of hail. Moreover, the production of thunderstorm electricity appeared to require active precipitation processes within the cloud. These and other considerations led us to search for an electrical effect associated with the freezing of water, which might serve as a thunderstorm charge generator. We found that water which is slightly contaminated with certain impurities likely to be found in the atmosphere, could separate large quantities of electrical charge during freezing.

Although the new electrical effect suggested a mechanism that appeared for a while to be adequate, it became difficult to account for the existence of negative charge centers at temperatures as low as -20 or $-30°C$, as reported by REYNOLDS and NEILL [1955]. Such a cold environment would appear favorable to ice crystals and graupel, but certainly not to wet ice, shedding water as required by the process envisioned. This question took us back to the cold box, where a great variety of tests for electrical effects of riming were investigated. Here again, nature seems to have provided a mechanism, although the physical processes involved are not well understood. By rubbing two pieces of clean ice together, it is possible to separate electrical charge if the rubbing is done in such a way that the area of contact on one piece becomes warmer than that on the other piece. In fact, it can be shown that it is not necessary to rub the ice, the only requirement being that of contact, with one piece warmer than the other. This process suggested the possibility that a falling graupel pellet which, of necessity, would be warmer than ice crystals against which it might impinge would, through the impingement, exchange electrical charge with the ice crystals. It was demonstrated by laboratory tests that such a process would be operative in the case of a relatively pure ice. It is expected, however that although the minute ice crystals of the atmosphere, formed as they are by direct sublimation, may be quite pure, the graupel pellets formed by the freezing of water droplets will be contaminated.

Here again, the physical action is favorable to the solution of our problem. We need to have a graupel pellet become negatively charged in order to satisfy the charge configuration observed for thunderstorms. This condition is satisfied in the case of relatively pure ice impacts, because the warmer ice acquires negative charge. In the case of ice contaminated with materials likely to be present in the atmosphere, the graupel will become negatively charged. As a matter of fact, the impurity condition seems to take control because it has been found that the contaminated ice will become negative, even though its temperature is considerably colder than the temperature of the pure ice with which it comes into contact. In the case of sodium chloride contamination, the rime particle may be as much as 20° colder and still acquire a negative charge on impact. I shall conclude by stating that, as of now, the charge-generating process which Reynolds and his collaborators propose is likely to be effective in thunderstorm charge generation, and it will provide for greater freedom in moving the negative charge center into colder portions of the cloud.

REFERENCES

REYNOLDS, S. E. and H. W. NEILL, The distribution and discharge of thunderstorm charge-centers, *J. Met.*, v.12, pp. 1–12, 1955.

WORKMEN, E. J. and S. E. REYNOLDS, Electrical phenomena occurring during the freezing of dilute aqueous solutions and their possible relationship to thunderstorm electricity, *Phys. Rev.*, v.78, pp.254–259, 1950.

INTERNATIONAL TERMINOLOGY

THE NEW INTERNATIONAL DEFINITIONS
OF HYDROMETEORS

CHARLES F. BROOKS

Blue Hill Meteorological Observatory,
Harvard University, Milton 86, Mass.

Summary—The new definitions were prepared by the Sub-Commission for the Study of Clouds and Hydrometeors, then modified by the Commission for Synoptic Meteorology of the World Meteorological Organization (WMO) at its Washington meeting in 1953 and subsequently edited by a temporary working group. The final editing is now in progress (Sep. 1955) in Geneva, adjusting the English and French versions. The definitions will be published by the WMO in the *International Cloud Atlas*, 1953, which should be available by early 1956. The wordings which I have and will present orally are those following the editing of 1954. Though there will be no change of substance in the final editing, now in progress, there may be some minor changes in wording. Therefore, the definitions as I am about to give them are for the information of members of this Conference, but not for publication, since they are not yet final and official.

Eighteen hydrometeors are now recognized and precisely defined: snow, snow pellets, snow grains, rain, drizzle, ice pellets, hail, ice crystals, fog (including ice fog), mist, dew, hoarfrost, rime, glaze, spray, spout and drifting or blowing snow. The following terms have been abandoned: granular snow, granular ice, sleet, snow and rain mixed, graupel, soft hail, and small hail.

DISCUSSION

Dr. James W. Ford—This point does not bear on the definitions, but merely on the usage. I wish to support a suggestion made some time ago by Chapman that the dual usage of the words 'above' and 'below' be used only in the case of altitude, and the terms 'warmer' and 'colder' be in connection with temperature, so that there should be no possible confusion.

Dr. Horace R. Byers—The only thing in the definitions that seems a little inconsistent to me is the division in hail, depending on size. Hail is always, even when it is large, some kind of a snow pellet which is coated with ice; but when it has a thin coating and is less than five mm in diameter the new definition changes the name entirely.

Dr. C. F. Brooks—It seemed better to differentiate them by the criterion of size than to try to get the observer to determine the origin. The same criterion holds in regard to identification of clouds. The whole system of cloud nomenclature is based on what the observer can see and not upon the interpretation.

Prof. Charles L. Hosler—As I understand it, we are abandoning the thunder and lightning criterion entirely. Even though thunder and lightning were audible and visible, we might have ice pellets instead of hail.

Dr. C. F. Brooks—Yes, you might. It would depend on the size.

Dr. Helmut Weickmann—It would have been nice to have some physical classification in this definition. For instance, we might have one particle type which is due to condensation or sublimation. Then the next type, due only to the process of accretion; and the last type, the mixed process, condensation and accretion. This would not necessarily be inconsistent with definitions based on observation. With snow, we usually have a particle whose growth is due to sublimation or condensation. A 'snow pellet' would be a particle which grew mainly by accretion.

Dr. Vincent J. Schaefer—We had a small committee which worked for several years on a classification system for snow crystals, which was submitted to the International Union of Geodesy and Geophysics (IUGG). We worked very closely with Dr. Nakaya and tried to get the opinion of as many other experts as possible. This apparently has not been taken into consideration in connection with these definitions.

Dr. C. F. Brooks—The difficulty is that some of the WMO symbols have been taken here and this tends to confuse the whole classification. We are in agreement on the symbols for hail and snow pellets, but we use your symbol for ice crystal strictly for ice needle, because the ice needle is a very distinct type of crystal which is important in the electrical nature of the snow.

Now I appreciate the problems you have, but it seems to me that your group should have tried to cover the really characteristic forms which anyone can easily recognize; for example, the cirrus-type crystal, the column, the thick plate, and the irregularly shaped crystal.

Dr. Weickmann—I agree very much with what Dr. Schaefer said. The Atlas seems to include several categories which define rime particles and only one for snow and ice crystals. However, I don't think it is quite so easy to distinguish between the snow-crystal types without a hand microscope and this might have been the reason for omitting more detailed classification.

A step toward a more physical classification was the substitution of 'ice crystals' for 'ice needles'. An ice needle is now a well-known snow-crystal type of a limited temperature interval. What was meant by 'ice needles' here, however, were real crystals, prisms, and plates as they occur throughout a wide temperature range which cause halo phenomena.

Mr. Charles E. Anderson—I was going to remark about the definitions themselves for two of the phenomena. The spout, in the definition, touches the ground. What about one that doesn't reach the surface; it is not a spout?

Dr. Brooks—No. It is called tornado aloft.

Mr. Anderson—My other remark concerns the definition of ice fog as crystals. I think studies of the particles found in ice fog show that they are some sort of spheroids with two rudimentary crystal faces; they are not truly crystals, but frozen water drops. I am speaking of the ice fogs that are reported around inhabited areas in the Arctic. Should these be called fog rather than ice crystals?

Dr. C. F. Brooks—Yes, the term fog is not limited to the liquid form.

FURTHER DISCUSSION

(at the closing session)

Dr. Byers—There was quite a bit of discussion subsequent to Dr. Brooks' presentation of The New International Definitions of Hydrometeors. Afterwards, a number of people stated that they would like to have some further discussion. One of the things that we can do is discuss here the possibility of expanding from that framework of definitions, and the possibility of further observations of hydrometeors.

A suggestion by Dr. Schaefer was that observers could be instructed in the rather simple techniques of classifying the different forms of solid precipitation. I think, in order to keep this discussion in some sort of order, it might be a good idea to start out by calling on Dr. Schaefer to tell us a little about the things he had in mind and then immediately I would like to have Dr. Brooks' comment on this. Then we can go ahead with further suggestions.

Dr. Schaefer—I would like to bring to your attention the publication *The International Classification for Snow* issued by the Commission on Snow and Ice of the International Association of Hydrology, IUGG, and published as Technical Memorandum 31 of the Associate Committee on Soil and Snow Mechanics, Snow and Ice Research in Ottawa, Canada, in August 1954. It can be obtained from the National Research Council in Ottawa.

Now, the foreword is by Gerald Seligman, President of the Commission on Snow and Ice, dated November 13, 1952; and there are references on the initial work started in 1948; and we submitted our report to the International Commission on Snow and Glaciers, in 1951 in Brussels. Subsequently it was turned over to the World Meteorological Organization.

We initially took all of the then available classifications, and of course, it is a fantastic job to try to get them all in a more or less uniform framework. In working we had George Klein who had been doing a great deal of work on snow and ice in Canada, Marcel deQuervain, head of the snow and avalanche research work in Switzerland, Dr. Nakaya, and myself. We had a number of meetings. I should say the main work was done by deQuervain and Klein.

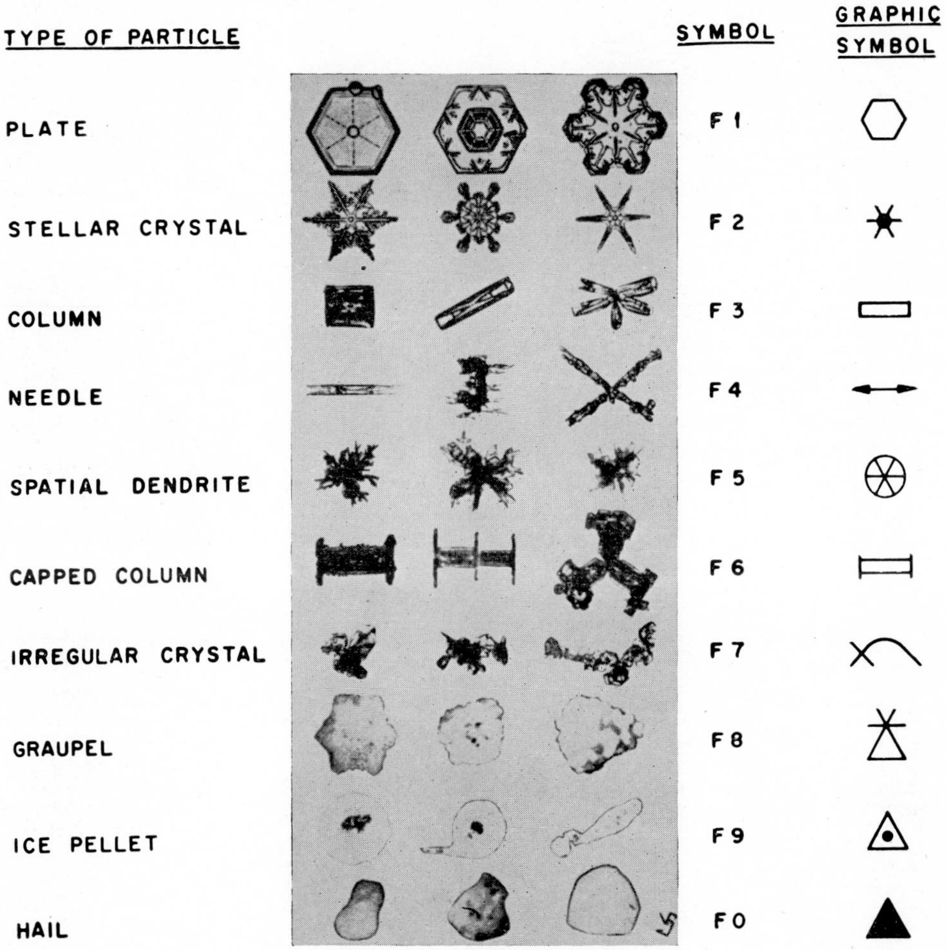

TYPE OF PARTICLE	SYMBOL	GRAPHIC SYMBOL
PLATE	F 1	
STELLAR CRYSTAL	F 2	
COLUMN	F 3	
NEEDLE	F 4	
SPATIAL DENDRITE	F 5	
CAPPED COLUMN	F 6	
IRREGULAR CRYSTAL	F 7	
GRAUPEL	F 8	
ICE PELLET	F 9	
HAIL	F 0	

FIG. 1—Tentative classification of frozen precipitation particles

What we finally came up with was a classification for falling solid precipitation, using ten symbols. The reason for using ten was so we could use the numbers zero to nine, if telegraphic communication was desired.

We had a great deal of discussion about the terms and symbols. We did our best to use all the then standard classification symbols. In fact, we modified ours a great deal to fit into the International Classification Method then available. We finally came up with the ten forms of precipitation shown in Fig. 1. I have used these at the Mount Washington Observatory and found it to be a fairly practical method of identifying snow types. With very limited training we found it feasible to get useful scientific information.

Just to give you an idea of the classifications we used, I refer to Fig. 1. F1 is a plate; F2, a stellar crystal; F3, a column; F4, needles; F5, spatial dendrites; F6, capped column; F7, irregular crystals; F8, graupel; F9, pellets; and F0 hail.

Now, I should point out that the main part of this memorandum concerns snow as it rests on the ground. The Classification was concerned particularly with subsequent changes of snow crystal forms for use in glacier studies and avalanches and so on. But some of us, especially Nakaya and I, directed considerable effort to the classification of falling precipitation because as far as we could see from our field observations, the ten basic forms pretty well included everything we had observed.

It is possible, of course, to subdivide any one of the ten types into fifteen or twenty sub-divisions, and for crystallographic studies this may be desirable. To give a general picture, however, our ten forms are sufficient. I think it would be unfortunate to make it more complicated.

Dr. Byers—Can these observations be made by the naked eye?

Dr. Schaefer—Yes.

Dr. Byers—No equipment of any kind is necessary?

Dr. Schaefer—No, except a piece of black velvet or a coat sleeve. The initial observations, to get an idea of what the forms are, may require a hand lens to fortify your belief as to what you have observed. But, after a little experience, one can glance at the collecting surface with the naked eye and classify it.

Dr. Weickmann—Are the types arranged in a certain manner, or could the arrangement be changed to a more physical one, to the arrangement I had in my diagram.

Dr. Schaefer—I originally had one designed along the lines you suggest, but by the time the various arguments were satisfied the results are as indicated.

This was initially presented not as a finished form but something we wished to have criticized. The classification still should not be considered as final. What we were hoping was that this would be used in the field for a while by people really interested in it and then perhaps five years from now we could come out with what might be a final classification.

Dr. Brooks—The Cloud Atlas Committee did consider this classification and there were considerable discrepancies between this and previous usage. We submitted it to the Commission of Aerology then to the Commission of Synoptic Meteorology. As I see it, the difference between what we have and this, is simply that we have here snow subdivided into seven different categories. Now, for ordinary synoptic purposes, we may find these categories are very valuable. The potentials have not yet been sufficiently investigated.

I think the best way to handle this, so far as the group is concerned, is to ask President Bleeker and the Committee which he leads, to add a footnote saying 'For study purposes, it would be desirable to recognize the following subdivisions of snow,' and then list these seven. I think that would be a very helpful thing, because it would then allow those students who wanted to go into detail to use this system and not start something else.

I remember in 1950, or thereafter, there was a letter system which had a hundred different divisions, and that was quite complicated. We used it in Blue Hill for several years. This system you have here is a very good reduction to the essential different types and I think that the best way, at the present time in this current situation, where the WMO definitions have been adopted and are in the final editing, would be to put a footnote and call attention to that.

Dr. Byers—I agree this would be a fine way to do it, because it would mean we don't lose the effort we have put into it and we shouldn't consider this final at the present time. In five years or so we can come up with something much better.

Dr. Nakaya—I think, when Dr. Brooks proposes to adopt these seven groups in WMO, it is proper to change the symbol of the double arrow for the ice crystal, because before the term indicated ice needle in your classification and we adopted this symbol from you. Now you change it to snow crystal.

Dr. Schaefer—We had it one way and then because of the WMO which had it the other way, we changed it, and now they have changed it back.

Dr. Byers—I think perhaps if we want to act here, we should designate a working group to act for us.

Dr. Schaefer—I wonder if it wouldn't be far simpler, since Dr. Brooks is in such close contact, if we just let him act for us. He could draft a letter to Dr. Bleeker of WMO.

Dr. Byers—All right. We will handle it that way.

(The matter was then put to a vote and it was voted unanimously that Dr. Brooks should write to the Synoptic Commission of the World Meteorological Organization suggesting the footnote involving the first seven forms of solid precipitation listed in *The International Classification for Snow*.)

Dr. Byers—Is everybody happy with the idea that graupel is not an accepted word?

Dr. Schaefer—It will still be used.

Dr. Byers—I think your philosophy there is very realistic. They say that the English language was not developed by experts but rather by the common people; perhaps if we can consider ourselves the proletariat, we might continue to express things our own way. However, of course, it is worth while to have meteorologists use a language which is quite generally understood.

Major Currie S. Downie—Dr. Byers, do you think it would be worth while to pursue your argument the other day, that is to use 'hail,' regardless of whether it is small, medium, or large, or whatever size is involved?

Dr. Byers—I would like to have Dr. Brooks' comment on that.

Dr. Brooks—We just felt that in view of the experiences with weather observers' reports that it is more important to know the size of the frozen particles as they come down than it was to try to ask the observer to differentiate between a layer or non-layer structure, or whether it is due to convective up and down movement or not. We would assume anything bigger than five mm would be due to strong convection. Whether or not anything less than that would produce strong convection, we don't know. We didn't feel the observer would be able to tell by glancing at that small particle. It is a matter of practical observation of what came in. Anything a man wants to put into his observation book in more detail about any particle he sees is all right. But, it did not seem desirable to make that subdivision. Therefore, soft hail, small hail, and hail; we are combining all hail into one package and eliminating the others.

Dr. Schaefer—What is the dividing line in size?

Dr. Brooks—Five mm. That is a fairly good size.

Dr. Byers—I am sensitive about that, because of having been raised on the coast of Washington State where most of the showers come in fresh maritime air, and many of them produce very small hail. It would mean that this would not be put into the records at all for such stations, because large hail almost never would occur in those localities.

Dr. Brooks—You'd still have ice pellets.

Dr. Byers—Yes, but people take these data and draw climatological charts on frequency of hail in certain places; and that I think would eliminate certain sections which characteristically have hail that would not fall into the hail classification.

Dr. Brooks—What are you trying to show? Are you trying to show the distribution of convective intensity or are you trying to show the distribution of particles of ice big enough to crack a windowpane?

Dr. Weickmann—If I may go back once more to this argument. I would like to state that I regret the omission of the graupel because of one reason. I think it was about the only particle in the shower precipitation class which was used internationally. But now I think every country has a different particle. The English call it small hail. In this country it is called soft hail, and I am afraid we are again up to some confusion.

Dr. James E. McDonald—I would like to add a comment to what you were saying about the climatic statistics and the slight difficulties these changes interpose. Aside from the question you raised, Dr. Brooks, of what one is trying to delineate with the hail data, and, agreed that it may be useful to show small size hail as ice particles, there is a very serious difficulty that comes into research just because of the change itself. It takes about two years before you have a new homogeneous record of these things, because observers don't seem to make these changes immediately. It argues for some conservatism. In cases like this where one can say there is a good reason for taking all ice particles as hail and using the old principle rather than changing to particle size, the conservatism has a real research value.

Dr. Workman—Could we refer these matters to a committee or correspondence or something?

Dr. Byers—I would suggest that it be handled by correspondence, if anybody has to add anything. But, in view of the urgency at the present time, Dr. Brooks should include in his letter to Dr. Bleeker, a statement of the sentiments expressed here. I don't believe that our discussion has yet reached the form where we would care to vote on some of these more ephemeral matters; but I believe we would all like to have these ideas known to the International Synoptic Commission.

APPENDIX 1

LIST OF PARTICIPANTS

Mr. Charles E. Anderson
Geophysics Research Directorate
Air Force Cambridge Research Center
Bedford, Massachusetts

Mr. Herbert S. Appleman
Special Techniques Branch
Hq. Air Weather Service
MATS, U.S. Air Force
Washington 25, D.C.

Dr. David Atlas
Geophysics Research Directorate
Air Force Cambridge Research Center
Bedford, Massachusetts

Dr. Hans J. aufm Kampe
Atmospheric Physics Section
Meteorological Branch
Signal Corps Engineering Laboratories
Fort Monmouth, New Jersey

Dr. Pauline M. Austin
Massachusetts Institute of Technology
Department of Meteorology
Cambridge 39, Massachusetts

Dr. Louis J. Battan
Department of Meteorology
University of Chicago
Chicago 37, Illinois

Mr. Arthur E. Bent
Ripley Lane
Weston 93, Massachusetts

Capt. F. A. Berry
Advisory Committee on Weather
Control
Room 1128, GSA Building
Washington 25, D.C.

Mr. S. J. Birstein
Geophysics Research Directorate
Air Force Cambridge Research Center
Bedford, Massachusetts

Mr. Duncan C. Blanchard
Woods Hole Oceanographic
Institution
Woods Hole, Massachusetts

Dr. Roscoe R. Braham, Jr.
Department of Meteorology
University of Chicago
Chicago 37, Illinois

Dr. Charles F. Brooks
Blue Hill Meteorological Observatory
Harvard University
Milton 86, Massachusetts

Dr. Edward M. Brooks
Institute of Technology
St. Louis University
St. Louis, Missouri

Mr. Andrew F. Bunker
Woods Hole Oceanographic
Institution
Woods Hole, Massachusetts

Dr. Horace R. Byers
Department of Meteorology
Univeristy of Chicago
Chicago 37, Illinois

Mr. Joseph Chase
Woods Hole Oceanographic
Institution
Woods Hole, Massachusetts

Dr. Robert M. Cunningham
Geophysics Research Directorate
Air Force Cambridge Research Center
Bedford, Massachusetts

Mr. Ralph Donaldson
Geophysics Research Directorate
Air Force Cambridge Research Center
Bedford, Massachusetts

Mr. R. H. Douglas
Meteorological Service of Canada
Toronto 5, Canada

Major Currie S. Downie
  Geophysics Research Directorate
  Air Force Cambridge Research Center
  Bedford, Massachusetts

Lt. Col. George Duncan
  General Sciences Staff
  Office Asst. Secy. of Defense for
    Research and Development
  Washington 25, D.C.

Dr. T. W. R. East
  Department of Physics
  McGill University
  Montreal, Canada

Mr. Gerard A. Faucher
  Geophysics Research Directorate
  Air Force Cambridge Research Center
  Bedford, Massachusetts

Mr. Alan J. Faller
  Woods Hole Oceanographic
    Institution
  Woods Hole, Massachusetts

Dr. James Ford
  Cornell Aeronautical Laboratory
  P.O. Box 235
  Buffalo 21, New York

Dr. E. M. Fournier d'Albe
  Instituto de Ciencias Aplicades
    Universidad Nacional De Mexico
  c/o Instituto de Geofisica
  Torre de Ciencias, 3er Piso
  Villa Obregon, D.F., Mexico

Mr. James E. Gallagher
  Geophysics Research Directorate
  Air Force Cambridge Research Center
  Bedford, Massachusetts

Mr. Paul G. Goldberg
  Geophysics Research Directorate
  Air Force Cambridge Research Center
  Bedford, Massachusetts

Mr. Milton Greenberg
  Geophysics Research Directorate
  Air Force Cambridge Research Center
  Bedford, Massachusetts

Dr. K. L. S. Gunn
  Department of Physics
  McGill University
  Montreal, Canada

Mr. P. E. Gustafson
  Geophysics Research Directorate
  Air Force Cambridge Research Center
  Bedford, Massachusetts

Mr. D. Lee Harris
  U.S. Weather Bureau
  Washington 25, D.C.

Prof. Charles L. Hosler
  Department of Meteorology
  Pennsylvania State University
  University Park, Pennsylvania

Dr. Wallace E. Howell
  W. E. Howell Associates
  P.O. Box 163
  Lexington, Massachusetts

Mr. J. H. Hughes
  Office of Naval Research
  Washington, 25, D.C.

Dr. Christian E. Junge
  Geophysics Research Directorate
  Air Force Cambridge Research Center
  Bedford, Massachusetts

Dr. Heinz Kasemir
  Atmospheric Physics Section
  Meteorological Branch
  Signal Corps Engineering Laboratories
  Fort Monmouth, New Jersey

Mr. John J. Kelly
  Atmospheric Physics Section
  Meteorological Branch
  Signal Corps Engineering Laboratories
  Fort Monmouth, New Jersey

Mr. William V. Kielhorn
  Woods Hole Oceanographic
    Institution
  Woods Hole, Massachusetts

Dr. Gilbert D. Kinzer
  U.S. Weather Bureau
  Washington 25, D.C.

Mr. Dwight Kline
  U.S. Weather Bureau
  Washington 25, D.C.

Dr. Joachim Kuettner
  Geophysics Research Directorate
  Air Force Cambridge Research Center
  Bedford, Massachusetts

Dr. M. P. Langleben
  Department of Physics
  McGill University
  Montreal, Canada

Dr. James P. Lodge
  Robert A. Taft Sanitary Engineering
    Center
  U.S. Public Health Service
  4676 Columbia Parkway
  Cincinnati, Ohio

Mr. James E. Manson
Geophysics Research Directorate
Air Force Cambridge Research Center
Bedford, Massachusetts

Dr. J. S. Marshall
Department of Physics
McGill University
Montreal, Canada

Mr. Kiah Maynard
Arthur D. Little, Inc.
30 Memorial Drive
Cambridge, Massachusetts

Dr. James E. McDonald
Institute of Atmospheric Physics
University of Arizona
Tucson 25, Arizona

Mr. C. B. Moore
Arthur D. Little, Inc.
30 Memorial Drive
Cambridge, Massachusetts

Dr. Ukichiro Nakaya
Hokkaido University
Sapporo, Japan

Miss Sally Naumann
Geophysics Research Directorate
Air Force Cambridge Research Center
Bedford, Massachusetts

Dr. R. Penndorf
Geophysics Research Directorate
Air Force Cambridge Research Center
Bedford, Massachusetts

Mr. Vernon G. Plank
Geophysics Research Directorate
Air Force Cambridge Research Center
Bedford, Massachusetts

Mr. Francis C. Ronne
Woods Hole Oceanographic
Institution
Woods Hole, Massachusetts

Mrs. Rita C. Sagalyn
Geophysics Research Directorate
Air Force Cambridge Research Center
Bedford, Massachusetts

Dr. Vincent J. Schaefer
The Munitalp Foundation, Inc.
R.D. 3, Schermerhorn Road
Schenectady, New York

Dr. Richard M. Schotland
Department of Meteorology and
Oceanography
College of Engineering
New York University
University Heights
New York 53, New York

Mr. Waldo E. Smith
American Geophysical Union
1515 Massachusetts Avenue, N.W.
Washington 5, D.C.

Mr. Edward R. Snow
Marshfield, Massachusetts

Mr. A. Theodore Spencer
Woods Hole Oceanographic
Institution
Woods Hole, Massachusetts

Dr. C. G. Stergis
Geophysics Research Directorate
Air Force Cambridge Research Center
Bedford, Massachusetts

Dr. David Turnbull
General Electric Company Research
Laboratory
P.O. Box 1088
Schenectady, New York

Dr. Bernard Vonnegut
Arthur D. Little, Inc.
30 Memorial Drive
Cambridge, Massachusetts

Dr. Helmut Weickmann
Atmospheric Physics Section
Meteorological Branch
Signal Corps Engineering Laboratories
Fort Monmouth, New Jersey

Dr. Raymond Wexler
Blue Hill Meteorological Observatory
Harvard University
Milton, 86, Massachusetts

Mrs. Frances L. Wheedon
c/o Chief, Research & Development
Division
Office of Chief Signal Officer
Department of the Army
Washington 25, D.C.

Mr. James D. Wilcox
Chemical and Radiological
Laboratories
Army Chemical Center
Edgewood, Maryland

Mr. Russell H. Woessner
U.S. Weather Bureau
Washington 25, D.C.

Dr. G. A. Wolff
Chemical Physics Branch
Signal Corps Engineering Laboratory
Fort Monmouth, New Jersey

Dr. Alfred H. Woodcock
Woods Hole Oceanographic
Institution
Woods Hole, Massachusetts

Dr. E. J. Workman
Research and Development Division
New Mexico Institute of Mining and
Technology
Socorro, New Mexico

APPENDIX 2

AGENDA OF MEETING

Sessions on Condensation Nuclei - Condensation - Droplets

First Session, Morning, September 7, 1955, Charles F. Brooks, Presiding

Remarks About the Size Distribution of Natural
Aerosols .. .. CHRISTIAN E. JUNGE
Distribution in the Atmosphere of Certain Particles Capable of Serving
as Condensation Nuclei
HORACE R. BYERS, JOHN R. SIEVERS and BARBARA J. TUFTS
Some Observations of the Geographical Distribution
of Giant Hygroscopic Nuclei .. .. .. E. M. FOURNIER D'ALBE
Electron-Microscope Studies on the Nuclei of Sea Fog
and Snow Crystals .. .. UKICHIRO NAKAYA
The Question of Meteoritic Dust in the Atmosphere VINCENT J. SCHAEFER
Some Facts about Meteoritic Dust .. .. .. CHRISTIAN E. JUNGE

Second Session, Afternoon, September 7, 1955, Horace R. Byers, Presiding

The Vertical Distribution of Aerosols Over the Ocean CHRISTIAN E. JUNGE
Recent Measurements of the Vertical Distribution
of Aitken Nuclei .. .. HELMUT WEICKMANN
Time Variations of Charged Atmospheric
Nuclei .. .. .. RITA C. SAGALYN and GERARD A. FAUCHER
Facts and Problems of Chemical Composition of
Condensation Nuclei in Unpolluted and Polluted
Atmospheres .. .. CHRISTIAN E. JUNGE
Techniques for the Chemical Identification of Micron
and Submicron Particles JAMES P. LODGE, Jr. and BARBARA J. TUFTS
Determining the Concentration of Fogs and Other
Aerosols by a Space-Charge Measuring Instrument
B. VONNEGUT, C. B. MOORE, JOHN EHRENFELD and C. R. SMALLMAN
Preliminary Investigation of the Distribution of Space Charge
in the Lower Atmosphere B. VONNEGUT, C. B. MOORE and M. BLUME
The Role of Adsorption in Water Condensation .. .. S. J. BIRSTEIN
Diffusional Growth Problems in Cloud Physics CHARLES E. ANDERSON

Third Session, Evening, September 7, 1955, W. H. Howell, Presiding

Droplet Size Measurements in Convective
Clouds .. .. .. LOUIS J. BATTAN and CLAYTON H. REITAN

Laboratory Measurements of the Growth and of the Collection
   Efficiency of Raindrops   Gilbert D. Kinzer and William E. Cobb
The Collision Efficiency of Cloud Droplets ..   ..   R. M. Schotland
Isokinetic Flow and Sampling of Airborne Particulates   James D. Wilcox
A Nomogram for the Calculation of Collision
   Efficiencies   ..   ..Helmut Weickmann

Sessions on Ice Nuclei - Ice Formation - Ice and Snow Crystals

Fourth Session, Morning, September 8, 1955, Vincent J. Schaefer, Presiding

Ice Nucleation and the Structure of Nuclei
   Crystal Faces ..   ..   James E. Manson
Observations of Freezing Nuclei over the Southwestern U.S.
         A. Richard Kassander, Lee L. Sims, and James E. McDonald
Remarks on the Theory of Heterogeneous Nucleation
   of Crystals ..   ..   David Turnbull
Studies on Re-Evaporation Ice Nuclei ..   ..   Charles E. Anderson
The Effect of Condensation Nucleus Size and Type
   on the Temperature of Ice Crystal Formation in
   Clouds ..   ..   C. L. Hosler and G. R. Spalding
Studies on the Effects of Certain Chemicals on the
   Inhibition of Nucleation   ..   ..   S. J. Birstein
Overseeding of Cumulus Clouds Roscoe R. Braham, Jr. and John R. Sievers

Fifth Session, Afternoon, September 8, 1955, H. J. aufm Kampe, Presiding

Surface Nature of Ice Crystals ..   ..   Ukichiro Nakaya
Thunderstorm Charge Generation   ..   ..   ..   E. J. Workman
Notes on the Structure of Ice ..   ..   E. J. Workman
Cinema on Crystal Growth   ..   ..   David Turnbull
The Growth of Ice Crystals   ..   .. G. A. Wolff
A First Experiment of Snow-Crystal
   Growth ..   ..   J. S. Marshall and K. L. S. Gunn
Physical Investigations of Snow Flakes ..   ..   ..   Ukichiro Nakaya
The Supercooling, Freezing, and Melting of Giant
   Waterdrops at Terminal Velocity in Air   ..   Duncan C. Blanchard

Sessions on Precipitation Particles

Sixth Session, Morning, September 9, 1955, Mrs. Pauline M. Austin, Presiding

The New International Definitions of Hydrometeors .. Charles F. Brooks
Precipitation of Convective Water Clouds   ..   ..   T. W. R. East
Size Distribution Generated by a Random Process   .. Walter Hitschfeld
Atmospheric Salt in Nuclei and in Raindrops ..   ..   A. H. Woodcock
Discussion of Raindrop Distributions Made During
   Project Shower, Hawaii, 1954   ..   ..   .. D. C. Blanchard
The Snow Crystal as Aerological Sonde   ..   Helmut Weickmann

Seventh Session, Afternoon, September 9, 1955, J. S. Marshall, Presiding

Observations of Space and Time Variations in the Radar
  Echo Intensity of Showers   PAULINE M. AUSTIN and RAYMOND WEXLER
Snow Growth and Aggregation in Generating Cells ..   R. H. DOUGLAS
A Discussion of Generating Cell Observations with
  Respect to the Natural Existence of Freezing or
  Sublimation Nuclei   ..   ..   ROBERT M. CUNNINGHAM
Radar Measurements of Precipitation Growth ..   ..   .. DAVID ATLAS
The Melting Layer   ..   ..   RAYMOND WEXLER

Closing Session

Eighth Session, Morning, September 10, 1955, Horace R. Byers, Presiding

(This was a general discussion session.   The Session Chairman took the
occasion to sum up the efforts of the Conference and to introduce subjects
on which further discussions seemed pertinent.   Where a discussion fits
into the discussion for a previous paper, these have been placed at the end
of the discussion of that paper.   The following items, however, do not fit
into such a plan.)
Cloud-Seeding Trials Using Common Salt   ..   E. M. FOURNIER D'ALBE
Discussion of the Question of Drag by the Cloud or Rain Particles in
  Initiating the Downdraft
Discussion of the Growth of Ice Crystals